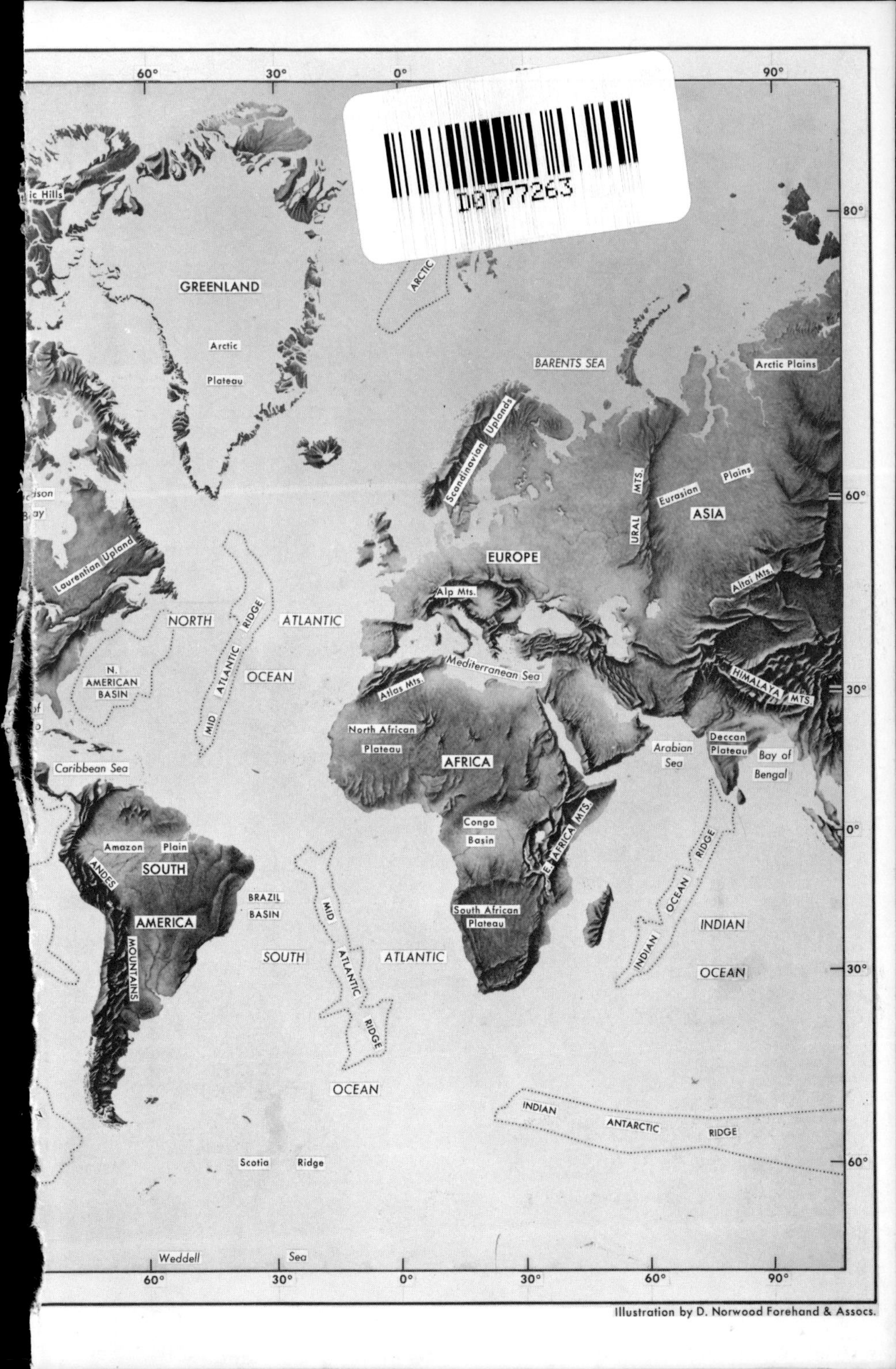

Illustration by D. Norwood Forehand & Assocs.

OUR DYNAMIC WORLD

The world's a scene of changes, and to be Constant, in Nature were inconstancy.

——ABRAHAM COWLEY, 1647

OUR DYNAMIC WORLD

A Survey in Modern Geography

A. JOSEPH WRAIGHT
M.S., Ph.D., F.R.G.S.
Chief Geographer, Coast and Geodetic Survey
Environmental Science Services Administration
U.S. Department of Commerce

CHILTON BOOKS
A DIVISION OF CHILTON COMPANY
Publishers
Philadelphia and New York

Published in Philadelphia by Chilton Company
and simultaneously in Toronto, Canada,
by Ambassador Books, Ltd.

Library of Congress Catalog Card Number 66-26584

Designed by William E. Lickfield
Manufactured in the United States of America

To all those hardy geographers who have not forgotten that geography is still the proprietor of all the sciences—physical, biological, environmental, and social.

Author's Note

Although it may be unnecessary to mention it, I would like to say that all statements and opinions expressed in this book are mine and mine alone and do not necessarily represent the views or positions of the U.S. Coast and Geodetic Survey, the Environmental Science Services Administration, the U.S. Department of Commerce, or any other agency, organization, or individual.

Foreword

Ours is a vastly intriguing world, which I have tried to share with the reader, be he a layman—young or old—or a student in college or secondary school. Because the scope of the book is so broad, some material has been handled in a general manner and certain fields of knowledge, such as astronomy and biology, have been integrated. This treatment may offend some specialists; it seemed unavoidable in a work intended for the average reader.

So many individuals contributed to the preparation of this book that it is impossible to mention them all. I do wish, however, to single out the help and guidance given by my friend and agent, Mr. Frederick Reinstein. Not only did he afford me valuable editorial assistance but he kept me from the many pitfalls inherent in book publishing. Those who assisted in preparing the illustrative material also deserve mention. Mr. William A. Stanley and Mr. D. Norwood Forehand worked on the maps and drawings, a task which required more than drafting ability. To Messrs. William Dennis, Elwood Bear, and Alfonse Benedict I am indebted for permission to use some excellent photographs. To all others who contributed to this book also goes the author's sincere appreciation.

A. JOSEPH WRAIGHT
Washington, D.C.

Contents

List of Maps

Maps appear between pages 257–277

Introduction

Within one week in September–October 1965 a large metropolitan newspaper in Washington, D.C., carried these scientific items as news:

The volcano on Lake Taal in the Philippines erupted violently, with heavy loss of life. . . . A new comet of the tenth magnitude was discovered in England. . . . The U.S. Coast and Geodetic Survey announced that the first complete hydrographic survey in thirty years was being made of the Severn River and Chesapeake Bay in the vicinity of Annapolis. . . . A private firm was awarded a contract for the construction of a huge seagoing platform to be used in a resumption of Project Mohole, the plan to sink a metal drill pipe six miles through the ocean in an attempt to penetrate the earth's crust. . . . A thorough search was advocated by a prominent scientist for various submerged "microcontinents" in order to prove that continental drift has taken place and that two supercontinents actually existed at one time in place of the six existing today.

In the older Webster dictionaries geography was defined as "the description of land, sea, air, and the distribution of plant and animal life, including man and his industries," but it is no exaggeration to say that within the past dozen years there has been an unparalleled interest in all these aspects of geography. Undoubtedly the exploration of space has generated much of this increased interest, so that today scientific discoveries and theories are considered to be of general concern and worth notice in the press.

By exploring the vastness of space we have become better acquainted with our own planet. Water, earth, and air have always been associated in the thinking man's philosophy, but only within recent times have we been able to realize how intricately the three are related. In a very real sense we have been forced to coordinate our knowledge of all three elements in order to launch successfully our space ships and earth satellites. The specialist has finally been brought in out of the cold to join his intellectual brethren in the pursuit of knowledge and truth. Bits of knowledge, long known but either never appreciated or considered impractical or worthless, have been assembled and coordinated, and gaps in our knowledge exposed.

Nowhere has this been more evident than in the field of geography, for this is one science where the individualist has long been permitted to pursue his separate studies. Now the entire world has been made available to the geographer, so that he may coordinate his research with allied specialists. The experience has not been entirely satisfying: frequently one is amazed to learn that the most basic geographic data are either lacking or highly questionable.

We have long known that the earth is some twenty-five thousand miles in circumference and about one-third this in diameter, but it is a surprise to find that the deepest penetration of the earth's surface goes a mere four miles. Oil wells off the Pacific and Gulf coasts have been dug this far, and there is a diamond mine in South Africa with a hole some two and one-half miles deep, but it was only within recent years that Project Mohole was organized to probe the earth's crust where it is thinnest, under parts of the ocean floor. The project was suspended in 1963, but a new contract was signed in September 1965 for a private firm to sink a metal pipe six miles.

Man has lived on this earth for perhaps millions of years, but only the very outer part of the earth's crust is our true habitat—and we know little enough of that. Yet this habitat, we are now convinced, is profoundly influenced not only by what goes on inside the earth but by what happens hundreds or thousands of miles away. Deep within the bowels of the earth, earthquakes originate that dramatically and drastically affect life on our earth; in outer space originate those natural phenomena which control our climate and thus the way man lives and works.

The dynamic aspect of our world has not been generally recognized until very recently, despite the observation of Heraclitus twenty-five hundred years ago that "there is nothing permanent but change." There are many reasons for this, especially man's need to concern himself with his own survival and livelihood; he simply has not had time or motivation to study the world around him. Now and then, it is true, a philosopher has taken the time and made the effort to think about certain natural phenomena, but he has always worked alone, and in most cases his theories were either ridiculed or ignored. What was required was the modern instruments to both probe more deeply and see more clearly.

Today we are in a position to do just that, and what we discover is as startling as the most radical theories of old. We find that our continents are not only adrift but actually moving in relation to one another. The earth's crust is getting warmer, whereas we used to think it was getting colder; we seem to be in a stage between ice ages, and it is possible that Greenland will once again support green vegetation as it did only a few hundred years ago.

As for the oceans which make up most of our world, we know so little about them that new data are being unearthed quite regularly. As I write this, the U.S. Navy has announced completion of its "Man in the Sea" project: for forty-five days three teams have lived and worked hundreds of feet underwater in a special craft, evidence that extensive exploration below the ocean surface has become feasible. There are high mountains under the water, as well as on land, and some of them reveal enormous cracks in their ridges. New islands or volcanoes are being thrown up out of the oceans here and there, and there may be greater wealth in the waters of the world than ever existed on land.

Most startling of all is the greater realization that the entire universe is and always has been in a state of flux and change, and our world could be destroyed. Nothing appears to be permanent, as Heraclitus so wisely observed so long ago. Basically, two types of dynamic force bring about change: the physical and the cultural. Physical forces are created by nature; cultural factors are the work of man. When either type is in imbalance, catastrophe may result.

Many of the physical forces in our shifting scene are so obvious that we may neglect them—until an imbalance occurs and we are compelled to take notice. Climate is one such force, always influencing man and his efforts. Another is soil, which we may take for granted until there is a change in its condition and starvation suddenly faces us.

Cultural factors are generally not quite so obvious. They include social institutions and techniques which are associated with particular localities and determine how people do things. (Today, for example, the oriental technique of using land is undergoing change, for it has never permitted the people to raise enough food to subsist.) A related cultural factor is population, a popular topic today because of the rapidly increasing number of people in most parts of the world; will there be enough food in the future to feed a population that increases continuously? Settlement pattern is another cultural factor of increasing importance in our day; in most western countries, with their emphasis on commerce, transportation arteries have great significance in determining the pattern of settlement. (Actually, in the United States it is no change from the past, as one finds that most important cities are situated on or near large bodies of water; for many generations the principal form of transportation has been via water.)

Use of land is the most important of the cultural factors—and also the most noticeable. It is both a force and a result, for use of land depends upon attitude toward land. Most land use falls into such categories as agricultural, pastoral, forest, hunting and gathering, mining, manufacturing, residential, or recreational. Frequently, an area will go through different stages of land use, culminating in what may be considered its best use so far as contemporary physical or cultural factors are considered. These changes, sometimes called "stages of occupance," may progress differently for similar areas. Thus in the deserts of southwestern Africa are to be found some of the most basic land uses anywhere in the world, while the Sonoran Desert of northwestern Mexico offers the most advanced irrigational-recreational use of land.

Regions of the world are best characterized by their similar physical factors. There are, for example, the rainy low latitudes and the dry low latitudes. The component regions within each of these large groupings usually differ from one another in their stage of development, yet a similar pattern of growth and change seems to exist for each group. This study will help us understand these and other parts of the world in their interrelations. We will also look intently inside, outside, and on the crust of the earth as we examine the working of our dynamic world, now and in the past.

If the scope of this book is broad, the specific discussions are rather limited, for the book is intended as an introduction to the subject of physical and environmental geography. This should be of interest both to the general reader and to students of high school or college level. To those who studied geography a generation ago, this book may well be startling, for the subject is much more broadly defined now and political geography, except to identify areas of discussion, has been entirely omitted. Furthermore, so much new information has come to light that subject matter and emphasis have had to be completely revised.

In a sense, this book is an interim study on world geography, for the subject is today under intensive examination from many directions and what is now accepted as fact may shortly be untenable. Not only is the world dynamic but our knowledge of it is equally changeable and uncertain. This may well be because we knew so little about our planet in the past and the new knowledge was relatively slow in coming to light. Today our frontiers of scientific knowledge are expanding faster than ever before, and the geographer must constantly re-examine and re-evaluate in the light of the latest research and experimentation. Thus we find the distinguished British scientist, Fred Hoyle, announcing in October 1965 that he now believes that our planet may have exploded into existence billions of years ago rather than having been gradually created over a period of time, as he had previously held. In many other matters we must expect to correct and update our geographic knowledge in the years ahead, as we engage in further exploration of space, the oceans, and the inner earth.

SELECTED REFERENCES

American Geographical Society Library. *Research Catalogue*. 15 vols. Boston: G. K. Hall and Co., 1962.

Huntington, Ellsworth, and E. B. Shaw. *Principles of Human Geography*. 6th ed. New York: John Wiley & Sons, 1951.

James, Preston E. *A Geography of Man*. 3rd ed. New York, Blaisdell Publishing Co., 1966.

———. *One World Divided*. New York: Blaisdell Publishing Co., 1964.

——— and Clarence F. Jones (eds.). *American Geography, Inventory and Prospect*. Syracuse, N.Y.: Syracuse University Press, 1954.

Kendall, Henry M., and others. *Introduction to Geography*. 3rd ed. New York: Harcourt, Brace & World, 1962.

Taylor, Thomas Griffith. *Geography in the Twentieth Century*. 3rd ed., enl. London: Methuen & Co., 1957.

White, C. Langdon, and George T. Renner. *College Geography: Natural Environment and Human Society*. New York: Appleton-Century-Crofts, 1957.

PART ONE

Chapter 1 / The Great Outside

From earliest days man has been awed by the fathomless space surrounding him. The scanty records of primitive man, now preserved as artifacts in many libraries and museums, indicate that he was curious about the nightly panorama in the skies that unfolded before him season after season and year after year. Perhaps before he was able to make records, man watched with bewilderment and fear the regular procession of stars across the sky and the augmentation and waning of the moon. He undoubtedly reckoned whatever crude regulations he imposed upon his life by the daily march of the sun in its course from east to west.

He certainly cringed during periods when an eclipse blotted out the great light for a brief time. In locations removed from the equator, early man must have seen that the sun at noon was lower in the sky during certain times of the year. Surely he must have considered the possibility that at some time the sun might not come back. We know that when the sun started its yearly cycle back toward him he marked this auspicious event. Many civilizations still have some kind of celebration shortly after the winter solstice, December 21. Probably more out of fear than interest, man always has somehow or other recognized his dependence upon and boundless relationship to the great outside.

This relationship and dependency is certainly no innovation of the current Space Age. We accept as commonplace the fact that sunlight has the capacity to make plants and flowers grow. Just as commonplace is the regular appearance of the moon and its various phases, but we have been negligent or misguided in our recognition of its full effects upon us. We have tended to ignore the potent effect of the moon upon the tides that move the great oceans that cover nearly three-fourths of the earth's surface.

Our earth is only one of nine planets revolving about the sun. It is the third planet out from the sun, approximately 93 million miles distant. Between the earth and the sun are two planets: Mercury, approximately half the size of the earth, and Venus, nearly as large as the earth. Beyond the earth lie Mars and then a wide belt of thousands of small planetoids or asteroids, until at about 483 million miles from the sun appears the next planet, Jupiter. After Jupiter is ringed Saturn, then Uranus and Neptune, with tiny Pluto being the outermost.

Earth is among the smaller planets, with its eight-thousand-mile diameter, yet it is about twice as large as Mars. Jupiter is ten times the size of the earth, and Saturn is nearly as large as Jupiter. Pluto is diminutive. All the planets are small in relation to the sun, which is at least a hundred times larger than the earth; its diameter has been measured as about 860,000 miles.

Sunspots

Heat and light, the basis of our life, come from the sun, a gigantic mass of incandescent gas, a huge nuclear furnace where hydrogen is changed into helium and energy is given off in heat and light. The sun's surface temperature is about 11,000 degrees Fahrenheit. This great gaseous sphere rotates about once every month.

Occasionally dark places appear on the sun's surface which are known as sunspots. They usually become visible in sequences or cycles, reaching their greatest activity about every ten or eleven years, then declining to minimum interim activity. The years of high sunspot activity are known as "solar years" or "geophysical years." The median years of minimum sunspot activity are known as "years of the quiet sun." The years 1958 and 1959 were geophysical years and 1964 and 1965 were years of the quiet sun.

The occurrence in cycles of these sunspots would be of minor significance if it were not for the effects upon the earth and its people. When these spots occur, charged particles travel to the earth and climatic conditions (affecting man) are altered. The spots are apparently caused by dense, dark gases released from the interior of the sun. They produce magnetic storms on the sun's surface, and great protuberances or swellings of incandescent gas are shot outward with violent thrust. These projections extend for thousands of miles and throw off millions of small particles, which travel through space to other stars and to planets in the solar system, including the earth.

During a time of high sunspot activity, many millions of these particles come into the earth's atmosphere and cause various phenomena. For one thing, radio communication is badly disrupted. It has been found that these particles penetrate and disrupt the protective part of the atmosphere above our breathing air, a layer called the "ionosphere." Radio waves from ground stations bounce along the ionosphere, which carries and propagates them. During geophysical years, these solar particles mangle the ionosphere and disrupt radio communication. Such disturbances are often referred to as "magnetic storms."

At the same time, some of these solar particles are also caught within the earth's magnetic field and are carried about in the great lines of magnetic force that surround the earth far out. Because of their charged condition, they constitute a large part of the well-known Van Allen radiation belts. They also light up certain gases in the ionosphere when they approach the earth in the region of the magnetic poles and cause aurora phenomena, much like neon lights. Many of us have seen the Aurora Borealis in the northern hemisphere and the Aurora Australis in the southern hemisphere. Commonly, these are known as the Northern Lights and the Southern Lights.

High sunspot activity affects more than radio communication. It specifically affects our climate and weather. Years of high sunspot activity are usually associated with cool, wet years; years of low activity with warm, dry years. Thus, cycles of climate parallel sunspot activity. This is particularly significant in areas where rainfall is marginal for agriculture—for instance, the Great Plains area in North America and the steppes of Asia. In these areas the years of low sunspot activity may cause not only severe drought and crop failure but even movements of people, such as the migrations from the "dust bowl" during the 1930's in North America.

These sunspot cycles are supposed to have had a tremendous effect upon historical events. The movements of barbarians out of Asia toward Rome during the last centuries of the Roman Empire are attributed by Arnold J. Toynbee and others to extremely dry times, which were, we now know, periods of low sunspot activity. Still other scientists and physicians, among whom may be mentioned the late Dr. Robert Wells, Head of Research Medicine, Cincinnati University, equate cool, wet cycles with times of prosperity and hot, dry cycles with times of calamity. Note also, if you will, that the Bible speaks of cycles of good years and bad years.

Sunspot activity during the recent series of geophysical years has been increasing, leading scientists to believe that there are master cycles lasting several centuries. Our timetable tells us that we may be approaching such an intense low-sun activity slightly beyond the end of our own century (Fig. 1).

According to C. E. P. Brooks, the British climatologist, the eleven-year sunspot cycles increase in magnitude or power when they are examined in a series of sequences. There are more sunspots at the peaks and fewer at the other end of cycles. They increase in this way for a period of forty-five years and then decrease or dwindle for a period of forty-five years. This makes a ninety-year cycle which includes eight of the smaller cycles. Such a sequence is called a "larger" cycle. In a similar manner, stormy-wet and dry-calm cycles augment and diminish.

Through a study of historical records and an examination of the rings of sequoia trees of California, which are centuries old, Brooks, together with his contemporary, Ellsworth Huntington, discovered even larger cycles. The ninety-year cycles also increase in magnitude to a peak every 270 years and then wane for the same amount of time. This 540-year span forms a

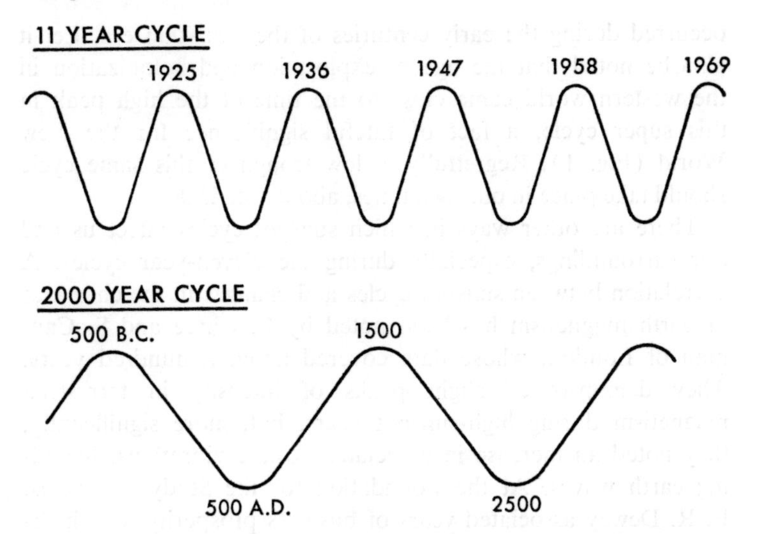

Fig. 1. Larger and smaller climate-magnetic cycles.

"master" cycle. To complicate matters, this 540-year period undergoes the identical process. It increases for 1,100 years and diminishes for an equal period of time, which totals 2,200 years. As might have been anticipated, this last cycle, composed of tens of centuries, has a suitably large label: a "super" cycle.

Both Brooks and Huntington found a relationship between sunspot cycles and climatic cycles. Take the 540-year cycle, for example. These scientists noted that the master dry periods occurred about A.D. 200+, A.D. 700+, and A.D. 1200+. During these times, great movements of certain peoples took place. We have already noted that while Christianity was gradually conquering the Western world, barbarians of all sorts invaded the civilized world (A.D. 200+) and advanced to the Eternal City itself. Five hundred years later came the spread of the Arabs and the rise of Islam, the pouring out of the Mongols from the Asian deserts, and the movements of the Slavs—a period of great restlessness and slaughter.

Let it be noted that the "lowest" dip of the last super cycle occurred during the early centuries of the Christian era. Let it also be noted that the age of exploration and colonization in the western world came close to the time of the high peak in this super cycle, a fact of fateful significance for the New World (Fig. 1). Regretfully, a low trough of this same cycle should take place in our own times, about A.D. 2500.

There are other ways in which sunspot cycles affect us and our surroundings, especially during the eleven-year cycles. A correlation between sunspot cycles and changes in the character of earth magnetism has been noted by C. Chree and S. Capman of London, whose data covered about a hundred years. They demonstrated slight peaks of intensity in terrestrial magnetism during high-sunspot years, but, more significantly, they noted an increase in associated cosmic vibrations, including earth waves. At the Foundation for the Study of Cycles, E. R. Dewey associated years of business prosperity with high-sunspot years. Reports from the American Medical Association indicate that general health is better during those years, and deaths from noxious diseases are down. Finally, the National Institute of Mental Health claims increased admittance to mental hospitals for this same period. In short, the high-sunspot years seem to be stormy and wet, cool and bracing, good for crops and business, and excellent for physical health—but they may be hard on the nervous system.

Another paradox has been pointed out. Cycle calmness and warmth appear to instigate and incite creative endeavors, the various renascences of art being a case in point. These creative times are associated with an increase in the stimulating ozone in the atmosphere, according to the meteorological evidence of H. H. Clayton, of Boston. The exact nature of the beneficial relationship that ozone has to creativity and mental health is not known; only the statistical association has been noted. We must not forget, though, that nearly all explorers have been impressed by the good nature of the natives of the Arctic, and measurements do show that the ozone content is much higher in these very cold regions than elsewhere.

The Earth's Orbit and Our Seasons

Much more intricately associated with our everyday lives is the constant, relentless activity of the sun. It is responsible for our day and night, our seasons, our calendar, our time measurement, and ultimately our records. First let us look at the movement of our earth around the sun once every year: that orbit is more than 600 million miles long (Fig. 2).

This orbit of the earth is responsible for our seasons. The axis of the earth—that is, a line through the earth from pole to pole—is inclined 23½ degrees from the axis of the sun. This means that the earth exposes different parts of itself to the direct rays of the sun in its yearly orbit. The earth's orbit is counterclockwise around the sun, as is the orbit of most heavenly bodies, and the 23½ degrees of inclination is outward, away from the axis of the sun. Therefore, the southern half of the earth's surface is exposed to the direct rays of the sun on the right-hand wing of the orbit, and the northern half is exposed on the left-hand wing of the orbit. Note that the eccentricity of the orbit actually puts our earth closer to the sun in winter than in summer.

The direct rays of the sun produce the greatest heating, whereas at larger angles the heating is lessened. Consequently, the areas which receive direct rays are hot, and these are generally the areas near the middle of the earth or near the equator. Those areas toward the poles are exposed to the angular rays of the sun and therefore get less heating. The direct rays of the sun strike wherever the direct portion or middle part of the earth is pointed at any given time of year. Hence, it is logical that in the right-hand side of the orbit the direct rays of the sun move to 23½ degrees south of the equator. In the left-hand side of the orbit, the direct rays move to 23½ degrees north of the earth's equator.

The limits of maximum movement, north and south, of the direct rays of the sun are known, respectively, as the Tropic of Cancer and the Tropic of Capricorn. When the sun reaches its northern zenith on June 21, the phenomenon is known as

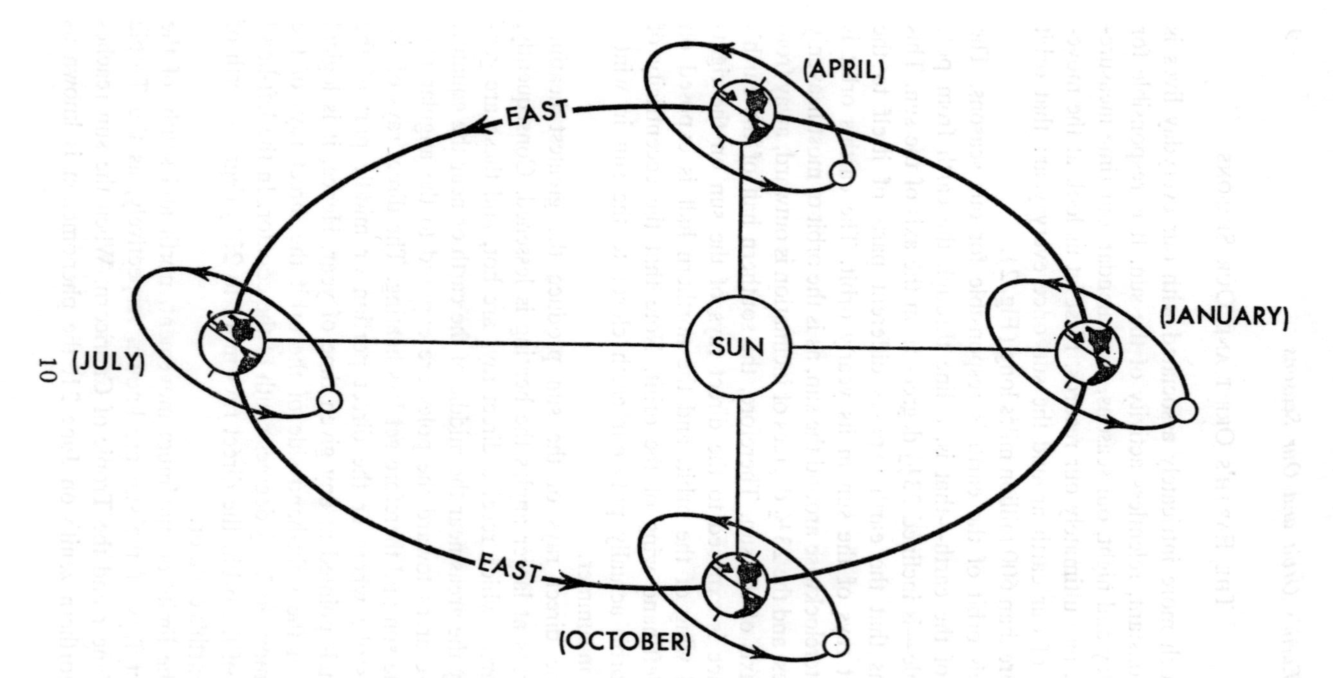

Fig. 2. The earth and the moon in their orbits about the sun.

the summer solstice. When it reaches its southern zenith on December 21, the phenomenon is known as the winter solstice. When the high sun crosses the equator in between, on March 21 and September 21, they are known, respectively, as the vernal or spring equinox and the fall or autumnal equinox.

The area in between 23½ degrees north latitude and 23½ degrees south latitude is known roughly as the tropics. This is because the direct rays of the sun are always in this area. Here the noonday sun is directly overhead at least one day out of the year at every place. The places which are very close to the equator experience the sun directly overhead many days.

The opposite is the case in the very high latitudes in both the northern and southern hemispheres. The North Pole is 90 degrees north latitude; the South Pole is 90 degrees south latitude. It stands to reason that if the direct rays of the sun migrate to 23½ degrees north in June and to 23½ degrees south of the equator in December, then somewhere near the North Pole there must be continuous daylight in June and somewhere near the South Pole there must be continuous daylight in December. In fact, above approximately 66½ degrees north latitude and below 66½ degrees south latitude there is at least one day of total darkness and at least one day of complete light. These two lines are known as the Arctic Circle and the Antarctic Circle.

The areas north of the Arctic Circle and south of the Antarctic Circle are also known as the north polar area and the south polar area. In between the Arctic Circle and the Tropic of Cancer and in between the Antarctic Circle and the Tropic of Capricorn lie what is known in general in both hemispheres as the middle latitudes. Some have characterized these as the temperate zones, because the tropics are hot, and north of the Arctic Circle and south of the Antarctic Circle it is mostly frigid. But these in-between zones are far from temperate. They are the zones of battle between the air masses of the tropics and the air masses of the arctics—between the forces of the low latitudes and the forces of the high latitudes. They are the zones in which most people now in the higher states of civilization live. It has been noted that the angle of inclination of the earth's axis is relatively constant with relation to the axis of the sun; thus, in the yearly orbit of our earth around the sun we have our seasons.

The Earth's Rotation and Time

We come now to the interesting phenomenon of the rotation of our earth on its axis. While the rotation is rather lazy, it appears to be most beneficial to life. Mercury, the nearest planet to the sun, is so locked within its gravitational field that it has no rotation of its own. It is baked on the side of the sun and frozen on the side opposite. Venus, the next planet out from the sun, is still very closely caught within its gravitational field. Hence, Venus has a very slow rotation, almost an eighth of a year for a day, and this appears to be retrograde owing to an alleged astronomical accident in a bygone age. Earth, with its 365 rotations in its year, seems to have an ideal relationship. On Venus one side gets extremely cold during its night and the other side in its day must get extremely warm. Violent storms—that is, strong movements of gases, which for lack of a better term we will call winds—possibly sweep the surface of Venus continuously.

On the earth the heating of the day and the cooling of the night is at such a moderate pulsation that it sustains life. Our daily habits of sleep and wakefulness are adjusted to it. Mars apparently has a day comparable to that of the earth, but indications lead us to believe that Mars does not have a dense enough atmosphere or enough water vapor or free oxygen to support the kind of life we know. The 1965 Mariner probe of Mars showed that the red planet may be completely dry.

The distant planets are too far removed from the sun's gravitational pull to slow down the speed of their rotation. Gigantic Jupiter, which is at least ten times the size of the earth, has a ten-hour day. It rotates so fast that its clouds become stratified, and this heavenly body has a banded look. Saturn is the same, and so it is for the rest of the planets. Neptune's equator, peculiarly, is not inclined in a fashion similar to the equatorial plan of the sun, as are the other planets; it lies on its side and spins in a manner similar to a knocked-over top.

The rotation of our earth, a complete round every twenty-four hours, indicates how we reckon time. Inasmuch as the rotation is at a speed of about a thousand miles an hour at the equator, the full circumference of the earth is rotated in twenty-four hours, more or less. Since the earth's equatorial circumference is divided into 360 degrees, which is called "longitude," the earth itself rotates about 15 degrees an hour. This, basically, is the framework of our time zones.

Decades ago it was recognized by scientists that some zero point for time zones and longitude should be recognized. Consequently, a line running through the observatory at Greenwich, England, was chosen. This was considered the zero meridian or the prime meridian.

With the prime meridian or zero hour at Greenwich, England, time is reckoned westward an hour every 15 degrees. Longitude, of course, is measured in degrees westward from Greenwich to 180 degrees west. Longitude is reckoned eastward also from the zero meridian to 180 degrees east. From both directions to the middle of the Pacific Ocean on the other side of the earth, at 180 degrees meridian, both east longitude and west longitude meet. This is called the international date line. Here, as one travels eastward, he moves from whatever time it is by his clock today to that same time yesterday. As he crosses this line westward, he moves from today to tomorrow. This line is arbitrary, naturally, but some place had to be set for the changeover.

Globes, Maps, and Projections

The division of the earth into 360 degrees of longitude around its circumference helps locate places. For example, New York is located at about 73 degrees west longitude and St. Louis at about 90 degrees west longitude. In addition, a similar system of lines based on the 360 degrees of a circle is used to locate places with relation to the earth's equator—that is, the belt around the middle of the earth. These are known as "latitude" lines. They are imaginary lines around the world parallel to the equator, and they progress from 0 degrees at the equator to 90 degrees at the North Pole and from 0 degrees at the equator to 90 degrees at the South Pole. They cross at right angles all longitude lines, including the prime meridian and the international date line.

On the other side of the earth these lines progress also from equator to both poles by 90 degrees, both north and south, respectively. They measure 360 degrees around the earth from equator to pole, to equator, to pole, and to equator again. New York, which is approximately 73 degrees west longitude, is about 42 degrees north latitude. St. Louis, which we said was about 90 degrees west longitude, would be about 38 degrees north latitude. In this way, places on the earth are described by the arbitrary breakdown of the circles. The degrees are divided into 60 minutes and each minute into 60 seconds, so that places can readily be located on the earth's surface with a high degree of accuracy.

On this basis globes and modern maps are made. With this system of latitude and longitude we can make a replica of the earth and draw thereon continents, oceans, and islands. We can locate cities, mountains, and seas.

All of us are familiar with globes. They represent the earth and its approximate shape, for the earth is essentially a distorted sphere. Most objects rotating in space take on the shape of a sphere or some similar form. If a body in space rotates too fast, the sphere becomes flat as in the case of Jupiter and Saturn. With a slow, lazy rotation like that of our earth, the flattening is only slight. The polar axis of our earth is only about twenty-seven miles shorter than the equatorial axis. Consequently, the earth comes pretty close to being a sphere.

The problem, however, lies not in making globes, although this is a very tedious task, but in making maps, which are flat representations on paper or other flat reproduction media of all or part of the earth's surface. It can be seen at once that it is impossible to represent a spherical surface or a part thereof on a flat piece of paper. There has to be some distortion—and there is. It takes the form of inaccuracy in area, shape, direction, or distance.

The old adage that a map is perfect is erroneous. It can be perfect for a certain purpose, or close to perfect, but obviously it cannot be perfect in every respect. Therefore, cartographers make maps for specific purposes. They arrange their latitude and longitude lines so they get as much accuracy as possible in one of the four aspects mentioned above. This arrangement of latitude and longitude lines is called "projection." On this projection, by reference to latitude and longitude lines, the peripheries of the continents and seas and islands and other features of the earth are drawn. Then other map detail, such as the locations of cities, is added.

The principle behind this arrangement of latitude and longitude lines is inherent in its name. Basically, it is the throwing of the latitude and longitude lines from a globe onto a flat piece of paper by placing a light in or somewhere near the globe and letting the shadows of the latitude and longitude lines reflect on the paper, which can then be rolled out flat. Now this flat paper can be placed as it is, without rolling, either on the side of the globe or held a distance from the globe. The light can be inside the globe or on the opposite side of the globe. Projections made like this are called "orthographic." We can also go about it differently. The piece of paper can be wrapped around the globe like a cylinder. Projections made that way are called "cylindrical." In other instances, the flat piece of paper may be rolled up in the shape of a cone, or dunce cap, and placed over a portion of the earth, and the latitude and longitude lines can be reflected thereon. These are known as "conic" projections.

As one might guess, these projections look quite different from one another. An example of the orthographic projection is seen in those familiar projections where two circles are drawn, each showing one half of the globe with the latitude lines as straight lines and the longitude lines converging to the poles. The cylindrical projection is characterized by both straight latitude and longitude lines, crossing at right angles to one another. Such a projection is used on many of the sailing charts of the world. The conic or polyconic projection is recognized by the latitude lines being curved lines and the longitude lines being straight lines converging toward the poles.

These are the principles by which maps are made. Actually, all projections are worked out mathematically rather than graphically, as just described, but the principles are the same. There are more than a hundred different projections, using combinations of the above. They are slanted for four different uses: (1) the showing of equal area, (2) the showing of true shape, (3) the showing of true distance, and (4) the showing of true direction.

The showing of **equal area** comprises the most common of projections and is the one used most in the classroom, for it allows comparison of areas throughout the world. It implies that the scale of the map, which simply says that a certain distance on the map is equal to so many miles on the ground, is constant. Consequently, areas of wheat production can be compared all over the world. Equal-area (sometimes called equivalent) projections are usually of the conic or polyconic type or adaptations thereof. Among them are Denoyers semi-elliptical projection, the sinusoidal projection, the Mollweide homolographic projection, the parabolic projection, the Boggs authalic projection, the Aitoff projection, and others (Fig. 3). Topographic maps, also, showing elevation and configuration of the land areas of the world, are mostly made on this type of projection.

Whereas the equal area projections are good for showing comparison throughout the world, they are poor for showing shapes of areas and distances and directions. We could not navigate well by sea or air by them. For providing **true shapes** of the land masses and water areas, the cylindrical type of projection seems to be best. The most common of this type is known as the Mercator projection. It was devised in the sixteenth century by a Dutchman named Gerhard Kremer, whose

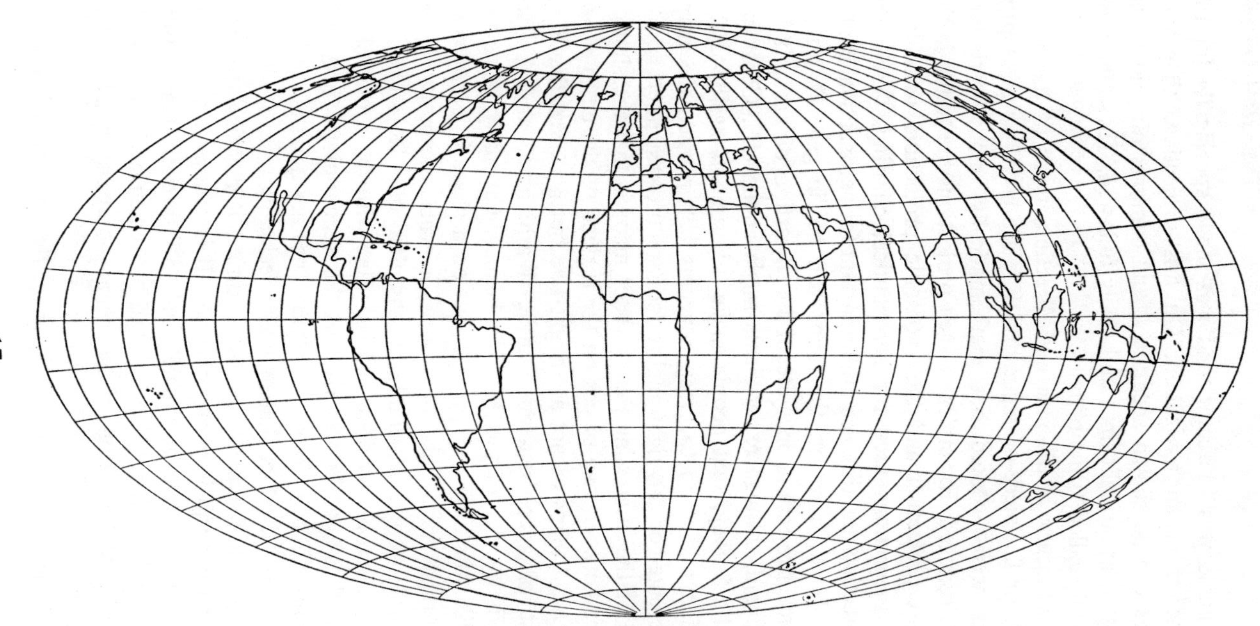

Fig. 3. Aitoff's equal-area projection of the sphere.

Latin name was Mercator, and was made specifically for the purpose of ocean navigation. On this projection, shapes of features can be shown accurately, and compass directions can be plotted as straight lines and easily followed. These lines are commonly called "rhumb" lines.

For **accuracy in distance and direction,** types of the orthographic or flat-piece-of-paper principle are used. As these projections were worked out mathematically, many variations were introduced. Examples of such projections are found in the Lambert projection and the gnomonic projection, as well as in the projections used for aeronautical charting. Obviously, true direction and distance are important for aeronautical charts. In this book, however, the maps will be, in general, on the Mercator projection, in spite of its distortion of area. It has been found, through experiments made at the U.S. Coast and Geodetic Survey, that people make adjustments easily to this distortion and seem to grasp concepts better when the maps are presented on this right-angle or square-grid system.

One of the interesting things about maps is that the shortest distance between two places on the surface of the earth shows up on most maps as not a straight line but a curved line. The shortest distance between Seattle, Washington, and Tokyo, Japan, is by way of the Aleutian Islands. On many maps this looks like the long way around, but on a globe it is obviously the shortest way. This, of course, is what is known as the great-circle route. It simply means that one is following a course around the world which is in line with the center of the globe and is the shortest distance between points. This concept is not difficult, for all longitude lines are great-circle lines.

In spite of the fact that mapping techniques have advanced greatly within the past several centuries, it remains true that much of the earth is poorly mapped. It is estimated that topographical maps cover adequately only a little more than a third of the earth's surface. Nautical and bathymetric charting—that is, mapping of the bottom of the oceans—only covers adequately the coastal areas of a little more than a third of the earth. The depth of the oceans is very poorly charted, where it is charted at all. Aeronautical charting of an acceptable accuracy is available for only about one-half of the earth. As for geodetic control—base locations on earth which are tied fast by fixes on stars (the actual basis for locating places by latitude and longitude)—it is available for only one-third of the earth.

Although modern aerial photography has advanced greatly, our world is not yet mapped on a large enough scale to be truly useful. Vast portions of the world—for example, the Gran Chaco region of Argentina and Paraguay, the Mato Grosso of Brazil, the interiors of Asia and Africa, and even parts of Australia—are yet to be done. The full use of our world that is our heritage can come only after it is adequately charted, and high-precision mapping cameras are now being placed aboard earth-circling satellites to take aerial photos suitable for reasonably large-scale mapping. With proper geodetic control, these photos are being compiled into maps which should eventually diminish the lag in world mapping and in geographical information in general.

We often consider mapping, as we know it, as a development of the modern age. This, however, is not entirely exact. We think of Columbus in the fifteenth century as a visionary who came to the conclusion that the world is a sphere and intrepidly sailed out into the unknown against all dangers. This, too, is a misconception, for the ancient Greeks knew of the spheroidicity of the earth. A globe made by a Greek mathematician, Crates of Mallos, more than a century before the birth of Christ, even outlined some of the basic continents (Fig. 4), visualizing to a certain extent the new world.

It has been hypothesized that long before the advent of the ancient Greeks there existed continents, attached to the present ones, which have since sunk beneath the sea. We are familiar with the story of Atlantis, the great microcontinent which was supposed to have existed in the Atlantic. Then there was Lemuria or Moria, which is thought to have existed in the Pacific. Gondwanaland may have covered much of the Indian Ocean and the South Atlantic (Fig. 5). Drawings and descriptions of all these continents existed among the ancients.

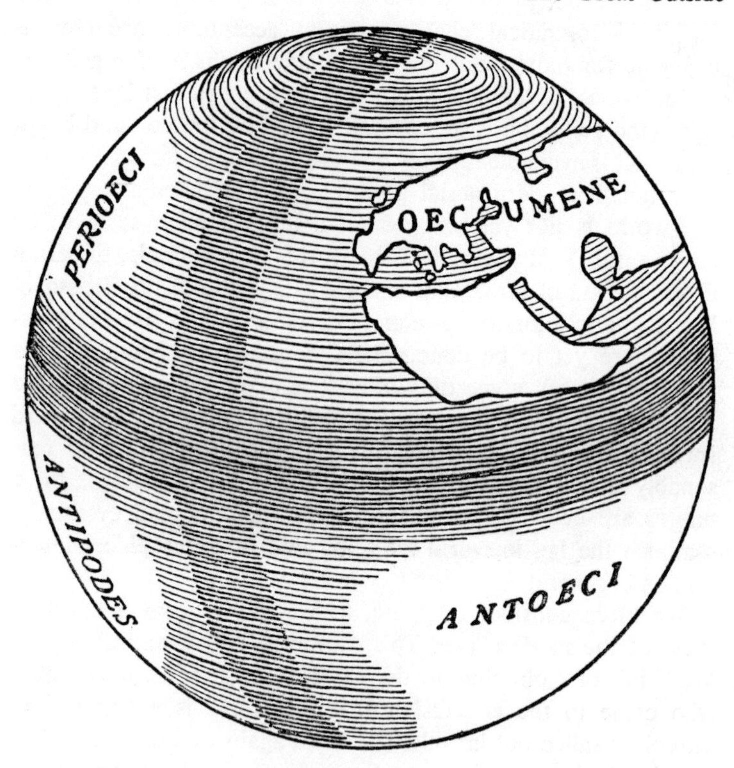

Fig. 4. Globe according to Crates.

It has been reported that Phoenician sailors navigated around the Cape of Good Hope hundreds of years before the birth of Christ and many centuries before the voyage of Vasco da Gama, although a violent controversy persists on this point. The New World was known to the early Vikings and to those who came before them. Among the earlier visitors to the New World, besides the Indians, were allegedly some of the "lost tribes" of Europe, Chinese sailors in their sturdy junks, and Japanese fishermen in Ecuador about 3000 B.C.! Recent archaeological discoveries by Dr. and Mrs. Clifford Evans of the Smith-

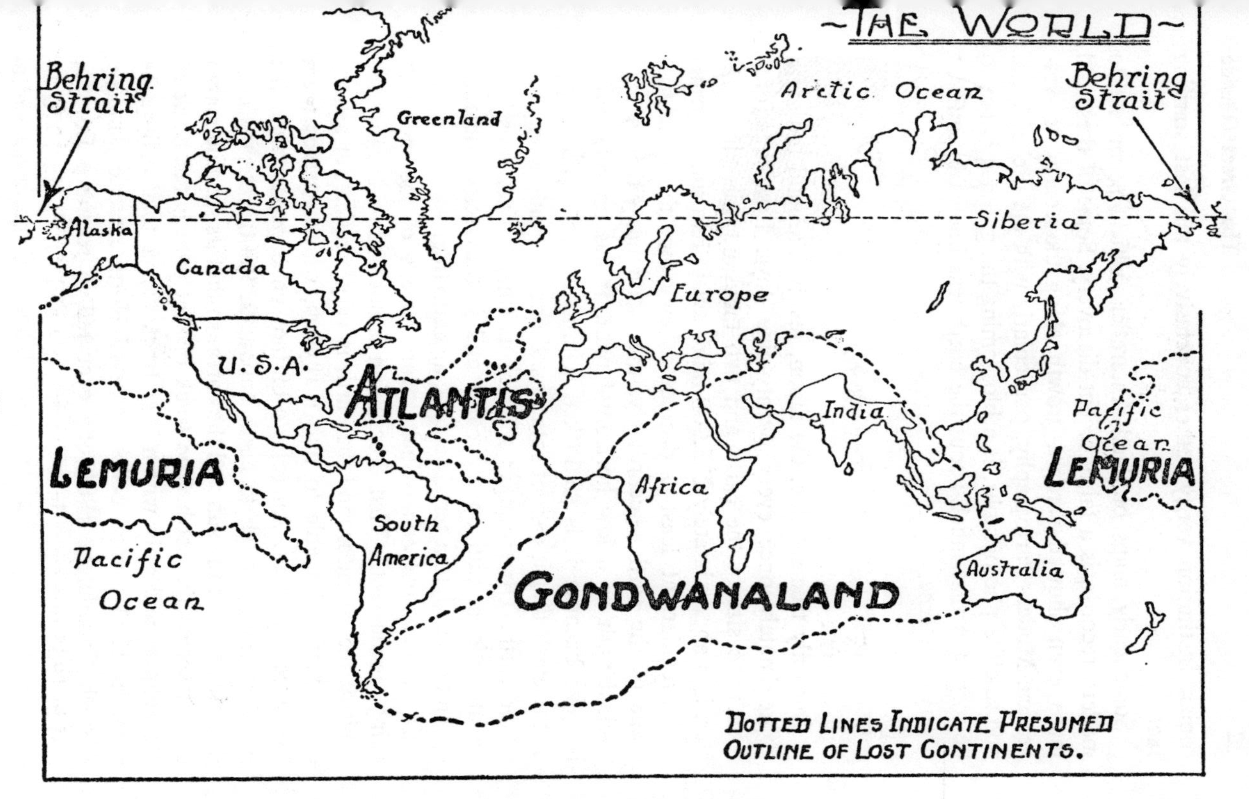

Fig. 5. Three lost continents.

sonian Institution verify rather conclusively this last startling fact.

Some early maps outlined Antarctica, which, according to modern records, is a fairly recent discovery. Some of these old maps even showed verdant growth along the coasts of Antarctica. Modern cartography, particularly with the use of aerial and satellite photographs, is a blossoming thing, but it is not to be forgotten that much about the earth was known by man at a very early time.

The Moon

Our only true satellite, the moon, revolves around the earth approximately once every twenty-nine days. Less than one-fourth the size of the earth and two thousand miles in diameter, it is approximately 235,000 miles away. Its orbit is erratic and irregular, at least 5 degrees askew from the equatorial plane of the earth. Accordingly, the moon has either a high vaulted path or a low horizontal path. It has no rotation of its own because it is so locked within the gravitational pull of the earth that it cannot rotate, and one side only is exposed to the earth. The moon, in spite of its smaller size, does have an attractional pull on the earth and is thus responsible for ocean tides and, to a certain extent, an earth tide.

In *Romeo and Juliet* Shakespeare speaks of the moon as being "inconstant." That description is not wrong, because the orbit of the moon around the earth is very erratic. Yet astronomers have been able to find a rhythm, which enables them to forecast eclipses. An eclipse of the sun happens when the moon is close enough to earth (about 233,000 miles) and is directly between the sun and the earth, so that its shadow makes a path across the earth. The track of that path is the track of the eclipse, and only within that track can a total eclipse be seen. In 1963 a total eclipse crossed North America, mostly through Canada. In 1961 one occurred in southern Europe, and in 1955 one came in southern Asia and Africa. In 1970 an eclipse will cross southern Mexico. There is an eclipse of the sun somewhere in the world at least once during every decade.

Eclipses of the moon are similar to eclipses of the sun, but they are possible only during the full moon, when the earth is between the sun and the moon. Generally, the orbit of the moon is such that light passes around the earth to illuminate the moon and show its fullness. However, when the orbit is so situated that the earth is squarely between the sun and the moon, a total eclipse of the moon takes place.

This brings us to what we may call the phases of the moon. In its twenty-nine days of orbit around the earth, the moon shows us its full face and then various parts of it until it is blanked out. Then it reappears practically as a crescent, at new moon, and grows bit by bit until it is once again full (Fig. 6).

The light we see from the moon is reflected light—light originating from the sun. It is easily understood that when the moon, in its counterclockwise orbit around the earth, stands between the earth and sun we are in the dark of the moon, and when it stands opposite the sun we have a full moon. Because of the moon's erratic orbit, light from the sun is usually able to get to the moon in spite of the earth's being in between, so at night we see the full face of the moon at full moon time.

The waxing and the waning of the moon has been studied for centuries. Farmers have planted and harvested and many other activities have been gauged by the regular activity of the moon in its monthly orbit. The greatest influence of this orbit, however, is on the earth itself. It has been definitely established that the moon has a gravitational pull on the tides in the water bodies of the earth. And there is even an earth tide—that is, a slight pulling of the land masses of the earth. Recent studies have shown tides also in the earth's atmosphere. These appear to be greatest in the autumn and may be partially responsible for the occurrence of hurricanes at that time.

It is not just the moon's gravitational pull but also its attraction, in conjunction with that of the sun, that affects our

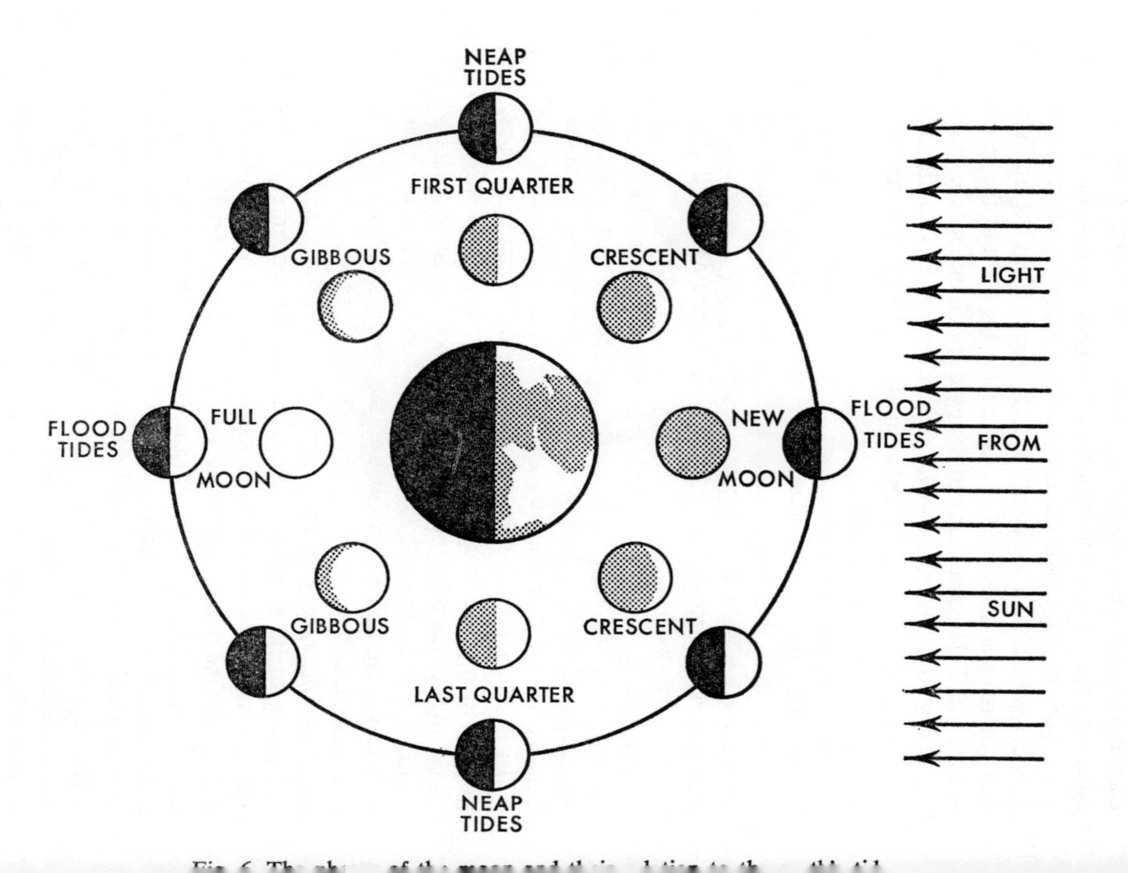

NEAP TIDES
FIRST QUARTER
GIBBOUS
CRESCENT
LIGHT
FLOOD TIDES
FULL MOON
NEW MOON
FLOOD TIDES
FROM
GIBBOUS
CRESCENT
SUN
LAST QUARTER
NEAP TIDES

tides. Tides are caused basically by both the sun and the moon's pull, and, as we know, two high tides and two low tides occur every day. The two high tides are about twelve hours apart, and the two low tides occur roughly about the same number of hours apart.

We know that we are exposed only once in one day to the moon. Why then are there two high tides? As the earth rotates and exposes an ocean basin to the moon, the pull of the moon raises a mound of water as it passes. This mound of water spreads its influence like pebble ripples on a pond, and it sloshes about the ocean basin and generates a high tide. After the ocean basin water is released by the moon, it settles back to normal and a low tide occurs. When an ocean basin on the other side of the earth is exposed to the moon, a high tide then occurs there. However, in the basin on the opposite side of the earth from the moon, the one that twelve hours earlier had had a high tide because it was then exposed to the moon, another high tide also occurs.

Why is there a high tide when the ocean basin is on the opposite side from the moon? The pull of the moon is direct when the basin is exposed directly to the moon's pull, indirect when it is on the opposite side. Naturally, the moon's pull is stronger on the side of the earth nearest it. It is the difference between the strength of these two pulls which explains the pull on the opposite side. In other words, in one place ocean water is being pulled up from the earth by the moon, and in the other place the earth is being pulled away from the ocean. In both cases a high tide results. Shallow seas adjacent to oceans often have little or no tide unless they are under the direct path of the moon. If their outlets are not in the path of the spread of the tidal bulge's influence or the sloshing in the ocean basins, they will experience a virtually tideless condition, such as in the Mediterranean Sea, or have only weak tides, as in the Gulf of Mexico. Some tidal estuaries, however, are right in the path of the surges and the sloshing, and in addition are constricted, and they experience tides as high as fifty feet, as in the Bay of Fundy on the east coast of North America.

As noted earlier, the pull of the sun affects tides much as the moon does. When the sun and moon are directly in line with the earth, they are pulling together and the tides are the highest. Those times are in the dark of the moon, when the moon is directly in line between the earth and the sun, and at full moon, when the moon is directly in line with the sun on the opposite side of the earth. Then the tides are higher and are often referred to as "high" high tides, "spring" tides, or "flood" tides. When the moon is at the half-moon stage, its pull is at a right angle with the pull of the sun, and hence the combined pull is much less and the tides are much lower. The tides then are known as "low" high tides or "neap" tides.

As tides come in, they break along the coast and where they strike at an angle they cause tidal currents. In some places these currents are considerable, and shipping has to adjust to them. (These currents and others will be discussed in Chapter 4 when we speak in detail about the oceans.) Let us not overlook the moon's influence on the land: where it causes marked tides in the water, it causes lesser tides on the more rigid land. These are hardly perceptible, but they do exist and are worth noting.

The supposed influence of the moon on individuals is legendary and has been noted since antiquity. The very word "lunatic" implies that the lunar pull has some effect upon the nervous system. It has been held that where the nervous system is marginally stable, the moon can make the difference between rational and irrational behavior.

In recent years man-made satellites have photographed parts of the moon's surface at close range. Consequently, we are learning more and more about the moon. There is no appreciable atmosphere, for the gravitational and magnetic fields are not strong enough to sustain it. Without a protective atmosphere, the moon's surface is exposed to the pitiless heat (more than 300 degrees Fahrenheit) of the sun on the exposed side and suffers extreme cold on the other.

Scientists have now been able to ascertain that the moon's surface is pitted by huge craters and large flat-bottomed areas known as basins or "seas." High mountains have been observed on the moon but no sign of vegetation or any sign of life. Scientists have suggested that the moon may possibly be constructed of materials similar to those of earth's crust—that is, granite and other types of siliceous igneous rocks. However, Charles R. Warren, of the U.S. Geological Survey, in a study released in 1964, suggested that the moon may be made up largely of a mixture of cosmic dust and ice. He thinks the large craters were made by meteors and meteorites striking the surface. The huge *maria* or seas supposedly were made by water which has since evaporated and escaped. Robert Dietz of the U.S. Coast and Geodetic Survey believes that the seas are actually the solidification of material melted into fluid at the time of meteor impact and then later hardened. Whatever the composition of the moon, it is possible that man's flight to it may come to pass in a very few years; a photographic rocket on July 31, 1964, landed on it. Soon we will have reliable knowledge about our natural satellite.

THE UNIVERSE

We have seen that the earth, with its moon satellite, is just one of nine satellites of our sun. Now let us see where the sun fits into the immense panorama of stars that pass overhead at night. As much as we may not care to admit it, the sun is not one of the larger stars but is actually among the minor heavenly bodies of the universe. It is only one of millions of stars in a great gathering which astronomers refer to as "our galaxy" and we often allude to as the Milky Way. In short, our sun and the millions of other stars in our galaxy form a huge spherical cluster which has been measured as being about 80 million light years across. Distances here are so vast that they have to be measured in terms of the speed of light, which is 186,000 miles per second.

Our galaxy, although spherical in shape, has its greatest concentration of stars along its equatorial plane. Hence, when we look into the heavens and see the Milky Way across the sky, we are looking along the equatorial axis of our galaxy. All the stars we can see with the naked eye are in our galaxy. One of the closest, brightest stars to us is the Dog Star, called Sirius. It is a little more than eight light years away. Our star, the sun, is located along the equatorial plane of our galaxy, about a third of the way out from the center. All stars in the galaxy are traveling at tremendous speeds counterclockwise around the galactic center or vortex. For example, our sun is traveling around this center at a rate of 180 miles per second.

As if our galaxy were not large enough, astronomers, with their huge optical and radio telescopes, have been able to ascertain that there are millions of galaxies similar to ours in the boundless universe. The closest one to us is the Magellanic Cloud, approximately 400,000 light years away, which was discovered by Magellan on his historic voyage around the world. The spiral galaxy which we most frequently see pictured is M 31 in the constellation Andromeda (constellations are simply convenient frameworks in which to place all the stars we see with the naked eye and the galaxies that we see with the telescope), more than 90 million light years away. Thus, the universe is practically infinite, and astronomers have detected that it is even growing larger. Stars and galaxies are moving away from one another at terrific speed, thus expanding the entire universe—the "great outside," as we may call it.

Even though our earth is only a tiny satellite of a small star in an immeasurable, cold, black universe, it appears to be, at least in present uncontested knowledge, the only place where life as we know it has developed and the only place where oxygen in a free form exists.

SELECTED REFERENCES

Abbott, Charles G. *The Earth and the Stars*. 2nd ed. New York: D. Van Nostrand Co., 1946.

Baker, Robert H. *Astronomy*. 8th ed. Princeton, N.J.: D. Van Nostrand Co., 1964.

Baldwin, Ralph B. *The Face of the Moon*. Chicago: University of Chicago Press, 1949.

Becker, Robert O. "Geomagnetism and Health." *Annals*, Veterans Hospital. Syracuse, 1962.

Beer, Arthur (ed.). *Vistas in Astronomy.* 5 vols. New York: Pergamon Press, 1955–1962.

Brooks, C. E. P. *Climate Throughout the Ages.* London: Ernest Benn, 1926.

Brown, Frank. "Magnetism of Animals and Man." *Proceedings,* American Institute of Medical Climatology. Philadelphia, 1963.

Brown, Lloyd A. *The Story of Maps.* Boston: Little, Brown & Co., 1950.

Chree, C. "Relation Between Sunspots and Terrestrial Magnetism." *Nature,* Vol. 115, 1925.

Clayton, Henry H. *Solar Relations to Weather and Life.* 2 vols. Canton, Mass.: Clayton Weather Service, 1943.

Defant, Albert. *Ebb and Flow: The Tides of Earth, Air, and Water.* Ann Arbor: University of Michigan Press, 1958.

DuBridge, Lee A. *Introduction to Space.* New York: Columbia University Press, 1962.

Dyson, Frank W., and R. R. Wooley. *Eclipses of the Sun and Moon.* Oxford: Clarendon Press, 1937.

Edgeworth, Kenneth E. *The Earth, the Planets, and the Stars.* New York: Macmillan Co., 1961.

Gamow, George. *The Birth and Death of the Sun; Stellar Evolution and Sub-Atomic Energy.* New York: Viking Press, 1945.

Greenhood, David. *Down to Earth.* New York: Holiday House, 1951.

Harang, Leiv. *The Aurorae.* New York: John Wiley & Sons, 1951.

Hoyle, Fred. *Astronomy.* New York: Doubleday & Co., 1962.

Huntington, Ellsworth. *Civilization and Climate.* New Haven: Yale University Press, 1924.

Kornbluch, Igno H. "Heating Potentials and Electromagnetism." *Proceedings,* American Institute of Medical Climatology. Philadelphia, 1964.

Ley, Willy. *The Days of Creation.* New York: Modern Age Books, 1941.

McLean, K. E. "Electromagnetic Therapy." *Proceedings,* American Institute of Medical Climatology, Philadelphia, 1964.

Menzel, Donald H. *Our Sun.* Rev. ed. Cambridge: Harvard University Press, 1959.

Miller, Freeman D. *Astronomy as a Career.* Boston: Bellman Publishing Co., 1963.

Mills, Clarence A. *Climate Makes the Man.* New York: Harper & Brothers, 1942.

Minnaert, Marcellus. *The Nature of Light and Colour in the Open Air.* London: George Bell & Sons, 1940; New York: Dover Publications, 1954.

Richardson, Robert S., and Chesley Bonestell. *Man and the Moon.* New York: World Publishing Co., 1961.

Ronan, Colin A. *Changing Views of the Universe.* New York: Macmillan Co., 1961.

Struve, Otto. *Stellar Evolution.* Princeton: Princeton University Press, 1950.

Toynbee, Arnold J. *A Study of History*. London: Oxford University Press, 1956.

U.S. Coast and Geodetic Survey. *Manual of Harmonic Analysis and Prediction of Tides* by Paul Schureman. Rev. (1940) ed. Washington, D.C.: Government Printing Office, 1941.

———. *Tables for Determining the Form of the Geoid and Its Indirect Effect on Gravity* (spec. publ. no. 199) by Walter D. Lambert and Frederick W. Darling. Washington, D.C.: Government Printing Office, 1936.

Van Allen, James A. (ed.). *Scientific Uses of Earth Satellites*. 2nd ed. Ann Arbor: University of Michigan Press, 1958.

Van de Kamp, Peter. *Basic Astronomy*. New York: Random House, 1952.

Von Braun, Wernher. *First Men to the Moon*. New York: Holt, Rinehart & Winston, 1960.

Watkins, Harold. *Time Counts; the Story of the Calendar*. London: Neville Spearman, 1954.

Whipple, Fred L. *Earth, Moon and Planets*. Rev. ed. Cambridge: Harvard University Press, 1963.

Wilkins, Hugh P., and Patrick Moore. *The Moon*. New York: Macmillan Co., 1955.

Chapter 2 / The Mysterious Within

On Good Friday, March 27, 1964, at 5:30 P.M., the most powerful earthquake ever recorded struck southern Alaska. It nearly wrecked the city of Anchorage, leaving wide crevasses in the ground and a devastation of collapsed buildings (*see illustration section*). One island, Montague, was raised about thirty feet, and the elevation of the land above sea level was altered as far away as Mexico. The distant movements of ground—in Washington, D.C., the earth rose a few inches—indicated vast disturbances within the earth (*see illustration section*).

This particular earthquake was registered at 8.6 on the Richter scale of 1 to 10, more potent than the 1906 San Francisco quake of 8.4 magnitude. In 1957 an earthquake in the Altai Mountains of Siberia had registered at 8.5. According to the World Seismological Center of the International Geophysical Union (with headquarters in Washington, D.C.), devastating earthquakes have been on the increase during the past several decades.

Serious volcanic activity, according to the same data center, has been increasing at least for the past three-quarters of a century. Recent volcanic eruptions have occurred in Hawaii, South America, the Philippines, and Asia. Ancient Vesuvius in Europe, asleep for centuries, has been active, and in Mexico Parícutin rose as a new volcano within a few days. One of the worst volcanic disasters in modern times occurred in 1902, when Mount Pelée, on the island of Martinique in the West Indies, ejected a fiery cloud containing temperatures of at least 800 degrees Fahrenheit that rolled down its slope at more than three hundred miles an hour to wipe out the town of Saint-Pierre and its 28,000 inhabitants.

Areas of Crustal Weakness

Besides the active earthquake areas of today (Map 1) which ring the Pacific Ocean and cross southern Europe, southern Asia, and northern Africa, there is evidence all around us of considerable earthquake activity in the past. "Block" mountains, which are blocks of the earth's crust thrust up as mountains by forces from within, are found in the great deserts of North America. Deep "block" valleys are depressions, such as those occupied by the Dead Sea in the Middle East and by the great African lakes. Broad plains and overthrust mountains indicate past shifting of strata in the earth's crust—for example, the Great Plains and the Lewis and Clark Mountains of Montana in North America.

The potentially active volcanoes, interestingly enough, lie in very much the same pattern as the earthquake areas of the world and also represent present-day areas of weakness in the earth's crust. The volcanic belt follows the same path as the earthquake belt across southern Eurasia and around the Pacific Ocean shore (Map 1), which has often been referred to as the "rim of fire" because of its many active volcanoes. Past volcanic activity has left its imprint, for many of the Pacific islands are remnants of dead volcanoes. The Columbia Plateau in North America and the Deccan Plateau in India are also indications of gigantic lava flows in the geological past.

It might well be said that all the continents of the world are held up by mountains. Mountains usually flank closely the edges of the continents, and broad plains or plateaus stretch between them (Map 1). Some of these mountains are young and rugged, with sharp, angular features and steep slopes. Others are rounded and smooth and appear very old.

The Himalayan Mountains across southern Asia are examples of young, rugged mountains, as are the Alps of Europe; many of the mountains of Africa; the Andes of South America; the Rockies, Sierra Nevadas, and coastal ranges of North America; and the mountains of Japan, eastern Asia, Indonesia, and New Zealand. It is fascinating to note, in addition, that these mountains still seem to be in the process of growing. Each new volcano, as well as every upthrust fault, adds to the mass of these slowly evolving ranges.

The older mountains of the world, which must have gone through the same processes in the remote past, are in more quiet areas of the earth today. Such mountains are found in the eastern United States—the Appalachians—and eastern South America. This seems to suggest that the areas of weakness in the earth's crust have varied geographically from time to time.

There are certain inner forces of the earth that have a vital and lasting influence upon each of us. One of these long-unnoticed manifestations has been revealed by a recent earth-circling satellite: *our continents are actually moving.* North America is drifting farther away from Europe; South America is moving away from Africa. Asia seems to be pressing toward Africa and the equator, and Antarctica is edging slightly toward the area of its heaviest ice accumulation. These movements only amount to a few inches in years, but they do indicate that our terra firma is not as firm as we had imagined. Alfred Wegener's theory of continental drift, much maligned fifty years ago, must now be seriously considered.

These movements have been verified by triangulation, a very accurate method of measuring areas on the earth's surface. From distant fixed points, like stars, a series of triangles are spread or fanned out below, forming a chain, and these triangles check one another at the points where they interlock. In the past the actual width of any ocean was not accurately known; triangulation depending upon line of sight could not span them. Now that we are in the Space Age, satellites can be observed against a background of stars, and a triangulation network can be carried across oceans, thus uniting continental systems. (The work has been carried on largely by the U.S. Coast and Geodetic Survey in cooperation with similar organizations in other countries in the world.) This means that the true width of the oceans, the true location of the continental shores, and the true size and shape of the earth can now be determined.

Not only are our continents moving apart but the world may

be getting larger, rather than smaller—as we used to think. Again, the period observed has been short and distances are inconsequential; nevertheless, the import of these revelations is startling, for it contradicts all previously held beliefs that our earth has been shrinking since its birth many eons ago.

Another example of the outward expansion of subterranean forces is the recently observed heat increase on the earth's surface. Until a few years ago, our best assumption was that the earth had cooled from a fiery mass, shrunk, forming our mountains, and was still getting cooler. We can no longer explain the formation of mountains this way. It is now evident that the earth is getting warmer.

Scattered data from observation sites on many continents had formerly pointed in this direction, but they had gone unheeded. Temperatures at given depth in mines had been observed to be higher in recent years, but no significance was attached to this information until temperatures were also taken along the ocean bottom. Scientists can now lower sensitive thermometers to the ocean floor which will pierce through the covering of ooze and get to the actual rock layer of the ocean bottom. With these instruments, investigators of the various maritime nations of the world have been taking temperatures in all the oceans.

Fortunately, a few brave souls had taken some ocean temperatures in the past. When these were compared with current findings, the latter were found to be much higher. Scientists have now been taking temperatures regularly at given places in all the oceans for more than a decade. The increase of heat noted is slight but definite; the trend has been established.

In the process of taking ocean temperatures, another interesting phenomenon came to light: the temperatures on the ocean bottom were not uniform. They seem to be cooler toward the continental edges and warmer toward the middle of the oceans, particularly in the Atlantic.

In the Atlantic Ocean nestles a huge chain of submarine mountains stretching nearly from pole to pole down the middle of the ocean basin (see endpapers). For the most part, its peaks are far below the water surface, so they are no hazard to navigation. The Azores Islands are an exception, for there the peaks of this ridge do break the surface. The submerged peaks seem to have all the characteristics of regular mountains, except that there is none of the usual vegetation on them. On the bottom of the Atlantic Ocean, beneath the bottom ooze, is heat which reaches its warmest point in the vicinity of the submarine ridge of mountains. It was also found that this ridge apparently has a huge crack following roughly along its crest. All of this suggests that the mid-Atlantic ridge has been formed by a gigantic upturn of the bottom of the ocean, which cracked open as it bent up, as if forced by some irresistible power below.

In the Pacific the greatest heat is not in the center of the ocean or down its center but closer to the North American continent. In fact the mid-ocean ridge, which persists in the South Pacific, actually comes to shore in the North Pacific to become the coastal mountains of North America. Elsewhere in the North Pacific are scattered hot spots that soon wane, suggesting that some localized heated areas are caused by release of energy from radioactive elements in places near the earth's surface rather than activity deep within the earth.

The general distribution of temperatures along an ocean's floor, especially in the Atlantic, leads to the suspicion that there are great heat waves coming up near the middle of the oceans. These waves then fan out, dissipate, and cool, dropping back down again near the edges of continents. This theory, advanced especially by Maurice Ewing of Columbia University, is in accord with the other theory of an expanding world because, as a rule, materials that heat up also expand (Fig. 7).

Slipping of the Earth's Crust

Charles Hapgood has suggested that heat near the earth's surface could cause a viscous or semifluid layer less than a hundred miles from the surface of the earth. He believes that

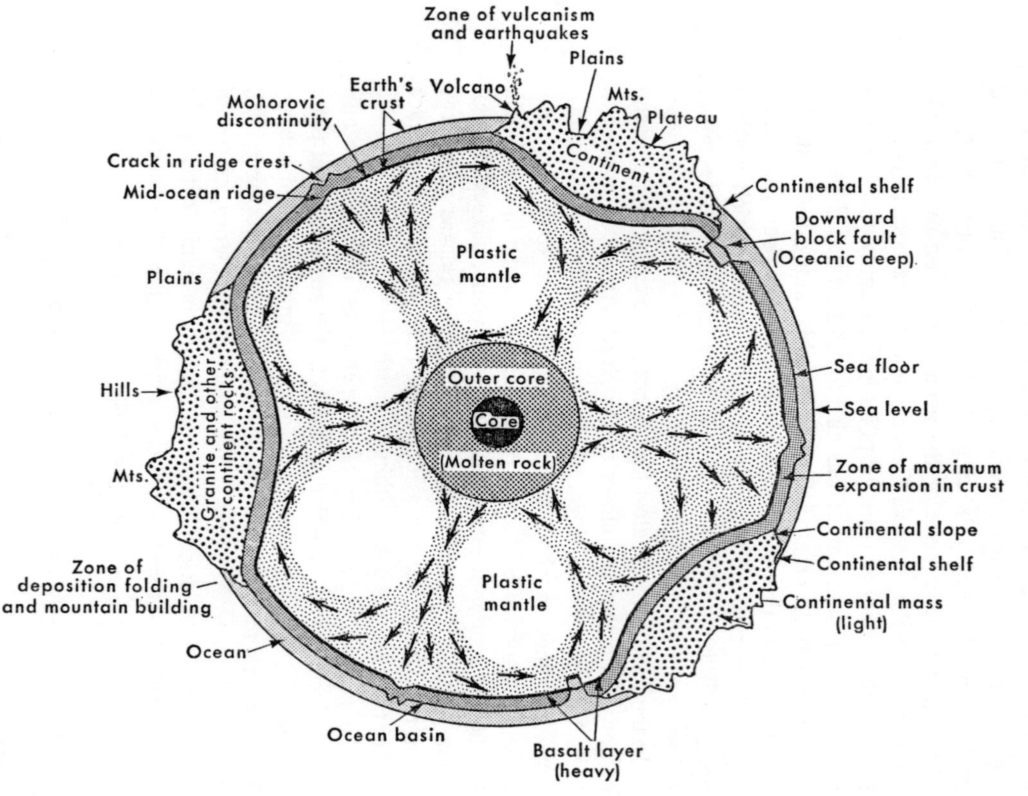

Fig. 7. Generalized profile of continental masses and ocean basins, with generalized flow of

such a layer does exist and on it the earth's crust has slipped, like the peel of an orange, from time to time in the geological past. He makes a strong case for his theory by showing that the ice we see now on the continent of Antarctica and on Greenland once covered equatorial portions of the earth in past ice ages. He does not claim that great ice caps advanced to the equator but suggests rather that the earth's crust slipped and put equatorial regions in polar areas and vice versa. His theory is further substantiated by the evidence of green vegetation found beneath the ice cap of Antarctica.

Hapgood shows how imbalances in the earth's crust could cause slippage. We know that the earth rotates about one thousand miles an hour at the equator. Imbalances of any sort in such a constantly rotating body are bound to develop stresses from centrifugal force, which means that the heavier objects in a whirling motion will want to fly off toward the edges. Hapgood suggests that imbalances in the earth's crust caused such stresses and brought about the slippage of the earth's crust in the past. The idea has even been advanced that this happened once during recorded history. Biblical writings speak of the sun being blotted out for an extended period and then coming up at a different place from where it used to rise.

The concept of a viscous layer less than a hundred miles from the surface of the earth is not without some logic. Seismological investigations indicate that there must be some sort of semiliquid material at that depth, because the S waves of seismographs, which are sensitive to such materials, pick up this layer. This kind of layer would have to exist if we are to accept also the Wegener concept of floating continents, which we know now has the most advanced engineering and scientific data to support it.

Hapgood's theory holds that the slippage occurred rapidly and with great violence, accompanied by overwhelming earthquakes and extremely furious volcanic action. The oncoming of such a period would be heralded by an increase in earth shaking and volcanic activity, which, unfortunately, we have been witnessing in our own times. Also according to this theory, the greatest activity takes place during the sudden rapid slippage of the crust, when a place like London might be relocated at the latitude and longitude of Singapore in a period of less than a day.

Hapgood appears to be the only scientist who has adequately explained the preserved condition of the woolly mammoths of the Holarctic Plains. These enormous, elephantlike animals were so quickly and thoroughly frozen in the far-distant past that their cell structure remained intact. To produce this state, as meat packers know, extremely low temperatures must be applied instantaneously, and Hapgood's theory contains a detailed explanation for this curious event. Volcanic gases, he says, were blasted far into the deep cold of space during the devastating eruptions of a period of crustal slippage. These gases, becoming super cold and heavy, then fell back to earth at a terrific speed. The beasts, grazing in the field, never knew what hit them. They were frozen solid in seconds—as were the subtropical grasses in their mouths.

Hapgood has speculated that the world may be approaching another period of crustal slippage. The increase in diastrophic and volcanic activity in recent decades, and certain rather ominous imbalances in our earth's crust today, superficially tend to bear him out. The most notable imbalances are on the continent of Antarctica, where tremendous thicknesses of ice have built up in recent centuries on the large plateaus closest to Australia.

Although the rotation of the earth is not as rapid in the polar areas as it is near the equator, a considerable amount of centrifugal force can be generated by such enormous weight so far removed from the poles (about 70 degrees south latitude). Hapgood intimates that this could cause a sudden shifting of our crust as much as 20 degrees of latitude. Thus, one who lived in the middle latitudes and experienced this catastrophe could wake up living—if he lived at all—in the tropics. Climatic belts themselves would not shift with the crust, only areas. This may not happen for centuries—but it could also happen within the next ten years.

Balance Adjustments: Isostacy

The consideration of balances in the earth's crust leads us to another concept which is often labeled "isostacy." It is a term borrowed from the Greeks meaning equal stability or equal balance. In this case, it means equal balance in the earth's crust. Let us recall the fact that an object rotating as rapidly as the earth will by centrifugal force throw any object that is out of balance toward its outer edge or even away from it. In short, unless the materials in the earth's crust are balanced as far as weight is concerned, the heavier pieces will tend to be thrown toward the periphery or toward the equator.

A theory regarding this phenomenon was developed early in this century by John Hayford of the U.S. Coast and Geodetic Survey. He proved by numerous observations and calculations that the materials in the earth's crust do tend to balance. He noted that, when they do not balance, stresses are set up, and under heavy stress catastrophes such as earthquakes take place. He dealt strictly with minor imbalances that could adjust themselves, without Hapgood's notion of crustal slippages. His theory, however, included some sort of viscous layer down in the earth, as assumed by Hapgood. If this were not so, how could masses in the earth's crust move?

Hayford's theory, although it did not envisage the slipping of an entire crust, did postulate the slipping of individual blocks of it together with crushing and folding among them. It is possible that the tensions set up by centrifugal force may be relieved by both means. The slippage and adjustment of individual blocks, as suggested by Hayford, could relieve most tensions and could keep the earth's crust in balance. Yet when strong, persistent, and large-scale imbalances develop, such as those in Wilkes Land in Antarctica, perhaps Hapgood's concept of a slipping crust is the only adjustment the earth could make.

Hayford's theory of isostacy assumes primarily that the materials of various weight in the earth's crust will tend to arrange themselves so that the crust will be of equal weight all over. To repeat, this is a natural, physical tendency for the surfaces of rotating bodies. By compiling and correlating thousands of gravity measurements, Hayford was able to present and substantiate his theory, which subsequent information has supported.

Hayford demonstrated that the earth's crust is made up of rocks and minerals of different weights. Continental areas are ordinarily composed of lighter rocks than those which underlie the ocean basins. Consequently, it would take a larger amount of these light rocks to cover, in balance, a given portion of the earth's surface, while it would take only a thin layer of heavy rocks on the ocean floor to preserve balance. Consequently, Hayford concluded that the continents, with their light rocks, would project higher into the air and, by the same token, lower into the plastic layer below the earth's crust.

It follows, too, that the continents, made up basically of granite rocks and their derivatives, would stand above the ocean level. Samples taken from the ocean bottom do show that it is made up of a heavy, dense, black, volcanic type of rock, which is called "basalt." It is also found in certain quarries, and anyone who has visited the Columbia Plateau in the State of Washington has seen this black rock in bold cliffs, particularly in the bluffs along the Columbia River. In central India this rock is exposed in the walls of stream valleys on the Deccan Plateau east of Bombay.

The lighter rocks, making up the continents, are crystalline. Granite is not the only rock found on land, but, as one of a group of siliceous rocks (acidic rocks from which sand, for instance, is derived), all of which are relatively light, it is the most typical.

With the many gravimetric measurements taken by Hayford, it was ascertained beyond question that the continental masses are anchored deeper in the earth's crust than are the basalt layers of the ocean bottom. Like an iceberg, a continent must have a certain amount below the surface.

The crust of the earth is, to sum up, a thin, dark layer with bulges or plates of light rock representing continents resting on it here and there (Fig. 7). These bulges locally depress the general level of the basalt layer. A well-substantiated theory states that the basalt layer does not completely pinch out underneath the continents, and reasonable evidence has been presented which shows that it merely thins out as it is depressed downward. Thus when erosion on continents and deposition in adjacent seas occur, minor imbalances in the earth's surface frequently result. Then certain movements, called "tectonic," take place inside the earth to adjust the earth's surface to an isostatic balance. Perhaps this is the reason that so many mountainous areas are close to continental borders.

Gravity is not only exerted at the surface of the earth; it also progresses to the center of it. Gravity pressure increases from the surface of the earth, from the normal air pressure of about fifteen pounds per square inch to more than twenty-five thousand *tons* per square inch at the center of the earth. This figure, which may be too conservative, is the result of many gravity observations, along with numerous calculations.

The pendulum or the plumb bob is used for measuring gravity. If a plumb bob is suspended, pointing toward the earth directly in line with a radius of the earth, and if the gravity is normal in the area, the weighted bob will point directly toward the center of the earth. If a gravitational anomaly or disturbance exists, the bob will not point toward the center of the earth but will be deflected slightly toward the nearby mountains or hills which may be causing the deflection. Many gravimetric anomalies have been and are being found all over the world. Surprisingly, a large portion of them occur in the areas where extra heating of the earth has been noted. They seem to coincide with weaknesses in the earth's crust and upheavals at the earth's surface.

What Is Inside? The Mohorovic Riddle

Of what does the "mysterious within" consist? We have the observations and investigations made by hundreds of seismologists over several decades to rely upon. These scientists work at colleges and other institutions throughout the world with seismographs, which record earth tremors.

These tremors are shock waves, emanating from an earthquake, which travel through and around the earth. The most violent or P waves, which are also the most noticeable, travel outward along the earth's crust from the seat or epicenter of the earthquake. Another set of waves, the S waves, which we previously said detect the viscous layers, bounce at an angle off the fluid outer core of the center while trying to pass through the earth. Still a third vibration travels obliquely through the earth, missing the fluid material near the center.

The seismograph is simply a drum with recording paper on it attached to a clock. On this paper several little inked arms, called "styluses," each record specific earthquake waves. The distance from a given seismograph to an earthquake is determined by the time interval between the arrival of the P and S waves, because they travel by different routes, the S waves taking the longer time. The epicenter of an earthquake can be located easily by intersecting arcs with the distances from which at least two seismograph stations have recorded the earthquake.

Among other things, these devices can also indicate whether a rock is viscous, molten, or solid, because S waves will alter their markings and decrease speed when passing through semi-fluid matter. The density and possible nature of the deep interior material can also be ascertained, but to a much less certain degree, by the action of these seismic waves; they will not penetrate the fluid outer core of the earth but will glance off it and back to the surface at an angle.

It has been established that the earth's crust averages about thirty miles in thickness. It is made up largely of the basic basaltic rock on the ocean bottoms and the light siliceous rock of the continents. Most volcanoes do not extend below this crustal limit, although some believe that materials beneath are sometimes thrown into volcanic action. Below this crust is believed to be the first of what geologists call "discontinuities," because each represents a distinct change in the character of the rocks.

This one is known as the Mohorovic discontinuity, after the name of its postulator, actually spelled Mohorovicic, but commonly shortened. No one, however, is really sure of this discontinuity—this drastic change in rock type and structure—which ends the earth's crust; no one yet has dug that far into the earth. Project Mohole has been trying for years to drill through the ocean floor to reach and learn for certain about this discontinuity.

Many believe that the rock in the vicinity of the Mohorovic discontinuity is viscous. There seems to be little doubt about the nature of the rock change from basalt to a heavier rock, for earthquake waves indicate this rather definitely. They also indicate an area of somewhat semifluid rock, which is most likely the lower limit of the basalt layer of the earth's crust. We noted before that the basalt layer, which is the only rock comprising the bottom of the ocean basins, also underlies in a much thinner layer the continental masses. In short, the layer of basalt is continuous immediately above the Mohorovic discontinuity (Fig. 8).

It is believed that the increase in heat which normally goes with increase in depth—about 1 degree for every sixty feet—overcomes a counteracting normal increase in density, preventing melting, for the basalt at a depth of about thirty miles. Hence the basalt becomes overheated and slightly viscous. This heating is probably aided by the release of energy from radioactive elements contained in the rock at those levels. At any rate, it appears that the lower portion of the basalt does become viscous near the vicinity of the discontinuity. This layer apparently is the one along which the earth's crust slips, in Hapgood's theory.

It is in this area that volcanoes are born. However, they are the result of more than just the changing of the basalt to viscous material, for this alone would not cause the fiery eruption of a volcano.

Below the Mohorovic discontinuity, extending almost two thousand miles toward the earth's center, is a layer of heavier rock known to geophysicists as the "mantle." This huge layer

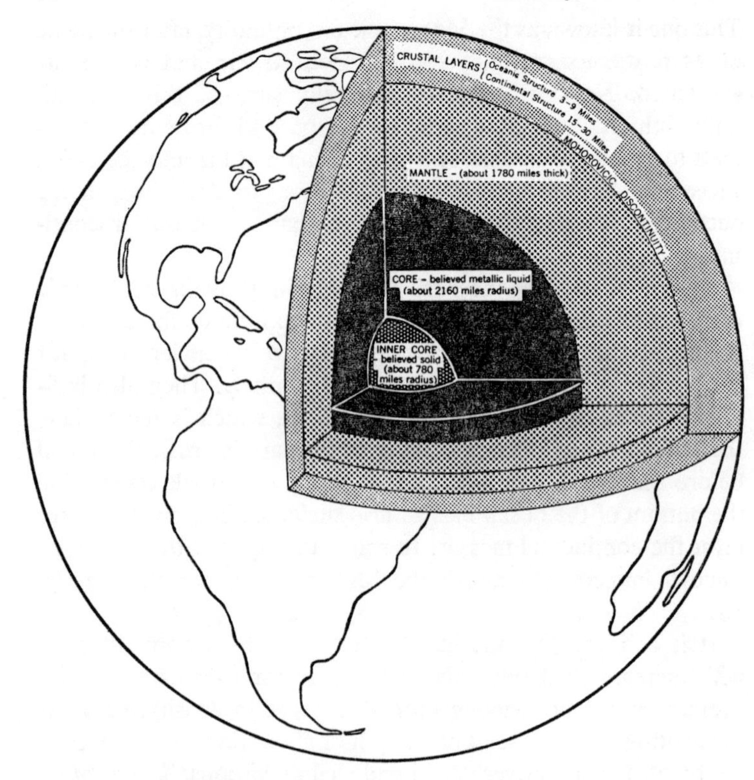

Fig. 8. Seismologist's concept of the interior structure of the earth.

is alleged to be made up of very heavy rocks and minerals known as peridotite and olivinite. Both peridotite and olivinite appear only occasionally on the earth's surface, where they are found and utilized as gem stones. Some of this heavy material gets through the discontinuity and into some of our volcanoes.

Seismic waves indicate that the greater part of the mantle is not truly solid but rather in a plastic state. This layer becomes more rigid again near the bottom, at the point where another discontinuity is reached; materials change again, and the core of the earth begins. It is believed that the portion of the mantle which becomes plastic or viscous is mainly composed of peridotite, whereas near the discontinuity with the earth's core the material is predominantly olivinite. Heat increase is not as great as expected at these depths, for it has leveled off at a much shallower depth to around 8,000 degrees Fahrenheit, and increased pressure could easily counteract the reduced rate increase. As a result, it is believed that some of the most plastic portions of the mantle are caused by radioactive elements releasing energy in that area. That the ancient fires still burn within the earth is not sheer fantasy, after all.

The Earth's Core and the Magnet Within

The materials in the earth change again at about two thousand miles, where the other discontinuity occurs, this time to what scientists believe were the original heavy materials of this planet—nickel and iron. This core occupies the middle of the earth for another two thousand miles until the actual center is reached. Seismic waves reveal that the outer half of the core is fluid or molten (Fig. 8) and the inner half solid but incandescently hot. Again, heating by radioactive elements or agitation by electrical charges could have caused this large earth furnace, and the very heavy outer pressure could keep the innermost core solid.

The presence of these fires inside the earth has promoted the notion of huge convection currents rising or boiling like heat movements. By measuring temperatures at the earth's surface and carefully plotting their distribution, scientists have developed a plausible theory about these convection currents. They believe that they rise or begin near the core of the earth, or in the outer core, at temperatures of at least 8,000 degrees Fahrenheit, and progress upward in waves, moving toward the surface in great volume, like water boiling in a kettle when the burner is located close to the center of the kettle's bottom. Continuing upward in huge currents through the hot mantle toward the surface, they are guided in their concentration, more or less, when they reach the outer mantle, by the undulations of the Mohorovic discontinuity.

This discontinuity dips underneath the continents to accommodate the larger mass of the continental rock and rises underneath the ocean floors (Fig. 7). The convection currents, according to geophysicists, are thus directed toward the highest places they can reach within the earth's mantle—the bottoms of the oceans. Therefore, the centers of these convection currents strike the discontinuity somewhere near the centers of the ocean basins, and in this way the increased heat of each ocean's floor near the center is explained.

Some light is thrown also on submarine elevations with cracks in the center, as are found in the mid-Atlantic ridge. When the convection currents are deflected in their upward movement by the discontinuity, they move outward from below the centers of the oceans toward the edges of the continents. While moving through the mantle, they cool somewhat and get heavy. On reaching the downward dip of the discontinuity at the edges of continents, these currents tend to turn and drift downward toward the center of the earth again. The downward pull of the returning currents may help explain the fact that the areas along continental margins are subject to downward block-faulting. By this we mean that appreciable hunks of the earth's surface break loose and drop many hundreds or thousands of feet as a block, leaving what we call "trenches" or "deeps" in the ocean near the edges of continents.

It should be noted that these convection currents in themselves generate a terrific amount of electrical energy. It is also believed that the fluid inner part of the earth may turn slower than the outer part, creating a huge dynamo. These currents, both from the convection force and the core dynamo, are supposed to be the origin of the earth's deep magnetic field. This magnetic energy is channeled outward from the earth through the south magnetic pole, which is located on the periphery of Antarctica in Wilkes Land, facing Australia. It has become common knowledge that these large lines of magnetic force travel around the earth at a considerable distance out in space and return to earth at the north magnetic pole, which is now located in northern Canada at the southern end of Bathurst Island (Map 2).

It must be emphasized that neither the north nor south magnetic pole is coincident with the actual earth poles. The lines of force carrying these magnetic impulses from the one magnetic pole to the other make a trap for some of the charged particles coming from the sun, other stars, and even other constellations. They trap them within multiple belts, the famous Van Allen belts to which we have referred in the previous chapter. In addition to this huge magnetic field of the earth, there are many minor magnetic fields throughout the world originating closer to the surface. These are probably caused by certain rock structures, localized heat centers, or special emanations from the huge inner dynamo.

The magnetism of the earth is a changing thing. The smaller areas of terrestrial magnetism are somewhat fleeting in nature. They grow stronger and weaker with varying conditions; some die away completely while others are born. Inside the earth, the magnetic dynamo itself, with its north and south magnetic poles, changes with time and conditions, altering gradually the location of the magnetic poles. According to a study released in 1963 by the Canadian Bureau of Mines and Technical Surveys, in 1831 the north magnetic pole was located on the Boothia Peninsula of northern Canada, whereas in 1963 it was established as being on Bathurst Island north of the Canadian mainland, more than three hundred miles away. Studies made by American geomagneticians and Australian scientists reveal that the south magnetic pole had wandered a similar distance during the same period, maintaining its relative position to the north magnetic pole. Since the north and south magnetic poles are both about a thousand miles removed from their respective geographical poles, magnetic declination lines indicating deviations from true north are required on many maps. It is obvious that the compass will point toward the magnetic pole, so an indicator is necessary to show the amount of deviation. Because of these changes, magnetic declination maps are published at least once every decade for the protection of compass users. Maps showing area variation in geomagnetic intensity are also published at intervals of five years to show time change.

There is evidence that both the deep-seated and the smaller centers of earth magnetism have a profound effect upon us as individuals and upon all forms of life in the animal and plant kingdoms. Recently several American horticulturists have described the effect of magnetic fields on the growing of plants. They say that certain areas are blest with the potentiality of good plant production, other things such as soil being equal, while other areas are "veritable scald spots." The latter places, in spite of good soil and climate, remain unproductive; they seem to be places of permanent magnetic sterility, yet places where little-understood earth waves emanate freely toward space.

Several New York physicians have studied this same condition with relation to human beings and animals, pointing out that certain areas seem to have a beneficial effect upon the humans who live there and certainly upon animals. In conjunction with studies made by earth magneticians, these doctors came to the conclusion that the beneficial effect, directly or indirectly, is through the magnetic composition of the areas. All animals, including man, are electrically charged and act as magnetic receptors or receptors of earth waves and cosmic impulses from space, according to their reports. It was suggested that the areas beneficial to man and other animals vary over the earth as does the magnetic field.

It also came to light that the earth's magnetic field changes with time, in accordance with influences outside the earth. It is known that the earth's magnetism increases during periods of sunspot cycles and decreases during years of the quiet sun. This applies to all magnetic fields of the world.

A growing volume of data points to the fact that the magnetic fields of the earth are affected by the moon as well as by other astronomical bodies. Minor magnetic fields appear to increase in intensity during periods of the full moon. And, as if horror stories come true, certain diabolical influences on animals (including man) in a marginal neurological state are claimed to exist. Although the reason is not yet known, it seems that earth and space magnetism affects man differently from that artificially created, for none of these effects was noted among people who worked around power-plant dynamos.

With the passing of certain stars and constellations, certain magnetic fields increase. The New York physicians showed that increased magnetism, working through one's own magnetic field, possibly attracting more cosmic impulses from space, affects the enzymal condition of the human body and, correspondingly, the nervous system. It appears that those who plant by the moon and judge things concerning themselves by the passing of the various astronomical bodies may not be so terribly far wrong. They make their judgments on the common-sense level, seeing results and relating them to coincidental or accidental phenomena which they attribute as causes.

Inasmuch as studies in magnetism seem to show these same relationships, it is possible that terrestrial magnetism could be the coordinating agent between earth and the universe of which it is a part. It is not inconceivable that elusive and basically beneficial cosmic impulses could come in with magnetism. Our world, we know, is just a small astronomical body in a great universe. We are, in effect, plain products of this earth, made of its material and, in a sense, bound to it. Isn't it conceivable that we are influenced by those very forces that guide our planet and, for that matter, the entire universe?

We pause here to mention the better side of the whole matter. Although admissions to mental institutions seem to go up during periods of high magnetic activity, the amenability to the cure of certain diseases also is said to increase. Ancient Egyptian physicians are said to have known of the potentiality of the earth's magnetic fields.

The earth's magnetism is measured in the field by use of the pendulum, the dip needle, the magnetometer, and other sensitive magnetic instruments. Hundreds of field observations are made every year, adding to data about the earth's magnetism, gathered finally at the World Magnetic Data Center. Little by little, these observations help to produce a picture of the entrails of the earth. Knowledge of the earth's magnetism, of the great inner fires, of the earth's gravity, of the Van Allen belts, and so on combines to project a ray of light upon the secrets buried deep within the earth.

The Origin of the Earth

Based on an analysis of the decomposition of radioactive material in the earth, the most recent calculation puts the earth's age at approximately five billion years. Earlier estimates, derived from the examination of fossil remains and records in rock strata, placed it at about two billion years. Measurement by the rate of breakdown of radioactive materials, however, is more precise and far more reliable. Most of the records of life we have are confined to the last one or two billion years—the traces of simple organisms found in ancient Pre-Cambrian rocks. More definite records exist for the last half billion years, starting with the earliest Paleozoic period, the Cambrian. From that time to the present, the fossils of living organisms engraved in the earth's rocks unroll a panoramic view of the history of the earth. Man—homo sapiens—seems to have existed on earth for at least a million or perhaps two million years, but only for about ten thousand years has there been any consistent system of written records. A knowledge of the origin and development of this planet may help us to explain the origin and distribution of most surface features of the world.

Looking at theories of the earth's origin and development, we first find some scientists claiming that a gigantic near collision of the sun with another star in the distant past caused large parts to break off from the sun; these parts whirled about as fiery masses in orbits about the sun, gradually cooling into the various planets in the sun's solar system, one of which is the earth. This is the star near-collision theory. It conforms with recent discoveries relative to the nature of the universe, wherein, as evidenced by the newly found bright Quesars, the entire universe is thought to be in expanding turmoil, creating the likelihood of collisions, as a result of a great cosmic explosion about eighty billion years ago.

Another theory was devised in the eighteenth century by the philosopher Immanuel Kant and later improved by the French scientist Pierre Laplace. This theory envisioned the sun as a huge, gaseous cloud which developed magnetic fields and heated to luminosity many billions of years ago. The cloud condensed into a whirling fiery ball, throwing off pieces which were too large and too much of a burden for the mass at whatever rate it was then rotating. These fiery pieces rotated in space and gradually cooled, forming the planets. The concentric structure of the earth is reconciled by the fact that it was a fiery ball in space for some time, perhaps billions of years. As the earth gradually cooled and shrank, its materials became stratified into layers in the course of the slow-cooling process. According to the Kant-Laplace theory, it is still shrinking and getting cooler today.

A more recent theory, the nebular-ring theory, envisages the sun as once being a huge, thin, gaseous, luminous cloud floating in a generally black part of the universe. This cloud gradually developed a core inside, possibly through a magnetic field and gravity attraction. The gases in this cloud were undoubtedly hydrogen and helium in an unstable ionized state, with untold billions of particles of cosmic dust mixed therein. The attraction of the particles for one another brought much of this cosmic dust to the center to form a small mass of hot material.

At this point it should be noted that in all the universe the most perfect form is the sphere. Materials attracted to one another tend to form a sphere and to rotate in a counterclockwise fashion. Thus, the assumption is that these hot particles formed a spherical ball of fire rotating within this cosmic cloud. The rotation of this protosun undoubtedly set up an immense magnetic field which, along with the lowering of temperatures involved in the creation of heavy elements, caused an ultimate implosion—the collapsing inward of this cloud—supplying tremendous concentrations of gases and particles to make up what is now the sun. These are the first assumptions of the nebular-ring theory, which will be explained further in succeeding pages. It is worth noting here that this is the way that most stars are formed.

There is one difficulty, however. Most cosmic clouds develop double nuclei, and implosion develops twin stars. Many of the observable stars in the universe are these twin or double stars—that is, two stars of common origin in close proximity, revolving around one another. Different from these, however, the sun's luminous cloud collapsed not into two vortexes but into one, making it one of the uncommon stars. It alone is the center of its system. Astronomers do not know whether or not any of the other single stars have planets. As far as we know, our sun may be the only star with satellite planets.

The nebular-ring theory goes on to show how this collapse of the luminous cloud left much luminous gas and a great deal of inert cosmic dust, together with the heavy elements—heavier than hydrogen—which the nucleus threw off, around the protosun. These, of course, were all affected by the rotation of the sun and tended to gravitate in rings along the sun's equatorial plane—"nebular rings." Within these various rings, which were probably not much different from the rings of Saturn we see today, magnetic fields developed and vortexes began, and the solid cosmic particles began to gravitate into spherical masses. These spherical masses ate up their respective rings and became fiery satellites rotating around the sun. Gradually they cooled, forming the earth with its concretionary stratification of materials and all the other planets. These bodies became smaller through loss of heat and finally took the form of the sun's planets today.

This theory assumes, as did the others, that the planets started as fiery masses, cooled gradually, and are getting smaller. We know that the "getting smaller" of the earth and the "cooling" of the earth are not necessarily true concepts: they do not fit the facts as presented by scientists today.

A new theory, sometimes referred to as the cold-earth theory, is now being rapidly accepted throughout the scientific world. It was developed partially by Frederick Whipple of the Smithsonian Institution and Robert Dietz, formerly with the Geological Electronic Laboratory of San Diego, California, and now with the U.S. Coast and Geodetic Survey of the Environmental Science Services Administration. Independently, these men examined more or less the same kind of data over a period of years and almost simultaneously came to similar conclusions. Earlier expressions of this theory were made by the astronomer, Gerard P. Kuiper, and the chemist, Harold C. Urey.

This latest version of the birth and development of the earth begins with a cosmic cloud, a great mass of black, inactive cosmic particles—dust—mixed with potentially unstable helium and hydrogen. There was no fire, no light at first, only darkness and cold. Then the inherent attraction of most particles for one another forced the materials in the cloud closer together. This caused collisions among themselves, generating electrical phenomena and luminosity and making the dark cloud a shining one. Heat was not yet great within the cloud. The cosmic dust particles may have become red hot, but they did not reach the tremendous heat to which they were later to be subjected.

Then, as in the nebular-ring theory, these cosmic particles near the center of the cloud began to feel further their mutual attraction and came together to form a spherical, fiery mass which began rotating. The rotation increased as more particles bombarded the mass at an angle. And as it grew, its center became hotter; while it became larger and hotter, its rotation speed increased. This rotating protosun set up a magnetic field which, together with tremendous heat probably generated by electrical energy, created heavy elements which lowered temperature and ultimately caused the collapse of the cloud and the dispersal of much luminous gas, as well as most of the heavy elements and many cosmic particles.

There is considerable controversy on this matter, but many scientists believe that the electromagnetic field then led to the formation of some of the elements found on earth today, which are heavier than those presumed to have been in the original cloud and protosun. The formation of such elements absorbed energy, so the protosun lost some heat, but then it shrank slightly and thus retained a good portion of its original heat. The loss it did suffer, however, was enough to impair its support of the cloud, hence the implosion. The shrinkage of the protosun then increased its rotation even more, and by centrifugal force it threw off its newly formed, heavier elements into the clouds of gas and cosmic dirt which hovered outside but relatively near.

Up to this point the cold-earth theory is similar to the nebular-ring theory, but there are now variations. In the ring theory vortexes formed within each of these rings, making fiery balls which cooled and shrank to become the present-day planets. According to the new theory, such did not take place. It is believed that the cosmic particles within the hovering cosmic clouds cooled somewhat and, independent of the helium and hydrogen gases, got together by magnetic force and gravitational attraction and became whorls within the clouds. These whorls grew into spherical masses, as in the ring theory, but they were not fiery masses. Some luminous helium and hydrogen gases may have been pulled into these spherical masses, but they did not attain enough volume and intensity to set up a nuclear furnace and make these rotating spheres fiery balls. The cosmic particles collected into these masses, according to Whipple, were reasonably stable, and the great bulk of the helium and hydrogen gases were drawn back into the sun by huge solar prominences at that time.

In contrast to former theories, the planets began as cold bodies, according to Dietz, and were smaller than at present—at least such was the case of the earth. Dietz believes that there was no concretionary stratification of materials within the earth at the beginning. Nor, according to Whipple, was there very likely any atmosphere as we know it, except probably some helium and hydrogen remaining above the surface, soon to be quickly drawn off.

The surface of—in fact, the entire body of—the earth was at first cold, and the deep fires that kindled did not begin until later. However, some unstable hydrogen and helium gases that did not escape were trapped within the earth, along with some unstable radioactive particles. The original crust of the earth was undoubtedly of the materials contained in those original cosmic dust particles.

As the sun contracted further, the coldness of space became even more oppressive upon the young earth. Contraction took place, and the small earth temporarily became even smaller. Moreover, the earth developed its own gravitational field, and, as noted before, gravity increased inside the earth to produce great pressures near the center. These pressures may have activated some of the radioactive material and the unstable hydrogen gases which were trapped. Consequently, the earth began to develop its own internal furnace. Some scientists believe that great electrical currents passing through the earth at that time helped to make the tremendous heat necessary to start the action. This must have begun about four billion years ago and is continuing today. The more severe aspects of the fiery revolutions of the earth, however, took place during the next few billion years of its existence.

With the development of the internal inferno, there came about stratification of the materials into the concretionary form found inside the earth today. Apparently, the iron and nickel particles were heavier and gravitated toward the center of the mass. The lighter siliceous materials, now formed into quartz and granites and other materials, were repelled toward the surface of the mass. Materials of medium weight and density filled the layer in between, which was eventually to become the mantle. The interior inferno itself localized where it had been trapped, in the outer core, where it has apparently continued to grow and increase in intensity.

With stratification of material and continuing increase of the heat within the earth, the mass began to expand, and the original rind eventually had to give way. Some of the compounds resting near the surface just below the rind reoriented into new materials and gases, which included water vapor, together with various other compounds containing oxygen, and these added to the internal pressure already being exerted.

The rind finally broke from the pressure within. The lighter crustal materials of molten siliceous rocks and basic rocks, like basalt, began pouring out of cracks and vents over the original rind. Great amounts of gas and water vapor were released during these stupendous volcanic eruptions and outpourings, but they did not escape; by this time the earth had developed a considerable gravitational field and was able to hold these gases and water vapor as our beginning atmosphere. This atmosphere must have stayed suspended as clouds for some time, for the eruptions were apparently world-wide and continuous for many millions of years.

Gradually, the volcanic period died down and the lighter materials making up the earth's crust began to settle over the original rind. The heavier of the two crustal materials, basalt, formed a complete layer around what was left of the original rind. The lighter siliceous materials formed a hard, capping layer around and above the basalt. In the meantime, the earth had become larger and lay quiescent, possibly for a few million years. It also lay reasonably featureless, overhung by clouds of potential atmospheric material.

The pressure of heat and gas from within the earth built up again after the granite cap hardened. This crystalline layer would not stretch like the fine-textured layer of basalt comprising the other layer of the crust just beneath; moreover, this granitic layer was thicker and much tougher than the original rind. We can imagine what happened: it finally broke from the terrific inside pressure—with shocking violence—and a second great catastrophe occurred.

The explosion must have been something beyond conception, unlike anything ever since experienced on earth. Hunks of granitic matter both large and small must have been blasted into space with a great boom. Flashes like those from a gigantic furnace must have illuminated nearby space, and more great clouds of gas and steam must have boiled up. The earth must literally have exploded, with some of the granite crust blown into orbit. The pliable basaltic inner crust of the earth adjusted and remained intact. Only several large slabs of the granite remained and floated here and there on the basalt—the continents of the future.

The Origin of the Moon

The granitic matter blasted into space from the earth may have got together later to make up the moon. Some scientists, however, believe that the moon was formed at the same time the earth came into being; that as the cosmic particles moved together to form the spherical mass of the earth, some of the lighter, siliceous materials made a ring around the proto-earth, along with hydrogen and helium. Like the earth, this ring of gas and light matter contracted, started a whorl, and attracted more matter into it until the satellite we know as the moon was formed. It could have been formed either way.

The diameter of the moon is only one-fourth that of the earth. In comparison, its mass is not great; neither is its weight, since it is allegedly made up largely of light materials. Consequently, the moon did not develop a strong gravitational field of its own, could not hold any of its gases, and developed no atmosphere. It did, however, prove attractive to meteorites and other space objects which plunged to pit its surface. Although it probably once had an original rotation of its own, this was soon lost as the earth grew in gravitational attraction. The result was that the earth locked the moon so tightly in its gravitational pull that the moon's independent rotation stopped.

The Origin of the Continents and Ocean Basins

In time, the earth began to grow larger. The continued heat inside caused more materials to reform and expand. In this way, continents and ocean basins took shape. As the earth expanded, the basalt layer, with its less definite crystallization and more potential plasticity, stretched, separating the broken slabs of the rigid crystalline outer layer by ever-widening intervening basins. Soon the basins grew larger than the slabs and became the original ocean basins; the slabs, of course, became protocontinents.

Then, according to some scientists, the great rains came. The quieting of the earth and the coolness of space condensed the great surrounding clouds and water fell, draining into the ready-made basins, and became our early oceans. It must have rained torrents for ages, for when it finally stopped the basins were almost full.

The continents were initially featureless, probably just barren slabs of rain-washed plains or plateaus rising above the incipient oceans. With the stretching of the earth's surface, the breaking up of the original continuity of the granitic crust into continental fragments and their ultimate separation, leaving intervening ocean basins, came some imbalances in the earth's surface. At first, the basaltic layer probably stretched uniformly throughout the world. This left the areas above, with the continental slabs overlying them, heavier than the other portions of the earth's crust. Two things happened: the basalt thinned out underneath these slabs, making them lighter, and at the same time it buckled, compressing these slabs into narrower straits to reach an isostatic balance. Hunks of the continental rocks both went deeper and buckled up higher into the air. Primeval mountains were born.

The continental masses, only two or three large ones originally, even then had slightly more weight than the ocean bottoms and by centrifugal force tended to break up into the present continents and drift apart. This process is still going on. At least some of the folding, faulting, and crushing of materials in the earth's crust, and further collapsings and foldings, are evidences of this. There have been repeated mountain-making epochs, adding to the mass of the continents. Geologists have uncovered at least ten such epochs in the history of the earth, three or four of which are well known (Fig. 9).

Recent mountain-making epochs have occurred near the western or southern edges of continents, leading many scientists to believe that, because of the earth's rotation, the various continental masses tend to drift westward and toward the equator and, meeting crustal blocks of resistance in the adjacent ocean basins, crush up against them and recoil. They explain the east–west-oriented Himalayan and Alpine systems by resistant blocks underlying the Mediterranean, India, and Australia.

ERAS	PERIODS c. million years ago	CATASTROPHES	OCEANIC VARIATIONS	BIOLOGICAL DEVELOPMENT
CENOZOIC	Pleistocene, 0 – 1 Coast ranges, western United States.	Ice sheets over vast areas of North America and northern Europe and Asia.	Sea level fluctuating.	Modern forests and grasslands. Man.
	Tertiary, 1 – 60 Alps, Himalayas, Apennines, Pyrenees, Caucasus.	Vulcanism in western United States formed Columbia Plateau (200,000 square miles of lava)	Submergence of lands. Limestone formed.	Great grasses. Mammals.
MESOZOIC	Cretaceous, 60 – 130 Rocky Mountains, Andes, Rising of Panama Ridge.		Europe and half of North America submerged. Chalk cliffs of England formed.	Giant forests. Dinosaurs.
	Jurassic, 130 – 155 Sierra Nevadas		Last invasion of sea into eastern California and Oregon.	Trees and grasses.
	Triassic, 155 – 185	Volcanoes in western North America; also in New England.		Giant ferns. More potential coal and oil deposits.
PALEOZOIC	Permian, 185 – 210 Appalachians south of New England	Volcanic Deccan Plateau of India. Glaciers in equatorial belt: India, Africa, Australia, South America.	Seas over western United States; world's largest salt deposits formed in Germany.	
	Carboniferous, 210 – 265		Central United States covered by sea for last time. Great coal beds formed.	Ferns. Coal and oil deposits formed in littoral swamps.
	Devonian, 265 – 320 Northern Appalachians			Fish in seas.
	Silurian, 320 – 360 Mountains of Great Britain, Scandinavia, Greenland.	Vulcanism in Maine and New Brunswick.	Invasions by sea. Salt beds formed in eastern United States.	Land plants appear.
	Ordovician, 360 – 440		Greatest submergence of North America – more than half of continent covered.	Vertebrates.
	Cambrian, 440 – 520±		Seas advance and withdraw.	Fossils.
ARCHEO-ZOIC	520± Mountains of Canada, Minnesota, Wisconsin. Their roots remain.	Earliest ice age.		Differentiation of marine plants.
PROTERO-ZOIC	2100 + Earliest known mountains (Laurentians of Canada) Earliest known sedimentary and volcanic rocks.			

Fig. 9. Earth's timetable.

Even some of the adjacent oceanic trenches, such as the Peru-Chile Trench, are attributed to being a remnant of recoil. Some scientists even equate mountain-making revolutions to sun activity cycles of far greater magnitude than those mentioned earlier in this book; still others relate them to times of slippage of the earth's crust.

With crustal weaknesses existing along mountain lines, there followed volcanic activity, associated with each historic period of mountain making. Materials as far down as the mantle were brought to the earth's surface and deposited on the continental masses. Earthquakes, which, as we have learned, are associated with the continental margins and volcanic realms and lines of weakness in the earth's crust, came from time to time.

Associated with the mountain-making eras, which occurred millions of years apart in the earth's history, have been periods of glaciation, where great ice caps crept over much of the land, except near the equator. At least two reasons have been set forth for these ice ages: changes in ocean currents or the temporary waning of the sun's heating power and influence on the earth's magnetic field. It is generally accepted that we are apparently in a mountain-making epoch today and in an interglacial period of that epoch.

Most of the features we see around us today came about during the last several mountain-making eras, beginning about half a billion years ago (Fig. 9). At that time a great mountain-making revolution took place which is referred to as the Laurentian revolution, when the mountains of eastern Canada, which are now worn down to a slight upland called the Laurentian (or Canadian) shield, were formed. In like manner were created the old mountains in the northern part of South America and in northeastern Asia. Some rudimentary mountains sprang up in Australia, Africa, and possibly Antarctica. By this time, life had already begun in the oceans of the earth, principally microscopic animals and plants.

After this revolution, the earth remained relatively quiet again for more than 300 million years, during what is known as the Paleozoic Era. Then, about 200 million years ago, another great mountain-making epoch occurred which is called the Appalachian revolution. During this era the Appalachian chain came into being as young, rugged mountains very much like the Alps and Rockies of today. Mountains in eastern Brazil and some mountains in northern India, northern South America, and northern Australia also took shape. At the same time, great outpourings of lava took place in northern and central South America, in India, and in Africa. An ice age is said to have accompanied this revolution.

By the time of the Appalachian revolution, land plants and animals had appeared on the earth, and the earth's atmosphere began to take something of the form we know today. In the 100 million years that followed, the Mesozoic Era, birds evolved and high reptiles dominated the land (Fig. 9). Great coastal swamps developed. Large fleshy fern trees grew and later fell of their own weight into the swamp waters, without decay. They were later compressed by overlying rock beds and formed many of our coal beds of today. Microscopic life thrived in abundance in broad coastal seas and, after dying, left their undecayed remains on the sea floor. These also became compressed by overlying sediments. Liquified and trapped in the pore spaces of rocks, they form our oil reserves of today.

During this period of momentous creation, the first warm-blooded animals and mammals appeared on the earth. In this period the North Pole is postulated to have been in the Pacific Ocean and, through the ocean's moderating influence, the climate of the entire earth is said to have been mild to hot. Later in this time the poles are said to have shifted to the general areas where they are now.

Less than 100 million years ago, the Mesozoic Era ended and the dinosaurs died off. In its wake, another mountain-making epoch ensued, the Laramide revolution. Many of the young, rugged mountains we see today came into being: the Andes in South America, the Rockies in North America, the Himalayas in Asia, the Alps in Europe, and the mountains of northern Africa, eastern Australia, and New Zealand. Following this period came another interrevolution time of about 99 million years, called the Cenozoic Era. Higher mammals and primates made their appearance then.

This last era ended a million or more years ago with the beginning of another mountain-making epoch and another series of glaciation, in which we still find ourselves. Some like to call this great alteration the Cascadian revolution. At least four great ice ages have taken place so far in this epoch, during which modern man made his appearance on earth. Recent findings indicate that man may have appeared even earlier. It is certain, however, that he was here during this epoch. The coastal mountains along the Pacific in North America and mountains in parts of Asia, Africa, and in the Pacific itself cropped up. The last of the four great continental ice sheets of these times covered the northern part of North America as far south as the Ohio and Missouri Rivers and the northern part of Europe and Asia as far south as the latitude of the city of Kiev. These great ice caps were very much like those now covering Antarctica and Greenland. The last continental glacial sheet receded a little more than ten thousand years ago, and, interestingly enough, recorded history soon began.

The most phenomenal aspect of our world was the development of our atmosphere. Remember that originally there was no atmosphere on earth. Practically all of the original hydrogen gas accompanying the earth's formation had been drawn away by the sun. Our atmosphere, then, came from inside the earth. Apparently, the cosmic dust comprising the early earth contained many elements, among which were those that produced the contents of our present atmosphere. The cosmic dust or particles were heated and altered when the primordial fires began burning. They took the form of gases and molten materials, which boiled out into the earth's surface during volcanic activity. Emitted through these volcanic vents and fissures were gases and, above all, *water* in vapor form. Aside from the oxygen tied up in water vapor there was ozone extant at that time, quite a different form of oxygen, certainly not the free oxygen that we breathe today.

These gases and vapors hung as clouds for millions of years

until the water vapor was precipitated in the rains that filled the ocean basins. The remaining gases were held to the earth by gravitation to form the atmosphere. This atmosphere contained nitrogen (originally ammonia gas until transformed by electrical charges), ozone (anatropic oxygen), and water vapor much as our atmosphere does today. The ozone eventually rose and formed a layer above the lower atmosphere, which we know now as the stratosphere. Carbon dioxide in the present atmosphere is alleged to be the electrical transformance of some original methane gases. Free oxygen later made its appearance.

After the continental masses took form and the waters of the earth were confined largely to ocean basins, microscopic life appeared in the ocean near the continental margins. This happened somewhere between two and three billion years ago, and life persisted in microscopic form for many millions of years. These microscopic forms developed photosynthetic functions and finally began giving off pure free oxygen into the atmosphere as a biological byproduct. Over a period of millions and millions of years, these tiny beings must have created much of the free oxygen that is now in our breathing air and is so vital to us today. As more life developed on earth, land plants began taking in carbon dioxide from the atmosphere and giving off free oxygen, perpetuating the beneficial processes begun so many eons ago.

These significant developments, we repeat, are traceable to the miraculous events that went on inside the earth. Scientists have been able to solve some of the mystery, but much remains to unravel. In what we have already learned about the earth there does appear, however, a certain unity in nature which can be benevolent.

SELECTED REFERENCES

Abetti, Giorgio. *The Sun*. Trans. by J. B. Sidgwick. New York: Macmillan Co., 1957.

Ahrens, L. H., and others (eds.). *Physics and Chemistry of the Earth*. 5 vols. New York: Pergamon Press, 1956.

Branson, Edwin B., and others. *Introduction to Geology*. 3rd ed. New York: McGraw-Hill Book Co., 1952.

Byerly, Perry. *Seismology*. New York: Prentice-Hall, 1942.

Carnegie Institution of Washington, Department of Terrestrial Magnetism. *Description of the Earth's Main Magnetic Field and Its Secular Change, 1905–1945,* by E. H. Vestine, L. Laporte, I. Lange, C. Cooper, and W. C. Hendrix. Publ. 578. Washington, D.C.: Carnegie Institution of Washington, 1948.

Clarke, Frank W. *The Data of Geo-Chemistry*. 5th ed. U.S. Geological Survey Bulletin 770. Washington, D.C.: Government Printing Office, 1924.

Croneis, Carey G., and William C. Krumbein. *Down to Earth: An Introduction to Geology*. Chicago: University of Chicago Press, 1936.

Dietz, Robert S. "Collapsing Continental Rises." *Journal of Geology,* Vol. 71, No. 3. May, 1963.

Dunbar, Carl Owen. *Historical Geology*. 2nd ed. New York: John Wiley & Sons, 1960.

Faul, Henry (ed.). *Nuclear Geology; A Symposium on Nuclear Phenomena in the Earth Sciences*. New York: John Wiley & Sons, 1954.

Gamow, George. *The Birth and Death of the Sun; Stellar Evolution and Sub-Atomic Energy*. New York: Viking Press, 1945.

———. *Gravity*. New York: Doubleday & Co., 1962.

Gutenberg, Beno (ed.). *Internal Constitution of the Earth*. 2nd ed. New York: Dover Publications, 1951.

——— and C. F. Richter. *Seismicity of the Earth and Associated Phenomena*. 2nd ed. Princeton: Princeton University Press, 1945.

Hamilton, Edwin L. *Sunken Islands of the Mid-Pacific Mountains*. New York: Geological Society of America, 1956.

Hapgood, Charles. *Earth's Shifting Crust*. New York: Pantheon Books, 1958.

Hayford, John F. *The Figure of the Earth and Isostacy*. U.S. Coast and Geodetic Survey spec. publ. no. 82. Washington, D.C.: Government Printing Office, 1909.

Hosmer, George L. *Geodesy; Including Astronomical Observations, Gravity Measurement, and Method of Least Squares*. 2nd ed. New York: John Wiley & Sons, 1930.

Kraus, Edward H., and Chester B. Slawson. *Gems and Gem Materials*. 5th ed. New York: McGraw-Hill Book Co., 1947.

Kuiper, Gerard P., and Barbara M. Middlehurst (eds.). *The Solar System. Vol. II: The Earth As a Planet*. Chicago: University of Chicago Press, 1954.

Leet, Lewis Don. *Earth Waves*. Cambridge, Mass.: Harvard University Press; New York: John Wiley & Sons, 1950.

Neumann, Frank. *Earthquake Intensity and Related Ground Motion*. Seattle: University of Washington Press, 1954.

Pearl, Richard M. *Guide to Geologic Literature*. New York: McGraw-Hill Book Co., 1951.

Perret, Frank A. *Volcanological Observations*. Washington, D.C.: Carnegie Institution of Washington, 1950.

Poldervaart, Arie (ed.). *Crust of the Earth.* New York: Geological Society of America, 1955.

Shepard, Francis P. *Submarine Geology.* 2nd ed. New York: Harper & Row, Publishers, 1963.

Simak, Clifford D. *The Solar System—Our New Front Yard.* New York: St. Martin's Press, 1962.

Stovall, J. Willis, and Howard E. Brown. *Principles of Historical Geology.* Boston: Ginn & Co., 1955.

Swick, Clarence Herbert. *Pendulum Gravity Measurements and Isostatic Reductions.* U.S. Coast and Geodetic Survey spec. publ. no. 232. Washington, D.C.: Government Printing Office, 1942.

Thompson, Henry D. *Fundamentals of Earth Science.* 2nd ed. New York: Appleton-Century-Crofts, 1960.

U.S. Coast and Geodetic Survey. *Directions for Magnetic Measurements* by Daniel L. Hazard. U.S. Coast and Geodetic Survey ser. no. 166. 3rd (1930) ed., corrected 1938. Washington, D.C.: Government Printing Office, 1938.

———. *Tables for Determining the Form of the Geoid and Its Indirect Effect on Gravity* by Walter D. Lambert and Frederick W. Darling. Washington, D.C.: Government Printing Office, 1936.

Van Valkenburg, Samuel, and Ellsworth Huntington. *Europe.* 2nd ed. with Colbert C. Held. New York: John Wiley & Sons, 1952.

Wegener, Alfred L. *Die Entstehung der Kentinente und Ozeane.* Berlin, 1915.

Whipple, Fred L. *Earth, Moon and Planets.* Rev. ed. Cambridge: Harvard University Press, 1963.

———. "The History of the Solar System." *Space Science Reviews,* Vol. XIII, Jan., 1964.

Wunderlich, H. G. "Continents Drifting Farther Apart." *The German Tribune,* Cologne. August, 1964.

Chapter 3 / Our Battered Crust

To one living on the surface of the earth the crust seems to be rough and uneven, but it really is not when looked at in perspective. Could the world be shrunk to the size of a billiard ball, its surface blemishes would be proportionately reduced and it would seem even smoother than a billiard ball. To any of us who have climbed mountains or worked on hilly land, however, the surface still is rugged. These variations in the crust will be examined in this chapter.

Types of Land Forms

There are four general categories of surface undulations—mountain, hill, plain, and plateau (Map 3). Mountains exhibit high relief and sharp angle of slope. ("Relief" is the difference between the highest and lowest places in a given region and generally is measured in hundreds or thousands of feet.) Hills are characterized by low relief and high angle of slope and are usually calibrated in hundreds of feet. Plains are areas of low relief and low angle of slope; they need not be featureless and many do seem to "roll" with swells and swales. Plateaus are elevated plains with a low angle of slope (except at the edges) but are perched in the air and thus have high relief.

Some of the forces responsible for these features of the earth's crust have already been discussed. These tectonic forces arise within the earth itself and are of two types, diastrophic and volcanic.

The diastrophic deal with the crushing and moving forces arising inside the earth that alter features on the surface. Folding of rock strata belongs in this category. The ridge-and-valley portions of the Appalachians are the results of such folding. Faulting, the displacement of one portion of crustal rock with relation to another, is the diastrophic force which also causes earthquakes, and many of the mountains rising above the ocean floor have this kind of origin.

The other major tectonic force, volcanism, is responsible for such features as the volcanic cone of Fujiyama in Japan, a specific kind of volcano. This type of mountain is the result of a series of eruptions. Another type of volcano which reflects the volcanic force within the earth is the shield, an example of which is the famous Kilauea on the island of Hawaii. It does not come to a point as does Fujiyama but is vast and round in shape, reaching appreciable heights. It takes the name "shield volcano" because from a distance it appears as a huge resting shield.

Other volcanic features represent the results of quiet lava flow. They may take a tabular form such as the Columbia Plateau in North America, which came about through the quiet outpouring of lava through cracks, or the Ozark Mountains in central North America, which resulted from the intrusion of volcanic magma (molten rock) into the country rock near the surface, while still inside the earth, and then exposed later by erosion.

Mountains. Mountains, plateaus, and hills that are formed by diastrophism and volcanism are often referred to as "gross" forms of the earth's surface. They are usually the large features created by the above set of forces and then worked upon by another set. The great mountain areas of the world were basically formed in this manner, and their distribution is essentially that of the areas of weakness in the earth's crust. Such are the ranges encircling the Pacific: the Andes in South America, the mountains of Central America, the Sierra Madres of Mexico, the Rockies, and the mountains of Alaska (*see illustration section*). Also to be included are the highlands of the Kamchatka Peninsula of eastern Siberia, as well as the mountains of Japan, the Philippines, and New Zealand.

Another vast system of mountain ranges along a line of weakness in the earth's crust crosses southern Asia and southern Europe, with offshoots along North Africa. Included are: the

Himalayas of Asia, the Caucasus of Asia Minor, the Alpine system of southern Europe, the Atlases of northern Africa, the mountains of the East Indies, and many ranges beneath the Pacific Ocean. Another arm moves northward from the Himalayas to include the Altai and other mountain groups of eastern Asia.

These are called the young mountains of the world, formed in the last two mountain-making revolutions, and they are the major mountains of today's world. The older mountains—the Appalachians in North America, the Urals in Asia, the Carpathians in Europe, and the mountains of Australia, Scandinavia, and the British Isles—are usually less lofty and have more rounded peaks.

Whatever the origin, mountains are the most impressive features of our planet. A few remarks of astronauts who circled the earth for a number of days in 1965 are worth noting in this respect. Their composite remarks are as follows:

The earth is splendid from up there—the continents and the broad oceans. The mountains are especially impressive. They resemble stones strewn over the ground, catching the sun's light at a weird angle and casting long shadows. The snow-capped peaks of North America stand as silent white sentinels, . . . while those in Central America stretch like a serpentine spine. They rise from their backgrounds of green or brown like the bold strokes of a painter, and they display brilliant colors seldom seen except through the inspired genius of the artist.

Plateaus. Many of the plateaus of today took shape as the result of the unchecked overflow of molten volcanic rock. The great plateaus of eastern South America, which pass through Brazil and Paraguay, and the plateaus in the Guiana Highlands of northern South America, were made in this way. The Columbia plateau of western North America and the Deccan plateau of India have been mentioned also as being formed in a like manner.

On the other hand, the Piedmont upland or plateau in eastern North America came about by uplift. Long ago it was an old, worn-down plain, but it was then uplifted by diastrophism to its present elevation of a semiplateau. The plateaus of Africa, Australia, and Antarctica were similarly raised. Incidentally, the high areas of Antarctica are an extension of the young, rugged mountains and plateaus of South America.

Some plateaus reach great heights—for example, the large intermountain plateaus in Mexico, on which are located many of Mexico's principal cities and other populated areas, average about eight thousand feet in elevation. Another example is the intermountain plateau in the Andes of South America, also uplifted by diastrophism, on which are located mining centers and much of the Indian population of Bolivia and Peru. It reaches nearly twelve thousand feet, and the Spanish conquerors referred to it as the Altiplano.

Following the crustal weaknesses to Asia, we find the populous Tibetan plateau in southern Asia, with an elevation of fifteen thousand feet, the Iranian plateau in Asia Minor with an average height of five thousand feet, the Anatolian (Turkish) plateau of three thousand to four thousand feet.

The plateau making up the bulk of the Arabian peninsula is about the same height as the Anatolian. In this general area lie the Dead Sea and the Jordan River Valley, a huge downward block fault diving to a depth of about twelve hundred feet below sea level in the vicinity of the Dead Sea. The Red Sea basin and part of the Persian Gulf are also results of this same huge downward block fault, as are the lake basins along the entire eastern side of the continent of Africa.

The East African plateaus are block mountains ranging from a few thousand to nearly ten thousand feet. Much of the Sahara is a low plateau, only hundreds of feet above sea level. The bulk of South Africa also is a large plateau, of medium elevation, but Western Australia is a block plateau of low elevation, measured in hundreds of feet.

Plains and Hills. The broad plains lands of the world and some of the hilly areas were formed by different forces, called by some "The sculptors," which will be discussed in this chapter. This refers to the forces or agents of erosion and deposition: continental waters, glacial ice, and wind. These forces are aided by a process called "weathering," which breaks up rock material so that it is easily eroded.

Under the plains of the world lie the original continental slabs, and it is the plains that are the receivers of the deposition picked up and transported by the sculptor agents. Formed in this way were the great plains of central and western North America, of the Amazon and Orinoco basins in northern South America, and of the Paraguay and Paraná Rivers of southern South America (see endpapers). We should also cite the plains of eastern France and northern Italy. Asia and Australia have vast plains similarly formed; those in Asia cover much of the north and central part of that huge continent.

Most of these plains were built from the deposits of the continental waters: streams, lakes, and underground water. A few, however, like the North Central plains of North America, were formed by continental glaciation. Often they are the remnants of old mountains or plateaus. Some were built up by wind deposition, as seen in the great desert areas of North America between the Rockies and the Sierra Nevadas. This type of formation occurs only in arid regions or areas where vegetation has not taken hold, for the wind is not an agent that can easily dislodge vegetation-rooted particles (*see illustration section*). Examples of hill features wrought by glacial deposition are found in North America on Long Island. Here at the terminus of one of the continental glaciers was deposited much boulder and associated material which now has become Long Island's rocky hills.

Waves and long-shore currents of the ocean also fashion beaches and small plains along the coastline. Generally speaking, the small beach plains cut by erosion are made by waves and long-shore currents along coastlines which tend to fall or submerge. On the other hand, the beach plains made by deposition are usually those along coastlines which have a tendency to rise.

The Continental Margins. We have seen how the major features of our world came into being and also noted that our continental platforms are made up of the lighter siliceous rocks in the earth's crust. How were the edges of the platforms covered by the oceans?

When the waters rose around the platforms they filled the basins not to the top of each platform or slab but only up to where the waters covered a little bit of the gently sloping part of the platform. The edge of the platform was submerged, as it is today, to a depth of from three hundred to six hundred feet. Beyond the edge of the platform, the slope breaks sharply from the usual gentle incline close to the shore to a steeper dip into the ocean basin. This steep dip is known as the "continental slope," which is supposed to contain great mineral wealth. The gently sloping area out to the three hundred to six hundred-foot depth is called the "continental shelf."

Diastrophism

As the agents of erosion—particularly the continental waters—erode the mountains, plateaus, and hill lands of a continent and carry the water to the sea, the deposition of that material is either on the continental shelf or in the ocean basin close to the foot of the continental slope. Over the years considerable amounts of this material are deposited, which affects the isostatic balance of the earth's crust and causes diastrophic movements such as folding and faulting.

As for the deposition along the continental margins, especially at the base of a continental slope, an excessive weight of material can gradually be built up. This results in one of two forms of diastrophism, depending largely on whether there is compression or tension in that coastal area—in other words, is the continental block pressing against the oceanic basalt slab or tending to pull away?

Where there is compression and the plastic basalt far below tends to thin out under the weight, the heavy load of deposition buckles the basalt downward and then folds itself upward into mountainous areas which add to the continental mass. Where there is tension and the plastic basalt again thins out and moves elsewhere, the heavy overload of deposition tends to cause a sizeable block fault. In this instance, a large slab of the thinned-out basalt gives away and the whole block of crustal rock with its overburden drops downward, pushing more of the plastic basalt aside and possibly even displacing some of the plastic mantle rock below (Fig. 7).

These latter features become the ocean trenches, the deeps in our oceans. Taking the Pacific for an example, the eastern side tends to be a coast of compression, whereas the western side is one of tension, owing to the tendency of continents to drift westward. The deep ocean trenches, such as the Mariana Trench with its 35,800-foot depth, are located in the western part of the Pacific (see endpapers).

As rock strata are displaced from one another along fault lines (persistent cracks), an earthquake is produced. Many of the known mountains on the central and western floor of the Pacific Ocean were formed by block faulting in the upward direction. Huge blocks of rock were pushed up along fault lines to arise as mountains. Other known mountains under the Pacific Ocean are volcanic cones or shields. All of them retain their original form, more or less, because the forces of erosion and deposition are not the same under the ocean. In fact, only an occasional current causes erosion and distribution on the ocean bottom.

Gigantic upwarpings of areas of land often accompany, and are a part of, diastrophic activity. (Recall the rise of land as far away as Washington, D.C., caused by the Good Friday earthquake in Alaska in 1964.) This suggests that there are great movements of materials within and beneath the earth's crust during periods of diastrophism. These movements undoubtedly take place in the lower viscous portion of the basalt layer of the crust and in the plastic rock of the mantle below. In all this the convection currents play an assisting role. We must remember that these powerful heat waves tend to rise within the plastic mantle from the fluid portion of the earth's core and move toward the surface at points beneath the oceans' floors.

In this connection, let us recall that the submarine chain of mountains known as the mid-Atlantic ridge was caused by an upheaval effected at the center of some of these rising convective currents. The advent of the huge crack in the crest of the ridge and the high temperatures on the ocean bottom in that vicinity substantiate this. We should recall, too, that the convection waves travel also beneath the ocean floor to the margins of the continents and then drop back toward the center of the earth after having been more or less cooled. This downward drop of the currents could exert enough pull to encourage the immense type of block faulting just described.

There are also block-fault trenches in the western Atlantic—the Puerto Rico Trench and the Cayman Deep in the West Indies, for example. These submarine trenches tend to have the same relative location as those in the Pacific.

We know that western coasts tend to be coasts of compression and eastern coasts ones of tension, so it is understandable that downward block faulting takes place more easily in areas of crustal tension. By the same token, upward block faulting takes place near the coasts of compression. Not enough deep bathymetric surveys have yet been made to substantiate these facts completely, but recent findings indicate that there are many blocks of submarine mountains or, as they are often called, "sea mounts," in the eastern Pacific, off the western coast of North America.

Nature, unfortunately, is not always simple. We have seen how diastrophic phenomena take place today, largely along the lines of weakness in the earth's crust. In the same manner, we would expect that the counterpart of the mid-Atlantic ridge would express itself along the middle of the floor of the Pacific Ocean. This is not exactly the case. A mid-oceanic ridge does appear in the South Pacific, but it bends shoreward in the North Pacific and actually becomes a part of the Pacific coast region of North America. As for the ridges in the middle of the Indian Ocean and in the Arctic Ocean, they follow courses slightly askew from—but reasonably close to—the center of the oceans. However, they are all joined in the high latitudes of the southern hemisphere. The closeness of the Pacific submarine ridge to the American continents can possibly be explained by the drifting of continents westward and toward the equator. The Eurasian continent probably drifts more rapidly because of its size, as evidenced by the island festoons left in its wake: the Japanese Islands and the Philippines.

VOLCANISM AND RELATED MATTERS

We noted earlier that the distribution of volcanism was practically synonymous with the distribution of diastrophism throughout the world. Both follow the lines of weakness in the earth's crust (Map 1). We would expect, then, volcanic mountains in all of the systems just described, and we do find them essentially so distributed. As a matter of fact, some of them accentuate their location by being turbulently active today (*see illustration section*).

There are at least seven active volcanoes in the Andes of South America, and in Mexico five are considered active. We know of active volcanoes in Alaska, and there are considerable data concerning such volcanoes along the western side of the North Pacific—in the Kamchatka Peninsula of Siberia and on the Japanese Islands. At least a dozen of them also persist in the East Indies and in the Philippines. (On September 28, 1965, a volcano on Lake Taal in the Philippines erupted suddenly, and hot lava, ash, and steaming mud spewed from the 980-foot peak in the early morning darkness. It was the nineteenth recorded eruption of the volcano, the last occurring in 1911.)

Along with the active ones, there exist scores of extinct volcanoes which have left behind impressive mountains (*see illustration section*). Following the line of crustal weakness across southern Europe and Asia, we come to the active volcanoes in the Mediterranean region, about which much is known, and to numerous extinct volcanoes which are scattered throughout the mountainous stretches of southern Asia. Several active volcanoes and a number of extinct volcanic mountains follow the line of crustal weakness down the eastern side of Africa.

Since volcanism is coincident with areas of diastrophism and regions of crustal weakness, we can readily assume that volcanism is associated with these phenomena. What, then, makes rock get so molten within the earth's crust that it has the power to rise to the surface and blast out into volcanic mountains of the size of Vesuvius? Several years ago the drama was unfolded before man's very eyes, when in a cornfield in Mexico a full-fledged volcano, called Parícutin, sprang out of the ground, continued erupting, and built a mountain in a matter of months. Scientists have been studying this matter for many years and have what they believe is a satisfactory explanation.

First of all, there must be deep cracks in the earth's crust. Such cracks occur most frequently along the lines of weakness in the crust, extending downward more than thirty miles. These cracks provide avenues for molten rock to get to the surface; yet the molten rock would not do so if it did not have some tremendous force behind it. This is apparent from the shotlike violence with which many volcanoes erupt. (We might mention here that the word "volcano" itself is derived from the name of the Roman fire god, Vulcan.) For a volcano, then, to erupt there has to be white-hot molten rock at the base of one of these fissures, with attendant gases and sufficient excessive volume to bring about the expulsion of this material from within the earth.

We know that the lower portion of the crustal basalt is viscous and the upper part of the mantle is plastic, but this does not mean that they are molten. At any rate, this volcanic phenomenon—the change of solid or viscous or plastic rock inside the earth's crust or upper mantle into molten magma—involves a combination of happenstances. Certain radioactive elements undoubtedly persist in the rocks at the level of thirty or more miles where most volcanoes are born. These, however, would not normally cause this metamorphosis at that depth were it not for a second condition, basically a change in the heat-pressure ratio of the rocks at those levels.

The implication seems clear that an imbalance between increase in pressure and increase in heat seems to occur as depth into the earth is increased. When this happens—particularly when heat increases—the radioactive elements are activated, probably by electrical action, and the rocks turn molten. This does not normally happen, of course, because the increase in pressure counteracts this heat increase. (Pressure increases at a rate of about sixty tons per square inch with each mile of increased depth.)

What volcanism requires is a decrease in the volume of the overburden at the earth's surface, cutting down on the increase in pressure in a given area. This allows heat to be prominent at a depth of about thirty miles, where temperatures are above 2,200 degrees and can melt rock.

Rock melting would still not be likely to happen, since much pressure remains; it is only lessened. However, the relatively increased heat apparently creates electricity and somehow activates and works with radioactive elements, and this combination causes a phenomenal increase in heat and the melting of rock to magma at about the thirty-mile level. When rock is changed from a solid or plastic or viscous state to a molten state, many gases are released and extreme pressure is built up. If a fissure or crack opening to the surface is present, a volcano is likely to develop and erupt. It would take one of the forms already discussed, depending on the size of the fissure.

Volcanic islands have been known to evolve in the Pacific and pop out of the water in a relatively short time as a result of such volcanism on the ocean's floor. Many of the atoll islands there, which are circular islands made of coral rock with an inside lagoon, are built on extinct volcanoes. This happens when the volcano, after becoming extinct, is either reduced in elevation by diastrophism or the sea level rises, whereupon the volcano becomes submerged below the surface of the ocean. Coral growing around the edge of the volcanic mountain, needing shallow water or surface contact for survival, builds up around the mountain as the waters slowly rise. After the mountain has long sunk beneath the waters, the coral ring remains and comprises the base of the islands. This rock is calcareous and whitish and is made from the coral form of life, which takes calcium from the water and leaves it in this hard form as a biological product.

Erosion and Deposition

How does the initial imbalance of pressure and heat develop in these regions of crustal weakness in the earth? Basically, it is due to erosion and deposition. It can also be due to the sudden melting of great ice caps and to other similar factors.

When mountains on land are worn down to hills and plateaus are broken into hills, the material is carried away largely by continental water—or, as some call it, running water—and is deposited in the shallow waters of the coast.

Most running water—rivers and other streams—deposit their material in the ocean. In this connection, we arrive at an established concept known as the "hydrologic cycle," which is simply the ultimate returning of all water to the ocean. In short, the waters which fall on the land usually have their origin in the ocean. Water is picked up by evaporation and becomes a part of clouds or water-carrying atmosphere, which travel over the ocean and then over the land. These clouds become disturbed when over land, either by convection currents, by displacement, or by being forced to rise over mountains. This disturbance causes them to precipitate or give off much of their moisture in the form of rain, snow, hail, or sleet. The water then rolls back to the ocean through streams, most of it directly. Some small part is carried as ground water but eventually gets into streams. Some water is taken up by plants, but sooner or later they give up water to the clouds, which precipitate again; most water finally joins this unending cycle.

The portion of the hydrologic cycle we are most concerned with here is the running water, or the water in streams. This running water carries away materials from mountains, plateaus, and hills after it has been loosened by weathering. Most streams carry a tremendous load of material back to the sea, material that was once land rock but is now in decomposed form. Some of this material is deposited on the plains to help build them up, but the greater part of it goes to the sea. Here it is deposited when the stream's velocity is checked at its mouth, either on the continental shelf, on the continental slope beyond the edge of the continental shelf, or in the oceanic basin beyond the continental slope.

It can be seen that when much material is eroded from mountains and plateaus on land, the pressure below those areas is decreased. But the heat down at the thirty-mile level is not. Now, with the decreased pressure and the consistent heat causing an imbalance underneath the eroded land, the process of volcanism already alluded to becomes activated, and molten rock is driven by gases through existing fissures to become volcanoes on the surface.

After the volcanic action has taken place and a great load of magma has burst from below to the surface of the earth, a certain void is left in the area where the magma was formed. The viscous lower portion of the basalt layer of the crust and the plastic mantle below move toward this area to make up that loss of interior material. This generally relieves the pressure of the overburden of deposition on the continental shelf and at the edge of the oceanic basin, because the material moves largely from there in creating an isostatic balance.

In areas where the coastline is one of tension, we noted that returning convectional currents beneath the ocean's floor tend to pull blocks violently downward while this readjustment of materials is taking place, and the oceanic trenches previously described are born. Where the coast is one of compression, the overburdened area buckles and mountains are formed. This often requires additional readjustment in that area of the earth's surface. More material is forced over into the volcanic area to cause more volcanism, possibly, but more likely faulting and other diastrophic phenomena.

Sometimes this faulting is violent; all faulting is not simple raising or lowering of large blocks of the earth's surface. Some occurs as the gigantic type of overthrust mentioned earlier. Some, too, may be lateral movements along fault planes in the earth's crust, such as those in California.

The convectional currents which are generated within the magma mass of a volcano are often credited with being the source of some of the minor magnetic fields of the earth. The large convectional current inside the earth, generated in the core and passing through the mantle, is believed to produce powerful magnetic forces. As noted earlier, convectional currents originate also from the fact that a dynamo is probably produced deep inside the earth, near its center. It is believed that the fluid material of the earth's core may rotate at a slower rate than the mantle and crust outside it. This, of course, would create a gigantic dynamo, which would give a tremendous additional amount of force to the earth's over-all magnetic field.

Weathering of Rocks

Although tectonic forces are credited with creating mountains and plateaus, the sculptor forces are responsible for most of our hill areas and for the plains. The sculptor forces, it should be recalled, are those which reduce mountains and plateaus to hill lands of varied design and which build up low areas into plains. These forces depend upon weathering to break down the rocks of the mountains and plateaus and hills, so they can eat them away and deposit them elsewhere. Weathering works by chemical or mechanical means. More explicitly, it breaks down rocks by the chemicals in the water that washes over or penetrates them, or it breaks them down by alternate heat and cold.

The chemical decomposition process often results from water seeping through vegetation, picking up chemicals which decompose some of the crystals within a rock. Some rocks are most susceptible to chemical decomposition and break down into smaller pieces, some of them to dust.

Mechanical weathering is a matter of alternate heat and cold in the earth's atmosphere. The various molecules and crystals which make up rocks have different expansion and contraction rates with the application of heat and cold. With this differential expansion and contraction going on continuously, rocks eventually break into small pieces and become susceptible to erosion. Some of this broken-down rock material may not be washed away. It then becomes the parent material for soil, which is formed when plants begin growing there, providing certain nitrogenous materials to make the weathered material arable, capable of being cultivated.

Since weathering breaks down rocks into soil or into unconsolidated material which can then be worked on by the forces of erosion and deposition, it is worthwhile for us to see just what kinds of rocks comprise the upper portion of our continental masses. We know that the bottoms of the oceans are underlain by basalt and that a thin layer of basalt underlies the continental masses. It is the lighter rocks making up the continental masses with which we are now concerned. These rocks are of three general kinds: igneous, sedimentary, and metamorphic.

Igneous rocks are those which are products of volcanoes, and we know from our consideration of the origin of the earth that these were the original rocks of the continents. They are basically siliceous, making up much of our mountain and hill areas and some plateaus. Sedimentary rocks are those secondary rocks which are composed of materials which have been eroded from other rocks, transported, and deposited in layers as sediments. These rocks underlie most of the plains of the world and many of the plateaus, and they have been folded by diastrophism into some hill and mountain lands. Metamorphic rocks are derived from either igneous or sedimentary rocks which, as the name implies, have been greatly changed by the heat and pressure in the forces of diastrophism or volcanism. These rocks are usually found in mountainous areas and in some plateaus.

Igneous Rocks and Ores. Igneous rocks include familiar stones such as the common granite, which has large crystals of quartz, feldspar, and other minerals—the result of slow cooling of magma just inside the earth's surface. Basalt is an igneous rock also, and when it occurs on continents it most certainly has been brought up by volcanic action. It is dark, fine-grained, and heavy, reflecting the fact that it was cooled rapidly after first being extruded to the surface. Such light material as pumice fits into this category, having been thrown rapidly out from a volcanic vent. In this group are also such rocks as peridotite, which, as we have seen, is a substance making up part of the mantle beneath the earth's surface, having been brought to the surface by volcanic action. As we noted before, these rocks are characteristic of the young, rugged mountains of the world, but they are also found in many plateaus and some of the old, worn-down mountains.

Most of the important ore bodies of the world are associated with volcanism and volcanic mountains, present or past, including many of the important ores, such as iron, copper, silver, gold, tin, lead, platinum, zinc, uranium, cobalt, molybdenum, and manganese. These ores are usually carried by the gas and steam of a volcano. As the magma of the volcano rises, gas and steam are forced in between layers and in cracks and fissures of the near-surface rock to the side of the main volcanic vent. When these gases and steam cool, they deposit their material, which was being carried in dissolved or suspended form, as pure ore veins.

We need only look at an atlas to confirm this distribution of ores. Iron is found in or near the Appalachian Mountains or Central Highlands of North America, which early in geological history were associated with volcanism; in the Laurentian (Canadian) shield; in Europe in the younger mountains of Spain, which are part of the Alpine system in Western Europe; and in central Asia, in areas which were also early associated with volcanism. Some is also found in eastern Africa, associated with volcanic rock; in India, Japan, and Australia; in Chile in western South America; and near Rio de Janeiro in eastern South America.

Copper is associated largely with the Andes Mountains in South America and the Rocky Mountains in North America, both largely of igneous rock. It is also associated with the areas of igneous rock in southeastern Africa; in central Asia, Japan, and Australia; and in the Scandinavian peninsula of northern Europe, which was associated with volcanism and contains many volcanic rocks from very early geological history.

Tin, which is rather rare, is found with igneous rocks in the Andes of South America, the Sierra Madre of Mexico, and the Rockies of North America. It is also associated with igneous rocks in eastern Europe and southeastern Asia, particularly the Malaysian peninsula, which had early and late contact with volcanic activity. It is also found in southeastern and central Africa, associated, respectively, with young and older igneous rocks. The same applies to the distribution of the other minerals mentioned and to many others associated with igneous rocks, such as chromite and tungsten.

These minerals, except possibly for gold, are all important in modern industry, which goes to great lengths to exploit them. It is fortunate that the actions of volcanoes place them, in their purer form, so conveniently near the surface of the earth. Some of these minerals can be seen as crystals, not worth recovering, in some rocks of this category.

Igneous rocks in general are crystalline, the crystals being formed out of the mineral elements when the rock was in the process of developing. Although these rocks are susceptible to chemical decomposition (as some of the crystals in the rocks would naturally be more soluble than others), they are most susceptible to mechanical disintegration by differential expansion and contraction of various crystals under alternate heating and cooling.

Sedimentary Rocks and Mineral Fuels. Sedimentary rock, if we recall, is associated with the large plains of the world and with several of the hill regions. It also comprises some of the great plateaus of the world, where a former plain has been uplifted to a lofty position by diastrophism. Sedimentary rocks that are familiar to many of us are sandstone and limestone.

Limestone is a common rock, generally appearing in layers and usually light in color and fine in texture. It is made up largely of calcium carbonate which long ago was precipitated chemically from coastal waters which had received the material from rivers out of the land. The thick layers of limestone we often see have taken millions of years to build, underneath the sea close to shore, before diastrophism lifted them up to become part of the continental mass. Other stratified rocks such as shale are also included among the sedimentary rocks of the world. They have, as a rule, the same distribution pattern as the others—the large plains and the flood plains of rivers throughout the world.

Limestone is particularly susceptible to chemical weathering, since calcium dissolves rather easily in chemically charged water, even rain water. It is for this reason that most of the areas of the world with underground streams and large caves occur in regions underlain by limestone. Waters circulating down into the earth easily dissolve the limestone layers and form underground channels which become underground rivers and caves. Often the roofs of these caves collapse and form, on the surface, a series of depressions known as sinkholes, comprising collectively what is known as "Karst" topography, named after the Karst region in the plains of Yugoslavia. Sandstone and shale are broken down less rapidly by chemical and mechanical weathering.

Areas of the world where oil and coal are produced contain sedimentary rocks. They are mostly the plains areas, but there are some hilly regions where these mineral fuels are found, especially where rocks have been folded and rendered into hills. We remember that both oil and coal are the results of incompletely decomposed organic matter, trapped within the layers of sedimentary rocks, laid down millions of years ago. Consequently, these mineral fuels occur always in areas that either are or have been regions of pure sedimentary rock.

The productive oilfields of today occur on plains in South America such as those of the Paraguay River basin, along the coast of Peru, in the Orinoco and Maracaibo basins in northern South America, and all through the great central lowlands of North America. Even the oil found in the hill country of the Appalachian Plateau in North America is in an area of folded sedimentary rocks. In Asia, oil is found in the great central plains, in the lake flats around the Caspian Sea, in areas associated with the rock-fault valley of the Persian Gulf, in the lowlands of Burma, and on the northern and southern edges of the islands of Borneo and Sumatra. In Europe we find oil in plains areas such as those in Rumania and in the East Indies, and in Japan oil is concentrated in those areas rich in sedimentary rock.

Coal, also associated with sedimentary rock, is found in both plains and hill areas. Coal in South America is mined at the southern end of the intermountain region in Chile. In North America it is located in the great central plain, and in Mexico on the intermountain plateau. Considerable amounts of coal are available in North America in the hill land on the western side of the Appalachians. This region is known as the Appalachian Plateau, an area of dissected sedimentary rocks—a former true plateau. In Europe coal is extracted from the hill lands of folded sedimentary rock in Great Britain and throughout western Europe. It is discovered among the sedimentary rocks in the great central Asian plains and plateaus, and in India it is found on the eastern side of the Indian peninsula, where sedimentary rock predominates. In Japan, southeastern Asia, Australia, and southeastern Africa, coal is similarly extracted from areas of folded sedimentary rock.

Metamorphic Rocks and Minerals. Metamorphic rocks have undergone such heat and pressure that the crystals have reformed themselves in the rocks, changing them entirely. They are new stones, and they very often have a banded appearance and bear names such as "gneiss" or "schist." Some of these rocks are familiar to us. Marble is the result of the metamorphosis of limestone. Quartzite, a very hard, resistant stone, is derived from sandstone. Slate, a highly flakable material, comes from shale, and the gneisses and schists are usually the result of the metamorphosis of various igneous rocks. Occasionally, sedimentary rocks such as bituminous coal are metamorphosed and become anthracite coal. This type of hard coal, which is mined in parts of western Europe and in the northern Appalachians, was brought about through the tremendous pressure of the crushing and folding sedimentary layers.

Metamorphic rocks are usually seen in hill lands and in some mountainous areas. The Laurentian or Canadian shield of northeastern North America is a land of low hills, worn down over millions of years from the upheaved land spoken of earlier, made up largely of very old metamorphic rock. The frontal range of the Appalachian system, known as the Blue Ridge

Mountains, is composed predominantly of metamorphic rock; the Piedmont upland immediately to the east of them is another case in point. Large sections of metamorphic rock are seen on the Brazilian plateau and in the eastern Brazilian highlands, where sedimentary rock has been subject to the intense heat of the outpourings of lava. Similar areas of metamorphic rock are found in the hill lands of the Scandinavian peninsula and in the hill lands of western, central, and southern Europe. Much of it is also found in the hill country of southern Africa, southeastern Asia, and western Australia.

Even metamorphic rocks are not without mineral or precious-stone value. Metamorphism can so reorient the atomic and crystalline structure of a rock as to change it even into a precious stone. This happens in the metamorphosis of such a sedimentary rock as coal, which is high in carbon content. The alteration of coal will lead to anthracite coal, and still further metamorphosis can produce forms of the highly precious carbon stone, diamond. Such metamorphism is responsible for the occurrence of diamonds in the Brazilian highlands, on the Brazilian plateau, and in the hill lands of South Africa.

Other precious stones such as garnet are found in areas of metamorphic rock throughout the world, representing more or less the end products of special lines of metamorphism. Mica, which is an end product of the metamorphism of certain igneous rocks, occurs quite frequently in areas of metamorphic rock. Mica has considerable industrial value, including its use in transistors, and is mined assiduously wherever it occurs. It is found in the Blue Ridge highlands of North America and in many of the other hilly areas of metamorphism throughout the world.

Metamorphic rocks are very resistant to weathering because they have already been exposed to most extremes of heat and pressure. Yet even they succumb eventually to forces of weathering and, like the sedimentary and igneous rocks from which they were derived, disintegrate to be carried away by erosion or to become residual soil.

Sculptor Forces

Let us see briefly how each of these sculptor forces—continental water, glacial ice, and wind—does its work.

The one we know best is continental or running **water.** It washes away loosened particles from the mountains and plateaus, carrying them in suspension or bouncing them along stream or river beds, and conveying them eventually to the sea or river-flooded plains for deposition.

Some of the great central plains of the world were built up largely by continental water, through a series of repeated floods which left behind thousands upon thousands of tons of sediment. Many others were made by these continental waters carrying sediments to the ocean, in geological ages past, and depositing the material near the shore. Such was the case of the southern part of the central plains of North America, which was once under a coastal sea known as the Mississippi Embayment. In more recent geological history, diastrophism upwarped this embayed sea floor to make it part of the central plains of North America.

Some plains were formed by the continental waters of lakes, many of which no longer exist. Lake Bonneville, which covered much of southern Utah, was responsible for leaving behind a large plain. Similarly, Lake Agassiz covered a large area of the northern part of the central plains of North America. This lake no longer exists, but it left behind a large rich plain which is now productive farmland. These lakes did not look much different in their day from the lakes which are perched on our continents today, the largest of which is the Caspian Sea. In geological time, these lakes were all of short duration, and their waters were eventually carried to the sea by the headwater erosion of some continental stream.

We know that continental waters in the form of streams have worn down the Appalachians from lofty mountains to the size they are today. This happened also to the eastern highlands of Brazil, the mountains of Scandinavian Europe, the hill lands of southeastern Asia, and many of the hill lands of Australia.

It might well be conceded that continental water, principally running water, is the greatest force among the sculptors in forming the features of the earth.

Glaciers are huge masses of ice that are capable of eroding, moving material, and making deposits. The glaciers we know today are those which occupy valleys near the summits of lofty mountains and those gigantic caps of ice which cover the continents of Antarctica and Greenland. They are of two kinds: mountain (or valley), and continental.

Mountain glaciers originate in valleys near the summits of lofty mountains, where weather conditions are always cold. They grow and push forward down the valley until they get to lower and warmer elevations, where they begin melting. When melting equals the amount of growth, the glacier stops advancing; when melting exceeds the rate of growth, the glacier recedes. The latter is the case with most mountain or valley glaciers today, especially those in Alaska which have been measured most carefully. This recalls our previous observation that we are in the warming period of an interglacial age.

Continental glaciers form near the cold center of a cold continent and build up and push forward in all directions over all features of the continent, sometimes reaching thicknesses of ten thousand feet. As more ice builds up at the center of the glacier through the packing of repeated snows, the glacier pushes forward, scouring hills and gouging out basins in its path. The continental glaciation that covered North America in the last glacial age scarred the hills of New England and Canada and was responsible for gouging out the basins of what are now the Great Lakes; that of the last ice age in Europe hacked out the English Channel and scarred the hills of Scotland and Scandinavia.

Like mountain glaciers, these continental ice caps begin to melt at their fronts when they reach warmer climates. When they recede they often leave behind sizable moraines—that is, rocky hills deposited as they depart. It was through the recession of the continental glaciation in North America that a large portion of the central plains of this continent is now covered with what is known as "ground moraine," in this case a thick deposit of glacial til—finely ground-up rock material. It comprises that large area south of the Great Lakes and north of the Ohio and Missouri Rivers of the central plains known as the corn belt. Here the receding glacier dropped millions of tons of finely disintegrated, rich mineral particles scoured from the metamorphic rocks in the hill lands of Canada. Extremely rich soil was produced, for the material was mechanically disintegrated rather than chemically decomposed; hence, it did not lose the mineral matter usually taken up by chemical decomposition.

The north German plain in Europe is a similar area endowed with the deposition of soil materials high in mineral content. Similar areas exist on the central Asian plains, where smaller glaciers receded. Some of the moraines left by the receding of continental glaciation are definite landmarks, such as Long Island, New York, which is one large terminal moraine.

Mountain or valley glaciers act very much in the same way, leaving ground moraine. But the most unique feature wrought by these glaciers is the manner in which they have gouged their valleys. When they recede they leave their former valleys in a U-shape instead of the usual V-shape. They also leave tributary valleys hanging high along the valley wall. This causes unusual-looking waterfalls, such as the Bridalveil Falls in Yosemite Valley, Califoria.

Wind erosion and deposition are less extensive; this force is the least effective of the three sculptors. The work of wind is done largely on plains and plateaus, usually in arid regions. There not much rainwater is available for transporting the decomposed material left by weathering. The wind, however, blows free in such areas—and strong. Without a cover of protective vegetation the wind moves materials freely in arid regions. In the plains areas of the great basin of western North America, the wind has denuded many plateaus to a rocky surface and deposited the material elsewhere to make part of it a hill land.

This type of hill land usually takes the form of dunes, which are crescent-shaped with the curved end oriented toward the direction of the wind. The sand-hills region in Nebraska is another hill area made by wind deposition. In northern Africa, many hill areas are made by the wind blowing sand and other small particles into dunes (*see illustration section*). In central Asia many large plains have been caused by the wind depositing very fine materials in a stratified fashion, known as loess. In western Australia and southwestern Africa, the wind is similarly the agent for denuding areas into plains and building up other areas into small hill sections.

We have seen that our battered crust is made up of large blocks of features formed by tectonic forces. We have seen also how these large blocks are weathered and altered by the sculptor forces of wind, ice, and continental or running water. These forces of our dynamic world produce the mountains, plateaus, hills, and plains. We understand how all these things are in a dynamic balance. Should erosion on a continent become too vigorous and wear down the features pushed up by diastrophism and volcanism and deposit the materials in the adjoining sea, then the isostatic balance in the earth's crust and various other forces go to work and push up new features. The cycle of erosion then starts all over again.

Once again we are confronted with the unity in nature. The alteration of the earth in many places by large engineering projects has given many scientists concern on this score. They fear the day when atomic power will be able to blow away mountains, create great lakes, change the course of streams, and alter hill lands, plains, and plateaus. They fear, and possibly rightly so, that these things will disturb the earth's balance and cause nature to make drastic adjustments to restore it.

SELECTED REFERENCES

Atwood, Wallace W. *The Physiographic Provinces of North America.* Boston: Ginn & Co., 1940.

Bateman, Alan M. *Economic Mineral Deposits.* 2nd ed. New York: John Wiley & Sons, 1950.

Eardley, Armand J. *Structural Geology of North America.* 2nd ed. New York: Harper & Row, Publishers, 1962.

Fenneman, Nevin M. *Physiography of Eastern United States.* New York: McGraw-Hill Book Co., 1938.

Fenneman, Nevin M. *Physiography of Western United States.* New York: McGraw-Hill Book Co., 1931.

Flint, Richard F. *Glacial and Pleistocene Geology.* New York: John Wiley & Sons, 1957.

Furon, Raymond. *The Geology of Africa.* New York: Hafner Publishing Co., 1963.

George, Russell D. *Minerals and Rocks: Their Nature, Occurrence, and Uses.* New York: Appleton-Century Co., 1943.

Hager, Dorsey. *Practical Oil Geology.* New York: McGraw-Hill Book Co., 1951.

Hapgood, Charles. *Earth's Shifting Crust.* New York: Pantheon Books, 1958.

Hussey, Russell C. *Historical Geology; the Geologic History of North America.* 2nd ed. New York: McGraw-Hill Book Co., 1947.

Jagger, Thomas A. *My Experiments with Volcanoes.* Honolulu: Hawaiian Volcanic Research Association, 1946.

Landes, Kenneth Knight, and Russell C. Hussey. *Geology and Man.* New York: Prentice-Hall, 1948.

Lobeck, Armin K. *Geomorphology, an Introduction to the Study of Landscapes.* New York: McGraw-Hill Book Co., 1939.

Longwell, Chester R., and Richard F. Flint. *Introduction to Physical Geology.* 2nd ed. New York: John Wiley & Sons, 1962.

Moore, Ruth. *The Earth We Live On.* New York: Alfred A. Knopf, 1956.

Pearl, Richard M. *Guide to Geologic Literature.* New York: McGraw-Hill Book Co., 1951.

Pettijohn, Francis J. *Sedimentary Rocks.* 2nd ed. New York: Harper & Brothers, 1957.

Pough, Frederick H. *A Field Guide to Rocks and Minerals.* 2nd ed. Boston: Houghton Mifflin Co., 1955.

Shepard, Francis P. *The Earth Beneath the Sea.* Baltimore: Johns Hopkins Press, 1959.

Stovall, J. Willis, and Howard E. Brown. *Principles of Historical Geology.* Boston: Ginn & Co., 1955.

Thornbury, William D. *Principles of Geomorphology.* New York: John Wiley & Sons, 1954.

Travis, Russell B. *Classification of Rocks.* Rev. ed. Golden: Colorado School of Mines, 1956.

Turner, Francis J., and Jean Verhoogen. *Igneous and Metamorphic Petrology.* 2nd ed. New York: McGraw-Hill Book Co., 1960.

U.S. Department of the Interior. *Mineral Yearbook.* Washington, D.C.: Government Printing Office, yearly.

Veatch, Arthur C., and R. A. Smith. *Atlantic Submarine Valleys of the United States and the Congo Submarine Valley.* Special papers no. 7. New York: Geological Society of America, 1939.

Von Engeln, Oscar D. *Geomorphology; Systematic and Regional.* New York: Macmillan Co., 1942.

Chapter 4 / The Oceans

The oceans are made up of one of the most marvelous liquids in all the universe—water. This liquid is known to exist in frozen form—ice—in many parts of the universe, but only on this planet have we found water in any great abundance in liquid form. Here, the hospitable temperatures allow water to remain liquid and to accumulate in large quantities, and this, of course, is most fortunate, for water is absolutely necessary to life. Our bodies consist mostly of water, and most of the food we eat is made up largely of this fluid; we know that we could not exist for long without it. In addition, our complex society today demands water for more varied uses than has any other society at any other time in history.

Except for their usefulness in fishing and commercial shipping, our oceans and seas were considered waste areas of the world until quite recent years. Now that booming population has posed a need for developing new frontiers in the exploitation of economic resources and for finding new sources of food, man is examining the oceans anew. We have always known that they played a vital role in the origin of life on this earth and in ameliorating climatic extremes, as well as providing means of sanitation, but now we are beginning to realize that this great reservoir is important to our life in many other ways. Today, extensive research is being carried on to design means and methods of using the untapped treasure of the ocean and to convert it to drinking use.

Let us look at some of the qualities of this liquid known as water, which comprises the oceans and seas of our dynamic world. First, water is mobile. It is a liquid, and it can move from place to place. With the ocean basins covering 71 per cent of the world, and with all of the oceans coming together at one place or another, this mobility of water is essential to its function as a great regulator of climate.

Another amazing quality of water, and a very unique one, is that it expands when frozen. (Most liquids will contract and become heavy.) Water, when chilled, will contract only to about 39 degrees Fahrenheit; then it will expand till it reaches the freezing point of 32 degrees Fahrenheit and changes to ice (28 degrees in the case of ocean water, because of the salt content), becoming lighter than liquid water around it. This fact is extremely important to life on this earth. If water were like other liquids and contracted all the way to the freezing point, the resulting ice would sink and the bottom of many of our oceans would soon become filled with ice, leaving only a thin layer of liquid water on top. Our oceans could not then be the great climatic regulators that they are.

Still another marvelous thing about water is that it will turn into vapor and back to liquid form in accordance with the changing conditions of the earth's atmosphere. It also dissolves and carries in suspension many mineral salts, and it supports numerous forms of life. It can absorb and carry heat readily, and, through its own convectional action, it can deliver heat to certain depths and bring coolness to the surface. The upwellings of water bring salts as food to many forms of life. In fact, the water of the oceans of the world is the great mother, the cradle of earth's earliest forms of life.

It is recognized, then, that the oceans and the seas, because of their ability to remain temperate in extremes of climate and because of the mobility of water, perform major functions valuable to mankind. We shall speak a little later about the ocean's role as mother of life. For the present let us look briefly at the areas occupied by the oceans and the shores they affect.

The Ocean Basins

The Atlantic Ocean stretches the full length of the globe from Greenland near the North Pole to Queen Maud Land in

Antarctica (see endpapers). Its total area, including appendages, is about 34 million square miles. The upper part is sometimes referred to as the North Atlantic and the lower part as the South Atlantic. The North Atlantic and its appendages—the Baltic Sea, the North Sea, the Mediterranean Sea, the Gulf of Mexico, and the Caribbean Sea—touch on the continents of Africa, Europe, and North America. The South Atlantic and its appendage, the Weddell Sea, occupy a basin from about two thousand to more than six thousand miles in width between South America and Africa, touching Antarctica near the South Pole. As we shall see, currents in the entire Atlantic Ocean carry temperate influences from the equatorial regions to the Arctic and from the Arctic to the lower latitudes.

The Pacific Ocean has many appendages—the Sea of Okhotsk, the Sea of Japan, the South China Sea, the Ross Sea bordering Antarctica, and the many waters of the East Indian Islands (see endpapers). Again, this great ocean, which stretches from the Aleutian Islands near the North Pole to the shores of Antarctica near the South Pole, is one huge basin, measuring as much as twelve thousand miles in width in the southern hemisphere and closed off with reduced latitude by the Aleutian Islands of Alaska in the northern hemisphere. Its total area, including appendages, is approximately 67 million square miles. Like the Atlantic, this huge basin is divided into the North Pacific and the South Pacific, the division being considered more or less the equator. Also, as in the Atlantic, the North Pacific Ocean has a system of currents carrying warm water to polar regions and cool water to the tropics. This pattern is duplicated in the South Pacific Ocean.

The Indian Ocean, with its two large appendages, the Bay of Bengal and the Arabian Sea, stretches from the southern shores of Asia to the frozen shores of Wilkes Land in Antarctica. It is about six thousand miles from east to west and touches India and southeast Asia on the north, Africa on the west, Malaysia and Indonesia and Australia on the east, and, of course, Antarctica on the south. Its total area is put at slightly more than 28 million square miles. Unlike the other two great bodies of water, the Indian Ocean is mostly a southern hemisphere ocean, but it too has a system of currents which carries tempering waters from the tropical regions to the cooler shores.

The Arctic Ocean, at the top of the world, is smaller, not more than three thousand miles in width, and, with its appendages—the Bering Sea, the Laptev Sea, the East Siberian Sea, and the Barents Sea—embraces an area of about seven million square miles. Because of its location, the Arctic Ocean is mostly frozen at the surface. Though the extreme cold of the North Pole area has frozen the surface water of the ocean, so that it has expanded and floats as ice on the top, the waters below are free and mobile. We recall that in recent years American submarines have traversed the Arctic Ocean beneath the surface ice. This ice is not one huge consistent mass, as sometimes depicted on maps and globes. It comprises numerous large chunks or islands of ice, which join together at times to make huge ice packs, which can again separate into individual floating islands. Flowing water may be seen between the islands.

During the cold night of Arctic winter, additional water is frozen, packing many of the ice islands together, and, by expansion, the great ice packs encroach upon surrounding shores. When the thaw comes in spring, some of the ice melts and, with frightening sound, the shore ice cracks from its grip on land and retreats as ice islands into the Arctic Ocean. Studies are now being made of the currents in this ocean, and more data will be available soon. What is known at present is that currents from the North Atlantic break into the Arctic Ocean and often bring warm water that melts Arctic ice in unusual amounts.

Still another ocean, the Antarctic Ocean, is identified by some people. This body of water is really not an ocean but rather makes up the waters that surround the south polar continent of Antarctica. Oceanographers have identified submarine ridges, which hem in the waters around the Antarctic continent at depths of several thousand feet in a rough ring around the continent, about six hundred miles from its shores. This is not a continuous ridge but rather a broken and partially oblique set of suboceanic ridges. Parts of this system of ridges are identified as the Atlantic-Indian ridge (Map 4). Although these features do not come up to the surface, it is possible that they do inhibit the flow of submarine counter currents which are the constant companions of surface oceanic currents.

THE MAKE-UP OF WATER

Before saying more about the ocean basins and the movements of the waters therein, let us look more closely at the characteristics of the water itself which fills the ocean basins, in order to understand better its gyrations. It is, in chemical terms, made up of billions of molecules, each containing two hydrogen atoms and one oxygen atom. This combination of atoms is not unusual in the universe, for numerous studies have shown that water in the form of ice is present in many places in outer space.

The peculiar thing about water on the earth is that it can persist in a fluid state. We know that water will turn to ice at 32 degrees Fahrenheit (28 degrees for sea water) and that it will vaporize at 212 degrees Fahrenheit. It is most extraordinary that the span of temperatures on earth corresponds closely with the span in which water remains fluid, when the vast range of temperatures in space is considered—from more than 400 degrees below zero Fahrenheit, which is the temperature of outer space, to several millions of degrees Fahrenheit on the surface of many of the hot stars of the universe. It may be recalled that our own sun has a temperature of 11,000 degrees Fahrenheit on its surface.

Since water is nearly colorless, it allows the sun's heat to penetrate deeply and warm it. On the other hand, it is always in a state of churning and is often exposed to extreme cold and loses heat just as readily as it absorbs it. The light of the sun penetrates the waters of our oceans only to several hundred feet. At a depth of about five hundred feet the light has gone, and from then on there is blackness. The oceanic life which inhabits the great depths has adjusted to this world of darkness.

It is fairly well known that the waters of the oceans and

seas are not pure. Salts and other materials are present, but in a surprisingly small proportion to the total volume—only about 3 per cent—and consist largely of mineral salts carried in solution. Four kinds of salts are mainly present: sodium, chlorine, magnesium, and sulphur. Sodium chloride is, of course, our familiar table salt; we are also familiar with sulphur and pure chlorine. Magnesium is less known. It is metallic in nature and is now being extracted from the ocean to make a metal which is light and strong and useful in aircraft construction.

Even though water is a relatively colorless fluid, the ocean looks far from colorless. The short rays of the sun are the most easily absorbed by the surface waters of the ocean, and these are the blue rays. Consequently, the color reflected back from the ocean's surface is usually blue.

In addition to the salts carried in solution in the ocean, many small particles are suspended: volcanic dust, plankton, algae, protozoa, skeletal fragments of microscopic animals, and so forth. The odd colors of the water are often due to the scattering of the sun's light by these minute particles. In some places they are able to scatter more effectively the darker waves of the sun's spectrum, and, as in parts of the Pacific, the water appears black. Near the coasts of continents the water often appears green, because of a different scattering of the sun's rays by the phytoplankton associated with coastal areas. In some places the water has a brownish or even reddish color, due largely to a different pattern of rays from the sun falling on certain types of algae abounding there. In general, however, the ocean's color at the surface is a varying shade of blue.

The temperature of the surface waters of the ocean varies somewhat, but the range is considerably less than that of the land temperatures of the world—from about 28 degrees Fahrenheit in the Arctic Ocean to about 90 degrees Fahrenheit in the surface waters of equatorial shores or in the Persian Gulf. As we have seen, the warm surface waters of equatorial regions are moved by currents to colder shores, and the cold waters from Arctic regions sink to great depths and travel toward the equator, to well up as cool currents invading tropical shores; hence the ocean's effect as a moderator.

As already noted, some of the surface water in the polar regions goes into ice, and the remainder stays in fluid form beneath the ice at slightly more than 28 degrees Fahrenheit. The ocean's water also gets colder with depth, regardless of the surface temperature. This decrease in temperature with increased depth is offset by the increased pressure of the overload of water; hence the waters in the great depths of the ocean do not freeze. As a result, the waters in the very deepest part of the ocean, more than thirty-six thousand feet down, are still fluid and capable of supporting life.

There is great increase in pressure with ocean depth. Skin divers and divers using self-contained breathing apparatus rarely go down more than a hundred feet; divers in heavy diving suits seldom go down more than five hundred feet. For descending more than six hundred feet a diving bell has been used, equipped with lights and provided with oxygen for the inhabitants of the craft.

With a bathysphere, a craft specially reinforced to withstand great pressures, man has been able to descend to the deepest parts of the oceans (*see illustration section*). In 1960 such a bell dove to the deepest spot known, the Mariana Trench in the Pacific, nearly 37,000 feet. The observers in this craft, with the use of their lights, were able to see that some form of life, adjusted to that dismal blackness and those terrific pressures, was able to survive. And pressures at those depths are terrific: at thirty thousand feet it registered 13,500 pounds per square inch. Near the surface of the ocean the increase in pressure is only about 50 pounds per square inch per one hundred feet in depth, but it increases rapidly with increased depth, although the proportion of increase is not geometric.

Underwater pressures affect life in the oceans, as they affect man in his attempts at diving and probing the shallow ocean floors near the continents. Divers with helmets and diving suits have to undergo a decompression process when they return to the air. This is necessary because the pressure of the water at the depths to which they descend is great enough to force certain material in the blood stream into fluid or solid form, which is released into a gaseous state or an expanded liquid form when the pressure is relieved. In short, unless the diver is decompressed slowly his blood will suddenly effervesce, and he will get what is commonly known as "the bends," which in some instances is lethal. In any case, the dangerous aspect of this increased pressure has been a serious drawback in man's exploration of the depths of the ocean.

Variations in density of ocean waters is a subject often treated at length by oceanographers, and some attention will be given to it here, since it is so closely associated with salinity. The density of the ocean's waters increases with depth, and waters that become dense at the surface will sink to a level commensurate with their density.

The average salinity of ocean water, as we have noted, is about 3 percent, made up of mineral salts carried in solution. The greatest part of the remaining 97 per cent is made up of regular water molecules. A small amount of true oxygen is also found in ocean water—that is, free oxygen—the molecules of which are lodged sparsely among the molecules of H_2O. There are also very small quantities of other minerals, including phosphorus and carbon.

Although the general salinity is 3 per cent, in parts of the ocean the salinity is higher, for example, in the Persian Gulf, where evaporation of surface water is high, taking away some of the water molecules and leaving a high percentage of mineral salts. The percentage of salinity is lower, of course, in certain areas along continental margins where large rivers, such as the Mississippi, dump millions of gallons of fresh water into the ocean, thus diluting the salinity. This is true of the mighty Amazon River of South America, which empties about 7½ million cubic feet of fresh water into the Atlantic Ocean per second. Seen from the air, the effects of this murky water on the ocean are noticeable for hundreds of miles out by a difference in color.

In general, it may be said that as the salinity of ocean water increases its density increases. Therefore, waters which have attained a high salinity, either from materials being added in solution or from excessive surface evaporation, become dense and will sink to a lower level. In the same manner, waters which have become cooled will become more dense and sink. This action is extremely important in the upper-level churning of ocean water, for it helps account for the equalizing of the extremes of earth temperatures. If cool water sinks to a lower level, then a warmer level is exposed at the surface to temper the air which is cooling the water. Consequently, there is a churning in the ocean's water to a depth of several hundred feet, which allows for the ocean waters to remain temperate and influence the climate of adjacent lands.

The surface movements of ocean waters also play a role in this moderating action, and they will be discussed later. Suffice it now to say that the action of the wind and the effects of the rotation of the earth often cause movements of surface waters away from given areas, particularly coastal areas, which allows for an upwelling of cold waters from great depths to replace the surface waters that have been removed. This is most evident when cold waters from the deeps are brought up along tropical shores.

The Atlantic Ocean

Before looking at the specific movements of the oceans and their effects upon us, let us return to examine more closely the individual ocean basins, which we have only outlined in general, since they have some effect upon the movements of the waters they contain. We have noted that the North Atlantic Ocean is bisected by a mid-Atlantic ridge, which snakes down the center of the basin. The equator is considered the arbitrary divider of the North and South Atlantic Oceans (Map 4). The ridge, with mountains as high as 14,000 feet, rises from the ocean floor, which is at an average depth of about 21,000 feet. The mountains are obviously no hazard to surface navigation, as most of the peaks lie thousands of feet below the surface.

At several places, however, the ridge does break through to become islands. One example is Iceland; another is the Azores Islands, a little east of the middle of the Atlantic Ocean and at about the latitude of Lisbon, Portugal.

We know of the unstable volcanic character of Iceland and the Azores, and geologists have been able to ascertain that the mid-Atlantic ridge is in truth unstable all the way up the middle of the Atlantic Ocean. Oceanographers are continuously substantiating the fact that in many places this ridge of mountains is topped by huge fissures, indicating that it might have been uplifted by gigantic upheavals. The existence of submarine volcanoes along the ridge is well known. Temperatures along the bottom of the ocean increase as this ridge is approached, as was explained in Chapter 2, indicating that the ridge was possibly thrown up by the action of the great convectional currents flowing from the earth's outer core. Nevertheless, with the exception of Madeira, Bermuda, and the Cape Verde and Canary Islands, this ridge provides most of the significant islands in the five-thousand-mile width of the great North Atlantic Ocean.

The floor of the North Atlantic on either side of this ridge is by no means flat and undulating. Only in certain places are low basins found, such as the Newfoundland Basin far to the east of Newfoundland Bay and the Canary Basin between the Canary Islands and the mid-Atlantic ridge (Map 4). Between and among these numerous basins are little side ridges branching off the mid-Atlantic ridge, individual block mountains of tremendous size, and huge plateau areas with rugged surfaces on their tops. Observations made from the U.S.S. *Explorer,* on oceanographic exploration off the southern portion of the North Atlantic basin in 1963, indicate that many of these plateaus and sea mounts are the results of block faulting, violent upthrusts, or warping movements of the ocean's floor.

An amazing thing learned on this voyage, revealed by photographs of the sides of the mid-Atlantic ridge and the slopes of many of the plateaus and hilly areas and mountains of the North

Atlantic basin, was that the stream valleys etching these features are comparable to those which we know on land. This agreed with information previously gathered about the great submarine canyons off the coast of North America, along the edge of its continental shelf (several hundred miles wide in the vicinity of the Newfoundland Banks).

Although the continental shelves along the European-African margin of the Atlantic basin have submarine canyons also, they are most marked along the North American continent. Here they etch far into the margin of the continental shelf, still beneath the surface of the ocean, carving canyons comparable to the Grand Canyon of North America. Many of these canyons appear to be continuations of the mouths of the land rivers, such as the St. Lawrence canyon, the Hudson submarine canyon, and the Chesapeake canyon. Although the continental shelf breaks at about six hundred feet in a 30-degree slant—known as the continental slope—to the depths of the ocean's basin, which is nearly twenty thousand feet here, the submarine canyons cut back into the continental slopes as if they were cut out by ordinary rainwater erosion, as were the canyons on land.

Even more amazing, it was noted that on the floor of the North American basin there was evidence of this type of erosion miles beyond the mouth of the Hudson submarine canyon. It was not in the form of delta deposits, as one might expect, but rather remnants of an apparently meandering land-formed stream continuing its flow from the mouth of the canyon for hundreds of miles along the floor of the basin. The implication seems to be that all of that area was above the ocean once, and the canyon was formed by our familiar land erosion. The same stream that broke out of this canyon must have, in a bygone geological time, meandered leisurely over a dry-land plain much as the Colorado River does after it breaks out of the Grand Canyon and flows through the southwest toward the Gulf of Baja California (Map 4).

Heated controversy has been going on among geologists and oceanographers for years about the origin of these submarine canyons. Some, such as George Sheppard and Douglas Johnson, have maintained that they were formed by land-type erosion when the land was pushed up out of the ocean by the heavy weight of ice caps farther north and west on the continents during the most recent glacial period. Others, such as Harris Stewart, author of *The Global Sea,* have suggested that these canyons could have been formed by submarine turbidity currents; and they explain the stream etching of the mid-Atlantic ridge in this manner. Still others, such as Robert Dietz, believe that this work was definitely done by land-type erosion, particularly the meanders at the mouth of the Hudson canyon, but they disagree that the continents or these areas could have been brought above sea level merely by the action of ice weight. They equate this with the theory of an expanding earth. They point out how these areas could well have been above the surface at one time and later sank because the earth stretched and could not support their frame. They perceive that the existence of a mid-Atlantic continent of Atlantis, and even the existence of the mythical continents of Gondwanaland and Lemuria, may not be as far afield as one might imagine.

The two large appendages of the North Atlantic Ocean on the west are the Gulf of Mexico and the Caribbean Sea. These two basins, shallower than the major basins of the large Atlantic Ocean and separated by the partially volcanic islands of the Greater Antilles group, appear to be parts of the ocean floor, the original basalt layer, exposed when portions of the North American continent pulled westward and toward the equator through centrifugal force, leaving behind island arcs as an expression of crustal tension. Although some claim that Puerto Rico, Hispaniola, and Cuba are really extensions of the line of weakness in the earth's crust from the Alps and Himalayan Mountains of Eurasia, the facts seem to show that these island festoons are comparable to those on the western side of the Pacific and are at least partially the results of continental movements.

These basins are excellent for the deposition of erosion from adjacent continents, particularly the Gulf of Mexico. A wide continental shelf and downwarping of sediments due to an overload of deposition seem to exist in the Gulf of Mexico and help explain the occurrence of oil beneath the Gulf waters, necessitating oilwell drilling on rigs miles off shore. Hudson Bay in North America is similar in its function as a catchment basin for sediment, as are the North, Baltic, Mediterranean, and Black Seas on the European side of the Atlantic basin. Glacial deposition and erosion had a part in the formation of the North Sea and the Baltic Sea and help account for their shallow depths and the conditions favorable for good fishing.

If tension were the only factor to be considered, it would seem incongruous that the Mediterranean and Black Seas—really just one sea system—should develop on the southwestern end of Eurasia, when it is assumed that continents are drifting or tending to drift westward and toward the equator. If this were the case, the Mediterranean area should be an area of compression, and no basin that looks like a tension basin, such as those of the Caribbean Sea and the Gulf of Mexico, should exist.

In reality, the Mediterranean basin is quite different in its formation. Apparently, it was formed much like the larger oceanic basins, but later, and by the stretching of the earth's crust. The Mediterranean is in line with a zone of weakness in the earth's crust and, with some recent expansion tremors of the earth's growth, the gap of the Mediterranean was opened and another portion of the floor of the basalt below was revealed. This block of basalt is still thicker than the basalt in the major Atlantic Ocean basins, allowing for depths of only about fourteen thousand feet in that body of water. It has been suggested that this development of the Mediterranean Sea and its basin took place during the period of the written history of man. Perhaps, some suggest, it happened during a recent period of volcanic and diastrophic violence when the stretching of the earth's crust opened the basin and breached the opening into the Atlantic at the Straits of Gibraltar. Could this —it has been asked—be the great flood spoken of in the Bible?

The North Atlantic Ocean is the only one that opens directly into the Arctic Ocean, since the Pacific is largely cut off by land in the vicinity of Bering Strait and by the Aleutian Island ridge and chain of islands. The mid-Atlantic ridge is parallel with the orientation of the ocean and hence the North Atlantic Ocean connects directly with the Arctic Ocean between Greenland and the Scandinavian peninsula of Europe. It can be readily seen that this would allow some of the warmer water of the Atlantic to penetrate north and has some significance in keeping northern Europe in a mild climate, while bathing part of the Arctic Ocean shores near Europe in relatively warm currents.

The South Atlantic is much like the North Atlantic, for it is split by a continuation of the mid-Atlantic ridge and has its basins, plateaus, sea mounts, and sea hills. It also has its bordering continental shelves and submarine canyons, such as the famous Congo submarine canyon off the mouth of the Congo River of Africa. One rather large diagonal ridge shoots off from the mid-Atlantic ridge and stretches all the way to the coast of southwest Africa; it is known as the Walvis ridge. Another series of east-west ridges, about 60 degrees south latitude, cuts the South Atlantic Ocean off partially from its influence upon the Antarctic Ocean. These ridges, where they approach the surface, keep some icebergs from the South Atlantic, whereas the lack of such protection in the North Atlantic allows the well-known ice floes there in winter.

It is interesting to note that the Scotia ridge, one of the submarine ridges separating the South Atlantic Ocean from the Antarctic, rises to the surface in several places and forms what is known as the South Sandwich Islands. One of these, appropriately named Deception Island, has a curious history: it seems that it disappears once in a while. Several different expeditions to that part of the world have located the island by reliable means and instruments. Yet other expeditions have failed to find the island at that location—in fact, they failed to find any island at all that answered to the description of this small volcanic feature. Explorations made by a ship of the Lamont Geological Laboratory of Columbia University indicate that this ridge is an extremely unstable portion of the zone of weakness in the earth's crust, characteristic of the ring around the Antarctic continent at about 60 degrees south latitude. It is hence possible that the island has sunk and risen from time to time in the past; other instances of this phenomenon have been recorded in other parts of the world.

It might be noted also in connection with both the North Atlantic and South Atlantic oceans that the submarine trenches, or deeps, appear on the western side of the ocean basins. As we noted in Chapter 2, these trenches are thought to have been formed by two conditions.

First, a coastal area of tension is necessary. The western margins of the entire Atlantic Ocean are considered such areas of tension, with the westward and equatorward drift of the respective continents of North and South America.

Second, the pull of the convection current has to be present—that is, the convection current from deep within the earth. We have already noted how this convection current rises to the surface through the earth's mantle to just beneath the crust in the vicinity of the mid-Atlantic ridge, and how the heat wave travels underneath the ocean floor and cools and returns toward the interior of the earth at the continental margins. This would not have much effect on the eastern side of the oceanic basins, which are allegedly coast lines of compression, but it would affect and possibly force the block downward, faulting on the western edges of these oceanic basins.

In the Pacific there are numerous examples of this, but in the Atlantic we have only a few definite indications of the phenomenon. In the North Atlantic lies the Puerto Rican Trench, adjacent to the island of Puerto Rico, which drops abruptly to depths of more than 27,000 feet from a normal oceanic depth of around 20,000 feet. Several other minor trenches exist in this area. There is also the South Sandwich Trench, in the South Atlantic, adjacent to the South Sandwich Islands near the Scotia ridge near the southern end of that ocean, which drops abruptly to a depth of more than 28,000 feet from a normal ocean bottom of less than 20,000 feet (Map 4).

The Arctic Ocean

Let us look now at a smaller ocean, the Arctic. This basin at the top of the world is less than a fourth the size of either the North Atlantic or the South Atlantic. It is also less deep, showing depths considerably less than twenty thousand feet in the few soundings that have been taken in recent exploration in that area.

This ocean is almost completely frozen over during winter (with the exception of a small area off northern Europe and northwestern Eurasia, where the warm North Atlantic current, the Gulf Stream, keeps such ports as Murmansk open a good part of the year). This frozen condition is what allowed Admiral Peary to reach the North Pole in 1907 by dog sled and on foot. In summer the ice breaks up along most of the coast, but much of it remains reasonably intact over the surface of a good part of the ocean (*see illustration section*). Where free water is seen, big ice islands appear, and here research scientists set up camp, making soundings and other observations.

Most of the appendages of the Arctic Ocean are similarly ice locked. The Bering Sea, the largest appendage, is not only choked with ice but also shrouded in fog because of the proximity of an ocean current that cannot get into the Arctic Ocean from the Pacific. The Bering Straits and the Aleutian Island ridge keep the Arctic Ocean shut off from the Pacific. Its only opening is into the Atlantic, and any warming influence by currents felt in the Arctic Ocean comes from that direction.

The mid-Atlantic ridge is supposed to continue underneath the central portion of the Arctic Ocean and come out in North America as part of the coastal system of mountains along the western edge of the North American continent. Archeological finds seem to indicate that the Arctic Ocean was, from time to time throughout the geological past, relatively free from shore ice, with human habitations adorning its shores. This seems to have been the condition during recent glacial periods, when the center of ice buildup was transferred to the North

American continent, and warm currents in the North Atlantic broke into the Arctic basin and warmed its shores.

It is alleged that migrations of aborigines from Asia into North America took place around the Arctic basin as well as over land then exposed along the Aleutian Islands ridge. It is held that the Mongoloids who migrated to North America during those times later went south to become the North American Indians and the Indians of Central and South America. There are even those who contend that during these same periods migrations came from northern Europe, taking advantage of the then clear and mild North Atlantic Ocean, to land in Labrador and Newfoundland and Nova Scotia, later moving southward and westward. The amazing similarity of ancient Egyptian architecture and science to that of the Mayas of Central America is advanced as proof of this. It is pointed out that even the signs used for various parts of the zodiac in Mayan are similar to those used by the Egyptians. Most of this, however, is accepted only as imaginative by experts in those fields.

Let us recall that the world experiences a full turn of a climatic "super" cycle about every two thousand years. The warmest part of the super-warm cycle occurred about A.D. 600 and the coldest part about A.D. 1500. We are now on our way toward another warming period near A.D. 2500. We noted that the sixteenth century was the time of western expansion and discovery, and we observed that A.D. 600 was in the middle of the Dark Ages for southern Europe.

It was no dark age, however, for northern Europe, or for people in northern climates in other parts of the world. This was a period of great expansion for the Vikings of Scandinavia. Their records show that icebergs were unheard of in the North Atlantic at that time. We learn from them that they established a colony in Greenland and eventually one in Labrador. A startling archeological find in 1964 by a Norwegian, Anne Stine Ingstad, provided conclusive evidence that a Viking colony did flourish in Newfoundland at a date earlier than A.D. 1000, probably between A.D. 700 and 900.

This was a period also of the beginnings of the Hanseatic

League along the shores of the Baltic, where various towns prospered from fishing and commerce and later joined together for their economic benefit. According to the Norwegian oceanographer, Otto Petterson, this was a time when the sun, moon, and several of the stars in space came into their proper alignment to exercise a terrific pull on the tides of the oceans, affecting the spill of warm waters into the Arctic Ocean and a great influx of Atlantic waters (with economically exploitable fish) into the Baltic Sea. This alignment of heavenly bodies at that time has been corroborated by astronomers.

In the light of the foregoing, one might give some credence to several early maps which have recently been discovered that depict Antarctica, centuries before the advent of Columbus or the modern era of exploration, as a continent with verdant green vegetation along its shores. If the Arctic could be ameliorated by these great tides, one might argue, then so could the Antarctic; the great tides were not so deep that they could not have easily overridden the submarine ridges around the Antarctic Ocean and brought warm South Atlantic, South Pacific, and Indian Ocean water to the shores of Antarctica.

It is believed, however, that a combination of circumstances, including the huge tides, were responsible for the unusual conditions of those times. We noted in Chapter 2 that climatic cycles appear to take place in relation to cycles of geomagnetism. It is very possible that the unique astronomical alignment previously alluded to could have been in part responsible for not just a cycle of oceanic activity but the entire combination of phenomena which reached cycle peaks at that time—that is, geomagnetism, climate, and oceanic conditions.

The Indian Ocean

We will now examine the Indian Ocean, that intriguing southern sea about which the least is known of all the waters of the world. For its size, it is rather shallow, with depths not exceeding twenty thousand feet. Of course, this is based on presently known depths, and until recently not a great deal of exploration had taken place in this body of water, in spite of the fact that it was one of the early oceans of the world to be used in trade, for the early routes between Arabia and India and the East Coast of Africa and later between Arabia and the Orient. It is known, of course, that the mid-Atlantic ridge continues into the Indian Ocean, after skirting around the southern end of Africa. This ridge runs northward a little west of the center of this body of water and ends in the Arabian Sea just west of the Indian peninsula (Map 4).

As in the Atlantic, this ridge has several minor branches, some of them capped with islands. One of them is the Madagascar ridge, and on it is the island of Madagascar, one of the largest of the world's islands. Another is the Seychelles-Mauritius ridge, containing the islands of the same names. Some scientists believe that a microcontinent, which has since sunk, once existed in the vicinity of the Seychelles. A number of basins and a series of independent mountains also make up a part of the floor of this mysterious ocean, the biggest of which are the basins occupied by the two appendage seas, the Arabian Sea and the Bay of Bengal.

The waters of the Indian Ocean tend to be rather warm, since they are largely in the low latitudes and are somewhat free of ice floes from the Antarctic Ocean. As is usual, a submerged continental shelf surrounds and underlies the Bay of Bengal and the Arabian Sea, both of which are considerably shallower than the main ocean, not being more than eleven thousand feet in depth. The waters in these two seas seem to be warm and hospitable and abound with nutrient materials brought in from the adjacent continent; hence they support varied sea life. The shores of bordering Australia and Africa seem to be singularly devoid of continental shelves of any appreciable width.

There does not appear to be a marked development of submarine canyons in this ocean, but several sea trenches have been discovered. One is located just south of the island of Java and northwest of Australia and is known as the Java Trench. This appears to be at the wrong side of the ocean for development by the pull of the downward convection current. Apparently, all oceanic trenches are not formed in that manner. Some arise in areas of definite weakness of the earth's crust, where sudden stretching of the crust has cracked and broken it open, causing a dropping of a sector of the crust. The Java Trench is definitely a part of the zone of weakness in the earth's crust.

A detailed survey of the Indian Ocean is now underway through the cooperation of many of the maritime nations of the world under the control of the Inter-Ocean Survey and the International Oceanographic Committee of the United Nations. In the summer of 1964 the U.S.S. *Pioneer,* on an oceanographic expedition as part of this international effort, found evidence of considerable magnetic hotspots underneath the Indian Ocean and evidences of anomalous magnetic disturbance.

It is well to note here that the International Oceanographic Committee of the United Nations, with its data center located in Washington, D.C., began in 1960 a ten-year program of examination and survey of the oceans of the world of which the Indian Ocean survey is only a part. Surveys have been and are being made also in the Atlantic, Pacific, Arctic, and Antarctic Oceans, and some of the mysteries prevailing for centuries about our oceans may soon be dispelled.

The Antarctic Ocean

Not much has been said about the Antarctic Ocean in these pages, first, because it is not a separate ocean in itself, and secondly, because its underwater systems that are known seem to be extensions of those of the South Atlantic, South Pacific, and Indian Oceans. Exploration of these oceans and geophysical explorations on the Antarctic continent have revealed, however, that the Antarctic may be larger than previously estimated; conversely, the Antarctic continent may be smaller than previously thought. Wide, deep channels have been discovered cutting across the Antarctic continent, the biggest one being between Marie Byrd Land and the western part of Ant-

Devastation in Anchorage, Alaska, March, 1964. *Photo by Alfonse Benedict.*

More earthquake damage in Anchorage, 1964. *Photo by Alfonse Benedict.*

Uplift of Montague Island, Alaska. The insert, lower left, shows area uplifted. *Courtesy U.S. Coast and Geodetic Survey.*

Rugged North American mountains.

Mountains in Central America stretched in a serpentine chain.

Young rugged mountains. Pikes Peak in Colorado, U.S.A., part of the Rocky Mountains. *Photo by William Dennis.*

Small sand hills are often developed by wind action. *Photo by William Dennis.*

Volcanic eruption in the Aleutian Islands, Alaska, U.S.A., 1918. *Courtesy U.S. Coast and Geodetic Survey*.

Volcanism often leaves behind impressive minor features such as Black Butte, New Mexico, U.S.A. *Photo by William Dennis.*

Sand hill in northern Africa. The direction of the wind is from the lower right of the picture.

A small bathysphere, 22 feet long, for oceanographic exploration in the North Atlantic. *Courtesy U.S. Geological Survey.*

On the shore of the Arctic Ocean. Ice chunks are pushed up by the expansion of the winter freeze. *Courtesy U.S. Navy Hydrographic Office.*

Unalakteet Inlet, Alaska. Longshore currents set in motion by the tides sometimes threaten to close such inlets. *Courtesy U.S. Coast and Geodetic Survey.*

Regular approach of ordinary waves, Florida. *Courtesy U.S. Navy Department.*

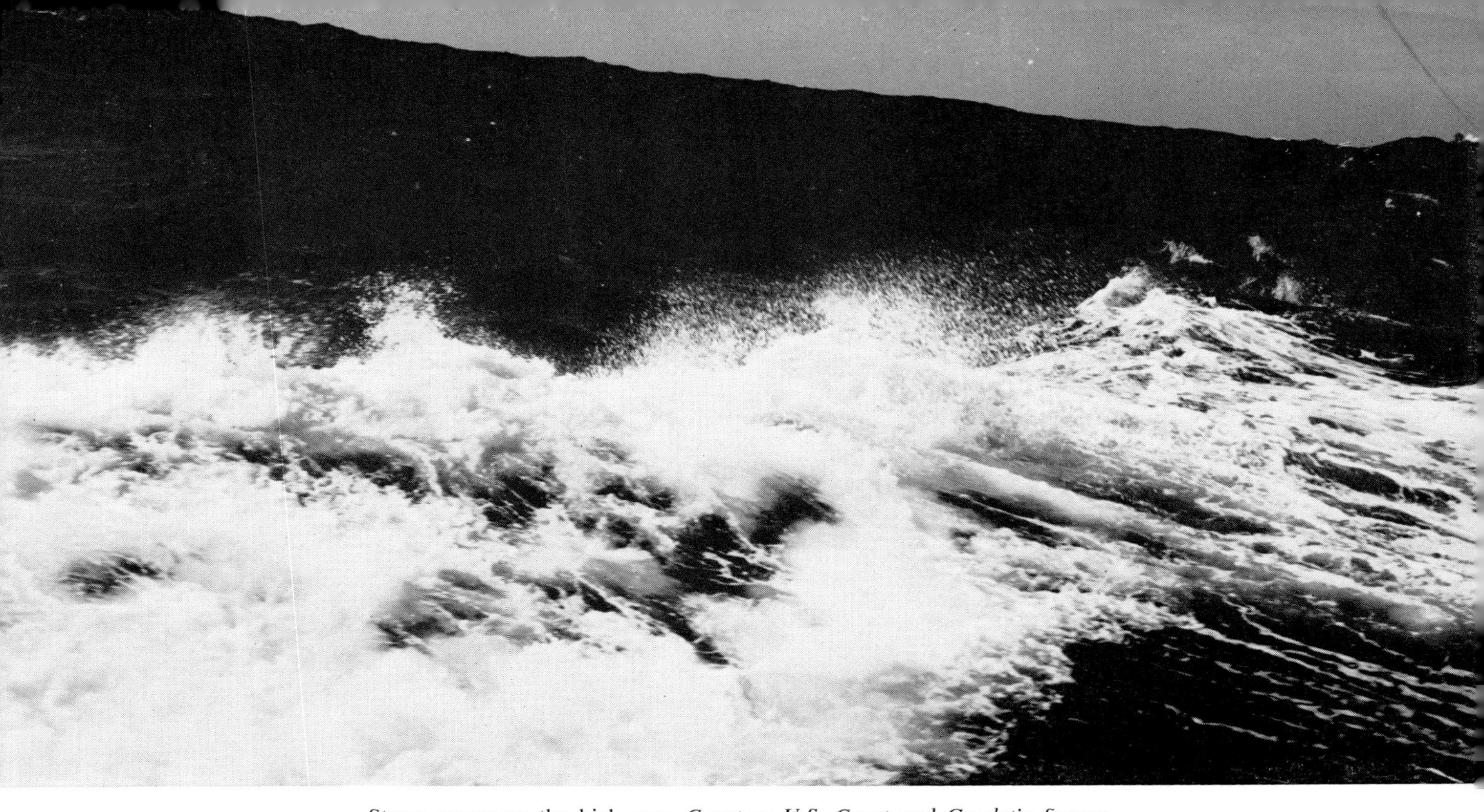

Storm waves on the high seas. *Courtesy U.S. Coast and Geodetic Survey.*

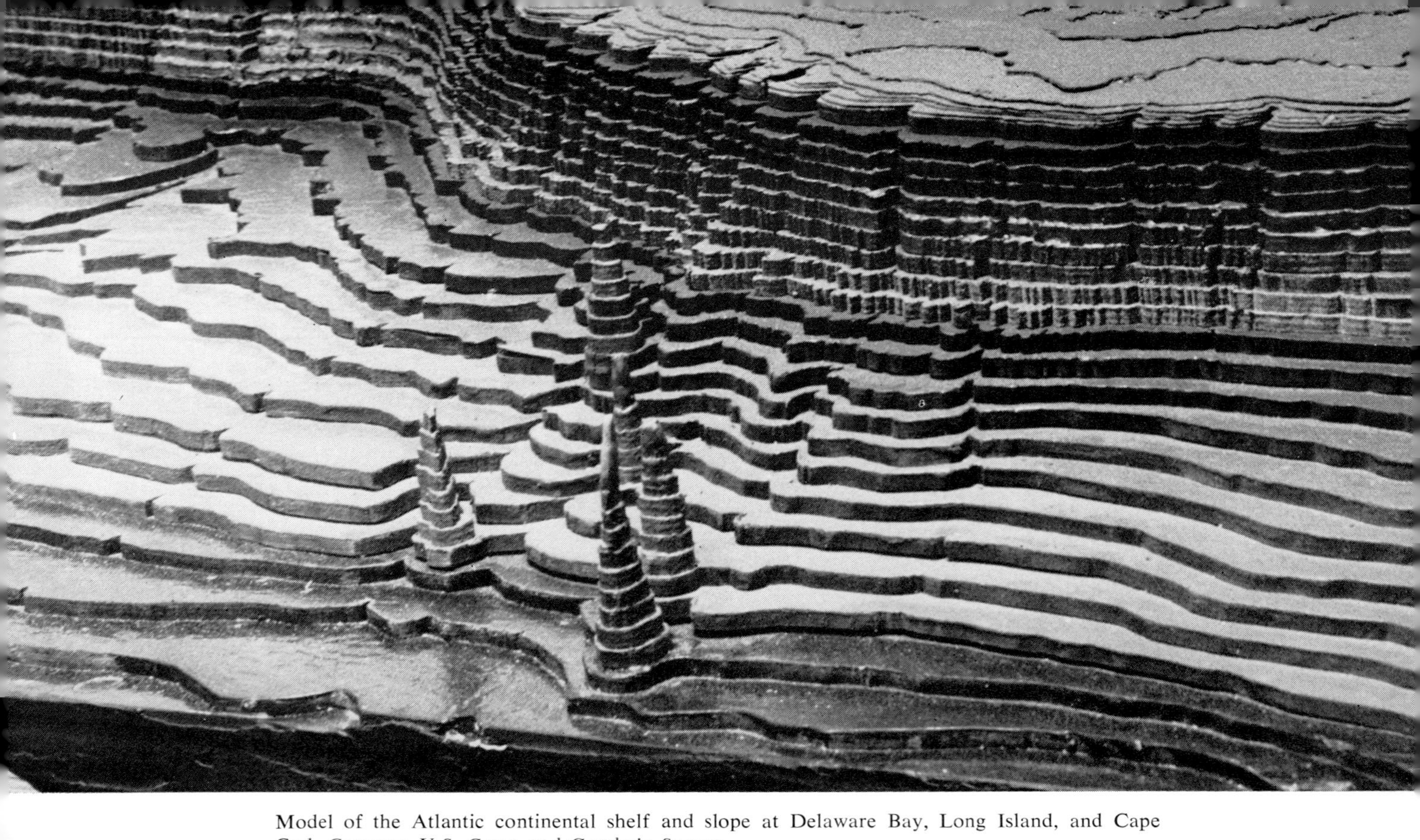

Model of the Atlantic continental shelf and slope at Delaware Bay, Long Island, and Cape Cod. *Courtesy U.S. Coast and Geodetic Survey.*

Recreational land use is developing rapidly in the Sonoran region. *Photo by William Dennis.*

Low-latitude highland area in Oceania. Picture was taken during rainy season. *Courtesy U.S. Coast and Geodetic Survey.*

Dry subtropical landscape in Central South America. *Courtesy U.S. Coast and Geodetic Survey.*

Village in the dry subtropical portion of the Meseta. *Photo by William Dennis.*

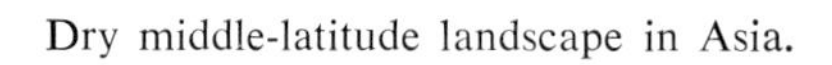

Dry middle-latitude landscape in Asia.

The Great North Woods, McKenzie taiga.

The Great North Woods, Hudson Bay taiga. *Courtesy U.S. Coast and Geodetic Survey*.

arctica. This channel, of course, has been covered by the huge continental ice sheet that embraces all of Antarctica.

The Pacific Ocean

Looking next at the largest of all the oceans, the Pacific, we note that it is arbitrarily divided more or less by the equator into the North Pacific Ocean and the South Pacific Ocean. This division is not entirely without logic, since one set of surface currents bathes the shores of the North Pacific and a separate set bathes the shores of the South Pacific.

The North Pacific Ocean contains the deepest known places in the entire world. The Mariana Trench, in the western part near the islands of the same name, drops from normal ocean depths of about 22,000 feet to nearly 37,000 feet. Several other deep trenches line the western portion of the Pacific Ocean —the Philippine Trench, the Japan Trench, the Tonga Trench, and the Aleutian Trench—all near the geographic features of the same name.

In general, the North Pacific is the deep ocean, with depths of 22,000 and 23,000 feet very common. Many submarine ridges, apparently of volcanic origin, are distributed throughout its over-all basin and interspaced by smaller basins, the topography of which is presumably undulating. Some of these ridges reach up through the surface and become islands, such as the Hawaiian Archipelago. In some places there are doughnut-shaped coral islands.

In addition to many underwater volcanic sea mounts and ridges, oriented more or less without pattern in the North Pacific, a number of apparently independent block mountains, brought about by faulting and diastrophic action, seem to be scattered throughout the submarine realm of the northern part of the Pacific. It has been suggested that some of these mountains and ridges might be the remnants of the ancient continent of Lemuria, which evidently sank beneath the ocean ages ago, as the basin stretched and could no longer support its weight.

As in the North Atlantic, submarine canyons indent the continental shelves ringing the North Pacific Ocean. An unusual feature is a series of east–west-oriented fracture zones crossing the eastern part, along which lateral movements in the earth's crust occur. Movements along these zones are responsible for the many submarine earthquakes in the North Pacific.

Most unusual of all, however, are the eccentricities of the oceanic ridge in this ocean. As noted earlier, it comes to shore along the coast of the North American continent to comprise the ridges making up the coastal ranges of western North America. The valleys behind these ranges, such as the California Valley, might geologically be considered a part of the Pacific basin. (Detailed studies will determine this fact, and it is already known that the coastal mountains of North America show many characteristics of mid-oceanic ridges.) This same ridge turns oceanward to become a true mid-oceanic ridge in the South Pacific Ocean, and of course in the northern end of North America it joins the Arctic Ocean ridge (Map 4).

Inasmuch as areas of coastal weakness are intensified on the North American coasts of the Pacific, it is not surprising that some oceanic trenches caused by the earth's expansion appear along the normally compressed western shore line of the continents. Such is the Mexican Trench off North America and the Peru-Chile Trench off the coast of South America. On the western margins of both the North and South Pacific oceans, the big trenches occur again, but these coast lines of tension produce trenches under different conditions, which have been described before, such as the Marianas Trench and the Tonga Trench.

The mid-Pacific ridge, in coming to shore along the Pacific coast of North America, forms the backbone of the lower California peninsula and comprises the coastal ranges of California, as well as the Cascade Mountains and the coastal ranges of Washington and Oregon, together with the coastal mountains and offshore island chains of Canada and Alaska. Explorations over the mid-Atlantic ridge by the U.S.S. *Explorer* in 1963 revealed that the shape of the general morphology of the crack in the mid-Atlantic ridge resembles somewhat the Willamette and

Puget Sound valleys of Washington and Oregon along the west coast of the United States, as well as the inland passage along the western coast of Canada and Alaska.

Some of the basins formed near these ridges are said to be the result of imbalances in the already unstable earth's crust in these areas, causing block faulting beyond the outer edge of the ridge and forming such depression trenches as the huge Aleutian Trench off southwestern Alaska. If exposed, the Aleutian Trench would be more magnificent than any trench or canyon known on land. It is an almost sheer drop from sea level to depths of more than twenty-five thousand feet.

The arclike shape of the Aleutians is in line with the form taken by buckling. With buckling movements, a tremor is set up within the earth; this happens rather frequently in the Pacific. Consequently, there are many submarine earthquakes and submarine volcanic eruptions, most of them taking place far beneath the surface of the quiet ocean. Naturally, they would be picked up by seismographs throughout the world, but they would get no further notice were it not for the fact that they often cause devastating sea waves.

Killer Waves

These huge waves wreak terrific damage when they crash on the shores of distant islands or continents. Under a perfectly sunny sky and from an apparently calm sea, a wall of water may break twenty or thirty feet high over beaches and waterfronts, crushing houses and drowning unsuspecting residents and bathers in its path.

How are these waves formed? When a submarine earthquake occurs, it is likely to set up a tremendous amount of shock, disturbing the quiet waters of the deep ocean. This disturbance travels to the surface and forms a huge swell in the ocean many miles across. It rolls outward in all directions, and the water lowers in the center as another swell looms up. Thus, a series of concentric swells are formed similar to those made when a coin or small pebble is dropped into a basin of water. The big difference is in the size. Each of the concentric rings of basin water traveling out toward the edge is only about an inch across and less than a quarter of an inch high. The swells in the ocean are sometimes nearly a mile wide and rise to several multiples of ten feet in height.

Many of us have heard about these waves, often referred to by their Japanese name of "tsunami." For ages they have been dreaded in the Pacific, as no shore has been free from them. An underwater earthquake in the Aleutian Islands could start a swell that would break along the shores and cause severe damage in the southern part of Chile in South America. These waves travel hundreds of miles an hour, and one can understand how they would crash as violent breakers when caused to drag in the shallow waters of a coast.

Nothing was done about tsunamis until after World War II. In 1947 a particularly bad submarine earthquake took place south of the Aleutian Islands. A few hours later, people bathing in the sun along the quiet shores of Hawaii were dashed to death and shore-line property became a mass of shambles because a series of monstrous, breaking swells crashed along the shore and drove far inland. Hundreds of lives were lost in this catastrophe, and millions upon millions of dollars' worth of damage was done.

Hawaii (at that time a territory) and other Pacific areas then asked the U.S. Coast and Geodetic Survey to attempt to forecast these killer waves. With the blessing of the government, the Coast and Geodetic Survey initiated a program in 1948 known as the Seismic Seawave Warning System, using the earthquake-monitoring facilities of the agency, together with the world seismological data center, to locate submarine earthquakes as soon as they might occur. With this information they could then tell how severe a submarine earthquake was and could set up a tracking chart, with the center over the area of the earthquake, which would show by concentric time belts the rate of travel of the resulting wave. This system would indicate when and where, along the shores of the Pacific, the swells caused by the submarine earthquakes would strike.

Such information, added to and confirmed by tidal stations all around the edge of the Pacific cooperating with the Seismic Seawave Center at Honolulu, Hawaii, could make possible the noting of any eccentricities of the waves. This information, too, could then be flashed to centers all around the Pacific. The expected time of arrival and the height of the breakers could be given to each of the places which might be affected. The system has been working successfully now for years. Nothing can be done to stop the waves, but the coastal areas in danger can be evacuated, valuable materials can be removed, and future buildings can be constructed so as to withstand the onslaught of the surges.

Ocean Mineral Wealth

Very generous predictions have been made about the mineral value that lies beneath the surface of all the oceans. The predictions may be overly optimistic, but it is known that mineral deposits in usable form have been revealed on the ocean floors all around the world. For example, deep-sea cameras have been employed to depths of more than thirteen thousand feet, and off the shores of Bermuda in the Atlantic, at depths much less, manganese nodules of economic value have been seen in great abundance. Similar nodules, which are likely concretionary in structure and quite small, have been observed in many other places on the floors of the oceans, most of them at depths of more than six hundred feet and sometimes more than one thousand feet. The nodules are numerous in the areas where they occur and if harvested could represent a considerable economic asset.

Unlike the extraction of salt and magnesium from ocean water, which is done by processing surface water, the gathering of manganese nodules presents a problem. They cannot be picked up by divers, because they are found well below the depths to which even helmeted divers can descend. They are worth going to the trouble to gather, however, for manganese is a rare mineral, vital in the making of certain kinds of steel and recognized throughout the world as a strategic element. Many programs have been proposed for the gathering of this wealth, most of them economically unfeasible. Deep-sea dredges are not practical, for the cost of lowering the dredges would outweigh the profit, and using diving bells with mechanical devices for gathering the materials is also considered uneconomical.

The problem may have been first solved early in 1964 when an independent experimental oceanographer, Dr. Edward A. Link, of Binghamton, New York, developed what he calls the "Sea Diver," a submersible, portable, inflatable "house" in which men can live for an extended period deep beneath the surface of the ocean to explore its depths and gather its riches. These riches, according to Dr. Link, even include raw diamonds lying on the ocean's floor and begging to be taken. He successfully tested his Sea Diver in waters in excess of six hundred feet near the Bahama Islands in September, 1964. He is still continuing his research and claims that man can work comfortably under the ocean at depths several times those he has already tested.

Dr. Link's Sea Diver is simply a rubber tent that is inflated with helium and oxygen under pressure. It is open at the bottom, but the inside of the sausage-shaped structure contains a mixture of air—97 per cent helium and 3 per cent oxygen. The pressure of the helium-oxygen gas inside keeps the water from entering from the bottom, and the men who live in this eight-by-seven-by-four-foot abode breathe this air successfully as they walk with their tent along the bottom of the ocean, carrying on their exploration. They can even don breathing apparatus and swim out and away from their abode, for the pressure inside is kept equal to the water at their depth.

Dr. Link proved not only that men can live under terrific water pressures but that they can work and explore the ocean bottom; his experimental divers stayed down two days and were in good condition when they were brought to the surface. He also showed that the recovery of minerals and other riches on the floor of the ocean may be economically feasible. These men, with short periods of sleep, could work the entire two days they spent on the bottom of the ocean. In contrast, if they were working with regular diving gear, they would have to be drawn to the surface every few hours and go through the long decompression process, which is both tedious and expensive. In the Sea Diver, men can stay continuously underwater at least two days, and only one decompression period is needed. Dr. Link estimates that the time men can stay at great depths can be multiplied a number of times.

The U.S. Navy conducted a similar experiment with success later in 1964, using slightly different equipment than Dr. Link but essentially the same principles. In 1965 the Navy engaged in more extensive underwater experiments. A specially constructed capsule named Sealab 2 was submerged for forty-five days and was occupied by three different teams of so-called aquanauts at a depth of 205 feet, and the men worked inside and outside the capsule with no observable ill effects upon their health. Officially it was announced, at the completion of the experiment in October, that man can now work underwater for long periods of time without physical harm.

The discovery of mineral wealth on the floors of the ocean has not been entirely by means of the deep-sea camera. Some has been detected through the use of a magnetometer towed behind a ship. This instrument sensitively registers variations in magnetism along the ocean's floor, to the degree that different kinds of minerals can be identified. The magnetometer towed behind the U.S.S. *Pioneer* and U.S.S. *Explorer* in the Pacific in 1963, as well as magnetometers towed behind ships in other oceans all over the world, have revealed numerous sources of such mineral wealth. The amount discovered thus far, however, does not merit the optimism exhibited by many ardent oceanographers.

These magnetometers also indicate the variations in the earth's magnetic field, both in the major field and in the occurrences of minor fields. They even reveal the location of magnetic poles throughout the world in the geological past. E. K. Runcorn, in 1955, was able to trace the migration of the north magnetic pole—that is, the earth's negative magnetic pole—throughout geological history, by notations of the magnetic character of areas around the oceans where the influence of the geomagnetic pole has been exerted.

The magnetometer picked up characteristic rocks, and the

orientation of matter therein denoted the former sites of the north magnetic pole. The indication was that, in early Pre-Cambrian times, more than a billion years ago, the magnetic pole may have been located somewhere in the North Atlantic. Later it shifted to what is now North America, and still later it was in the North Pacific Ocean. In the Paleozoic Era, about half a billion years ago, it was still in the North Pacific but closer to the Asian coast. By the Mesozoic Era it had reached the continent of Asia in the vicinity of Manchuria. It then migrated northward across eastern Asia, and by the end of the Mesozoic Era it was in the Arctic Ocean. During the last one hundred million years it has wandered erratically in the Arctic Ocean, sometimes touching the continent of North America.

We have noted that its last movement was northwesterly from the continental shores of North America, some three hundred miles away, wandering since 1831 toward the true pole. This widespread movement of the earth's magnetic pole throughout geological history seems to give credence to the theory of the shifting of our true poles from time to time in the geological past, for it has been ascertained that the earth's magnetic North Pole never varies more than about twenty degrees from the true pole. If this is true, the earth's crust must have shifted considerably in the past. It might be said that the earth's climate as a whole must have been very mild when the North Pole was over the Pacific and the South Pole over the Indian Ocean. Both of these oceans are large enough to moderate the extreme cold of the poles by their circulation systems and hence not let ice build up as in the present landlocked Arctic Ocean.

Oceanic Movements: Tides and Waves

The dynamic aspects of our world need not be sought in the past; they can be seen today, particularly in the gyrations of our oceans. Most of us are familiar with some of the ocean's movements—that is, with its waves and its long-shore currents. We are also familiar with its tides, for we see them or read about them regularly. If we live near the ocean, we can see the waves on the surface of the water. We can also see how the tide comes in and recedes twice every day, and we observe the little currents that develop along the shore, usually parallel with the coast as the result of the action of wave or tide.

What we may not see, by standing on the shore looking out to sea, are the great surface currents of the ocean, which are much too vast for our casual eye. We also do not see the deep countercurrents flowing in opposite directions from the great surface currents to keep the balance of the ocean. Nor can we observe the very deep slow currents flowing far beneath the ocean surface and traveling at a snail's pace, sometimes taking nearly one hundred years to carry a drop of water from the Arctic to the tropics. We cannot see the turbidity currents, either, which are caused by sediments and erratically flowing waters operating beneath the ocean's surface and effecting considerable erosion along the continental shelves. We may perceive, however, that the ocean is in motion and is carrying materials and plankton—that is, microscopic life—from one part of the world to another, while also conveying heat from warmer to cooler parts and vice versa, acting out its role as the great moderator.

The Tides. As noted in Chapter 1, the pull of the sun and of the moon is reflected in a bulge in the various oceans as they pass under the gravitational pull of these astronomical bodies. Since the moon is closer to the earth, its pull is greater. The influence of the bulge travels outward like a wave from a dropped pebble as the bulge moves along its path. The height of tide at a given place depends on its attitude toward this wave. This influence is felt in the ocean basin on the other side of the earth because the earth is, to some extent, pulled away from the ocean at that end. Consequently, each ocean basin gets two high tides each day, one when the moon is passing directly over it and one when the moon is passing over the other side of the earth. The tides are low when the ocean's water has returned to a more normal state.

Each individual ocean basin, with its peculiar topography, also influences the way the tides slosh about in the ocean basin. This is an involved subject and justifies the highly complex tidal science of today, which helps to explain the variations in tide that can occur in individual ocean basins. For example, the tides in the southern part of the North Pacific Ocean, both on the American and Asiatic sides, are relatively low and are measured in inches, but the tides in the northern part of the Pacific are great and measured in feet. Tides along certain parts of the North Atlantic Ocean are extremely high also, reaching fifty feet in the Bay of Fundy, and some of the tides in Alaska are more than thirty feet. Consideration is being given in many parts of the world to harnessing the tides for the generation of electrical power. Inasmuch as these tides do not strike the coast at a direct angle, they often set up tidal currents that may be responsible for erosion and deposition along our coast lines (*see illustration section*).

Waves. Besides gravity, the other forces capable of moving ocean waters are the wind and the rotation of the earth; sometimes seismic disturbances will cause movement also. Although some currents in the ocean are caused by wind, the main product of wind activity over the ocean is the generation of waves. Most of us are familiar with the regular run of waves, which are not more than a few feet high, and we have seen pictures or heard stories of huge waves which are reported as being at least ten times the ordinary size (*see illustration section*).

Much has been written about waves, but an erroneous concept is still extant: most people think that water is traveling with each wave. It appears as such when a wave breaks on a shore; however, water does not actually travel in a wave but rather a vibration of a disturbance does the traveling. When a wave is born on the ocean by the action of wind friction on the water, a disturbance is set up which is more or less a circular motion—that is, the water rises and drops and the impulse moves on toward the shore, lifting and dropping water as it advances. The individual particles of water, however, stay pretty close to where they were originally. When the impulse gets close to the shore, the circular motion of the particles of water cannot be completed for the circle drags the bottom; hence, the water falls forward of its own weight, resulting in a breaker. It can be noted, though, that with the passing of a wave the individual particles of water go only with the circular motion of the impulse and then return close to the place where they began. Consequently, waves in general are not movers of water except in a very limited sense.

The wave's length is measured from the trough, and its height is the number of feet it rises above the general level of the ocean. Its shape is actually ellipsoid. Most waves are not more than a few feet high and travel to break on some coast at a regular rate of several per minute (*see illustration section*). A constant exists between the wave's height and length, for its height never exceeds one-seventh of its length. If waves are created during stormy weather, very often the ellipsoid that is formed is compressed and the ratio of seven to one is broken; thus the wave gets too high for its width and topples over of its own weight, forming a whitecap. The toppling of waves because of the bottom drag along the coastline exerts great erosional and depositional power, and considerable energy is released. This may be partially responsible for the rarefying of the air along coastlines and the higher ozone content in those areas, according to the results of British researchers.

Storm waves are not only much higher than the average but they appear much more dangerous. Most ordinary waves never reach more than three feet in height, but many storm waves extend more than thirty feet high. Only a few, however, get up to forty or fifty feet. These are awe-inspiring, for when a ship is in a trough between two such waves passengers on deck can often see the crest of the waves above the level where they are standing.

Monstrous waves have been reported from time to time, such as ones of eighty or ninety feet, in unusual storms in the Pacific. The highest wave that has ever been reported which can be reasonably well documented was 112 feet. This was reported from the steamer U.S.S. *Ramapo* in the Pacific during a storm in 1933. An officer of the ship while on watch was able, by means of geometry, to measure rather accurately the height of this wave, using the length of his vessel, the height of its mast, his position on the ship, and the line of sight to his eye. It was truly a mountain of water, and the accuracy of the measurement cannot greatly be doubted. In general, however, waves are not large in size and are not great movers of water over the face of the earth. They are conservers of a great amount of energy, as they represent the energy caused by the friction of the wind on the water, and many programs are now being developed to harness this energy.

The tsunami or seismic sea wave has been discussed before. It is so large that it is imperceptible at sea but crashes with devastating violence whenever it is forced to topple over along shallow coast lines. It is not caused by wind friction, as are most waves, but rather by the terrific vibrations emanating from a submarine earthquake or volcanic eruption. Similar, but smaller, swells have been known to be generated by peculiar wind friction in the North Atlantic, causing considerable damage along coasts.

Oceanic Movements: Global Currents

Surface Currents. By far the most important movers of ocean waters are the currents, and the most important of these are the global surface currents. We have heard of the Gulf Stream, the equatorial current, the Humboldt current, and others. They move billions and billions of gallons of surface ocean water from the equatorial regions to polar regions and vice versa. The currents are, above all, the means by which the ocean becomes the moderator of climate throughout the world (Map 5).

Currents are often set in motion simply by the rotation of the earth and the friction of wind on the waters, particularly in the low latitudes or the region of the trade winds. We noted earlier that the earth rotates at about a thousand miles an hour from west to east in the equatorial region. Water, being fluid, does not necessarily have to move at as great a speed as the solid earth. Consequently, there is a tendency for water to drag in the vicinity of the equator where the earth is rotating the fastest. In addition, the air, which is also an agent independent of the solid earth, tends to rotate slower than the earth in the low latitudes. This backward or westward drag of the air in the lower latitudes takes the form of the trade winds, flowing toward the equator from the northeast in the northern hemisphere and from the southeast in the southern hemisphere.

The drag of the ocean water and the easterly wind direction tend to set water moving in a westerly direction in the vicinity of the equator. This surface flow of water in a westerly direction, which is not more than ten knots, is known as the equatorial current. It moves the surface waters but not the waters at great depths. The sheet of water moved is not more than several hundred feet in depth, but it is enough to carry the heat stored in the water by the tropical suns ultimately to cool regions and to move the microscopic life, plankton, to different places throughout the world. This equatorial current is in reality two currents, for one sector moves from east to west above the equator and another sector moves from east to west slightly below the equator. In between there is a backward movement of water to compensate for this westward displacement, and a counterequatorial current moving from west to east hovers closely along the equator.

In the North Atlantic Ocean the equatorial current north of the equator is known as the Atlantic north equatorial current, and it moves from the coast of Africa in the vicinity of the Gulf of Guinea westward across the Atlantic Ocean, hundreds of miles wide, to the northeast coast of South America. It then passes through the Caribbean Sea and the Gulf of Mexico and exits from the Gulf of Mexico through the ninety-mile-wide Florida Strait in a swift, constricted channel (Map 5). Part of it, however, goes on the outside of the Caribbean and the Gulf of Mexico, joining up with the other and moving northward along the eastern coast of North America. In this area it is known as the Gulf Stream. This would be the normal bend of this current in any event, if we recall Ferrel's law (sometimes called Coriolis force)—that is, objects moving on the surface in the northern hemisphere tend to deflect toward the right. The northward deflection of this equatorial current up the eastern coast of the United States is thus a natural tendency.

This is still a very warm current, for these waters have stored much of the heat of the sun while in the equatorial regions and are now carrying them northward along the eastern coast of North America. It passes closer than ten miles to the coast in the vicinity of Cape Hatteras and then tends, by Coriolis force, to bend eastward and northeastward across the North Atlantic. As the North Atlantic current, it crosses this stretch and then bathes the shores of England and northern Europe in the still warm waters it has carried from the tropics. Part of this warm current breaks off to the east and north and warms Scandinavia and the Arctic shores of Europe. Finally, the main part of the current bends southward again, which is its tendency, and now, cooled, flows down the west coast of Europe and northern Africa again to join the north equatorial current. This warm current bathing the shores of England and northern Europe is largely responsible for the mild climates there, for England's latitude is about that of cold Labrador and Scandinavia is about the latitude of the frozen Hudson Bay country.

After this current is again deflected rightward and flows down along the western coast of North Africa, it is then reasonably cool and is partially responsible for the dryness along that coast. This aridity is also encouraged by the tendency of the current to pull away from the coast in that area—that is, by the Coriolis force it tends to deflect again to the right to rejoin the north equatorial current farther to the southwest. The tendency of the surface water to pull away from the coast allows for the upwelling of deep waters along the western coast of North Africa, bringing to the surface cold waters from great depths. Consequently, the waters off the coast of Rio de Oro in North Africa are cold, as ocean waters go. These cold waters chill and dehydrate any air passing over them and, consequently, any moisture-laden air that tends toward the North African coast has had the moisture chilled out of it into fog before it reaches land—hence the aridity.

It might be noted that in the middle of this great whorl of water in the North Atlantic Ocean is a relatively calm spot, like the eye of a hurricane. In the case of the North Atlantic, the eye is considerably west of the center of the ocean, closer to the North American continent. It has a name familiar to us, the Sargasso Sea. Here, as in the dead center of any slow eddy, great accumulations of debris occur, and the abundance of seaweed in the Sargasso Sea is well known.

It should be noted also that some of the warm waters of the Gulf Stream or the North Atlantic current as it reaches Europe pass through into the shoreward portion of the Arctic Ocean north of Norway. That is how the ports of Murmansk and Archangel on the Arctic Ocean are serviceable a good part of the year as ocean ports. At the same time, cold water from the Arctic Ocean tends to flow southward, is of course deflected to the right, and tends to flow westward to the north of the North Atlantic current and strike the North American coast along eastern Canada and northeastern United States. This is known as the Labrador current and is the reason that the coastal waters in that vicinity are so cold. This is why, too, the North Atlantic is so stormy: the warm North Atlantic current is in close juxtaposition with the cold Labrador current in the northern part of this ocean, and the air masses over them, being warm and cold, respectively, clash. The drag of currents away from the coast in the vicinity of New England also allows for the upwelling of water from great depths. This is partially responsible for the Grand Banks and the New England fishing industry, for these upwellings bring to the surface rich mineral salts on which plankton feed and which attract the great schools of fish upon which the industry was established.

The south equatorial current forms a comparable whorl in the South Atlantic Ocean (Map 5). It drifts across the South Atlantic just below the equator as the warm south equatorial current. In the vicinity of the bulge of Brazil, it turns southward along the South American coast. This is natural, for the Coriolis force stipulates that objects moving along the surface in the southern hemisphere are deflected to the left. Its flow southward as a warm current is along the South American coast to about the latitude of Rio de Janeiro. Then, by Coriolis force, it is deflected again to the left and travels eastward across the South

Atlantic as the South Atlantic current. By then it is cooled and, by the same force, it deflects northward just west of Cape Town, South Africa, and flows as a cool current, known sometimes as the Benguela current, up the west coast of South Africa to join the south equatorial current again just south of the equator. Along the west coast of South Africa the Benguela current tends to deflect away from the coast, and again upwellings of cool water come in from the depths and extreme aridity is experienced along this coast.

It might be noted that in the South Atlantic, as well as in the Indian and South Pacific oceans, all of these great circular-moving currents meet up with a drift of cold water moving from west to east around the Antarctic continent at about 60 degrees or less south latitude. This "drift" is moved by the violent westerly winds in that vicinity, which makes that part of the world an inhospitable part of the globe.

In the large North Pacific Ocean, the whorl of currents is similar to that in the North Atlantic Ocean (Map 5). The North Pacific current travels from east to west, bends to the right—that is, to the north—along the eastern coast of Asia, and flows northward, becoming the warm Japanese current. It bends to the right opposite the northern island of Japan and travels eastward toward North America as the North Pacific current. It bends to the right again as it nears the west coast of the North American continent in the vicinity of southeastern Alaska, and, now cooled somewhat, it flows southward along the west coast of North America as the relatively cool California current. In the vicinity of lower California, it tends to deflect away from the coast, again bending to the right, eventually to join the Pacific north equatorial current north of the equator. Its bending away from the coast in the vicinity of southern California and the lower California peninsula causes an upwelling of cold waters from below, and the bringing to the surface of food nutrients in the form of mineral salts, which is partially responsible for the fishing industry off the California coast.

An equatorial countercurrent is evidenced in the Pacific, as in the Atlantic, and is responsible for the cool waters noted in some of the islands along the Pacific. As in the Atlantic, the polar current from the Arctic Ocean passes through the Bering Strait southward to the Aleutian Islands ridge—where it is stopped. The juxtaposition of the warm North Pacific current and the cold Arctic current in the vicinity of the Aleutians is responsible for the notorious fog shrouding those islands. Unlike the North Atlantic, the North Pacific has no well-defined "Sargasso Sea." It has a few minor eddies of currents in the eye of the huge whorl which bisects the great North Pacific Ocean. The relatively mild climate of even southeastern Alaska is due largely to this whorl, just as the countries of northwestern Europe are affected by the Atlantic whorl.

The South Pacific is in most ways a counterpart of the South Atlantic. The south equatorial current travels westward across the South Pacific close to the equator, bends to the left—as is the case in the southern hemisphere—in the vicinity of Australia and New Zealand, travels southward along these coasts, and then bends eastward again at the southern end of New Zealand to travel eastward across the South Pacific, there being cooled by juxtaposition to the cold waters of the Antarctic current. In the vicinity of the southern tip of South America it bends to the left again, by Coriolis force, and, now cooled, moves northward along the South American coast as the Peru or Humboldt current. In the vicinity of the equator it joins again the south equatorial current.

Like the Benguela current off South Africa, the Peru current is pulled away from the coast by Coriolis force to join the south equatorial current farther to the northwest. Upwellings of cold water along the coast of northern Chile and Peru lower the temperature of the air off these coasts and, consequently, convert any movement of air toward them into dense fogs, removing moisture and making the winds that finally reach the shores extremely dry. As a result, the coasts of northern Chile and southern Peru are among the most arid in the world, yet thick banks of fog lie just offshore a good part of the year.

Currents in the southern part of the Indian Ocean tend to be similar to those in the South Atlantic and South Pacific; as a result, the western coast of Australia, which is bathed by a current similar to the Peru current, also tends to be extremely dry. The northern part of the Indian Ocean has a current system similar to that in the North Atlantic and North Pacific. It is, however, curtailed by the limiting of the land mass at about 25 degrees north of the equator. These currents, then, although making the complete whirl as in the other northern hemisphere oceans, do not tend to have a moderating effect because they are always in the low latitudes. Consequently, the northern portion of the Indian Ocean is warm and supports abundant sea life, with some of the warmest water temperatures in the world to be found in the appendages of the northern portion of the Indian Ocean, such as those approaching 90 degrees in the Persian Gulf.

Surface currents in the Arctic Ocean are the not-so-frigid waters, and they tend to display an irregular motion in such areas as are not locked by ice. But waters that are not frozen tend to cool and compress in the Arctic Ocean, as well as in the Antarctic, and get heavy and drift to the bottom. These waters, then, drift southward at great depths as countercurrents to replace the surface waters that are washed into the Arctic Ocean.

Countercurrents. It is natural that all of the water that leaves the equatorial regions does not get back. Some of it is lost by evaporation, some of it cools and sinks to lower levels in the higher latitudes, and some of it escapes into the Arctic Ocean or Antarctic Ocean and forms surface currents there or gets locked up as ice. The equatorial countercurrents are upwellings of waters that do get back to the equator by subsurface flow between the north and south equatorial currents, tending to make up for that loss of water, and forming the cold counterequatorial current which flows naturally at a counter direction to the equatorial currents.

Water seeks its own level, so the oceans of the world try to keep an ocean level. That is the reason for the upwellings causing the counterequatorial currents, and it is of course partly the reason for the upwellings along the western coasts of continents at about 30 degrees north or south latitude, where the surface currents tend to pull away from the coasts. This is the reason, too, for deep countercurrents in the oceans all over the world. They are generally less than a thousand feet below the surface and follow the pattern of the surface currents, particularly those flowing southward carrying cold water at those depths to the equatorial regions, possibly to supply the water which wells up to form the counterequatorial current.

The best known of these is the countercurrent beneath the Gulf Stream in the North Atlantic Ocean at depths from about five hundred to a thousand feet. This current flows exactly underneath the Gulf Stream in the opposite direction, carrying the cold waters of the ocean's depths toward the equator. It has been studied by the U.S. Coast and Geodetic Survey since it was discovered during the historic voyages of the steamer *Blake* in the 1880's and 1890's. Some have romantically labeled these currents as "rivers under the sea," but they are merely a part of the ocean's attempt to keep its own level. In the same manner, oceanographers have observed a very deep, almost bottom current, or flux, in the ocean, which moves very slowly from the Arctic to the tropics. This is merely some of the cold water from the Arctic Ocean that has spilled over barriers and is slowly drifting along the ocean's bottom toward the tropics. Oceanographers have estimated that it takes years for a particle of water to travel all the way to the tropics by these very slow currents.

Turbidity Currents. The last of the oceanic movements are the turbidity currents. These are merely ephemeral parcels of water along the continental margins which have become heavy and laden with sediment and debris. These bodies of water tend to become heavy and sink—not to their own level, but all the way to the bottom—with their sediments. When they sink along the continental slopes or near the edges of the continental shelf, they tend to break down the unconsolidated sediments of the continental shelf. Thus they cause tremendous erosion by their weight and rapid downward movement in these areas, gouging out huge canyonlike features along the continental slope (*see illustration section*).

The turbidity currents are credited with moving billions of tons of material along the continental margins yearly. Many oceanographers believe that they are the makers of submarine canyons, since most of the large submarine canyons are somewhere near the mouths of rivers which throw out much of the material which make up these currents.

It has been suggested that the ill-fated submarine *Thresher,* mysteriously sunk off the Atlantic coast of North America in 1963, may have been caught in one of these turbidity currents. The dense water of the current (a mixture of sediment and water), the theory contends, could have caught the *Thresher* at the mouth of a submarine canyon and carried it with it as it cascaded down the continental slope to the deep part of the North Atlantic (submarine) basin. The sudden downward thrust could have been too rapid for the *Thresher* to regain its buoyancy, and hence it collapsed.

The Genesis of Life

Now that we have seen how the oceans equalize climates throughout the world, let us look briefly at the other major role of the ocean and see how it functioned as the cradle of life. We know, of course, that the oceans teem with living things, that fish of various sizes swim in all of them, including the Arctic, and that microscopic life, both plant and animal, known as plankton abound in most waters. Plankton is the food on which fishes live, and plankton in turn lives on the mineral salts in the oceans. Consequently, areas rich in such salts, particularly where there are upwellings, have a tendency to abound in marine life. Warm oceans, also, like the northern part of the Indian Ocean, where much nutrient matter is washed in from land, tend to swarm with life.

We have noted that all ocean depths have some form of thriving life, and that the fluid waters of the oceans range in temperature from about 28 to 90 degrees Fahrenheit. This is a comfortable temperature range for living things as we know them, and this is one of the important factors that allowed the ocean to become possibly the original incubator of all life on earth.

It is estimated that life on our planet made its appearance between one and two billion years ago, and most scientists agree that it undoubtedly originated in the ocean. It is logical that the cradle of life should have been the ocean, because it contains all the materials which go into the make-up of living protoplasm. It is only in the hospitable temperatures of the ocean, with these materials assembled in a fluid, that elements could unite to form the huge and complex molecules of protoplasm, which, by clustering together and putting a wall around themselves, formed a living cell with the power to divide and form new cells and thus could create new ones of their own kind.

Special conditions had to exist on the earth. First, it had to be at the right distance from its sun, to have oceans at all and to have temperatures favorable for developing life. If the earth had been closer to the sun, as is Mercury, the oceans would have dried up; if it were farther from the sun, as is Jupiter, all water would be in the form of ice. Moreover, the age and development of the central sun had to be just right. As it now is, the sun is still a relatively cool star, not cold, like one of the red giants, but far from the white-heat of the white dwarfs, those stars in the sky whose temperatures reach millions of degrees Fahrenheit. The average temperature of the sun is about 11,000 degrees Fahrenheit, allowing for equitable temperatures here. When the sun gets older and becomes a white star, it may scorch life from the world, but two billion years ago the sun helped develop life.

The size and density of the earth were also important in this miracle. The earth was large and dense enough to have sufficient gravity to hold an atmosphere, and this is important, for a shielding blanket was essential to maintain equitable ocean temperatures and protect the earth from harmful radiation.

The speed of rotation was equally important, for a lower speed would cause the side exposed to the sun to get extremely warm and the side away from the sun to get extremely cold, causing great rushes of wind from the warm to the cold sides and back again as the planet rotated. (This is the case on Venus, where the rotation is much slower, nights are much longer and colder, and days are longer and hotter. Great storms and winds sweep the surface of Venus and probably preclude any form of life. Jupiter, on the other hand, is much farther from the sun, is less affected by its gravitational hold, and hence has a very rapid rotation. As large as Jupiter is, it has only a ten-hour day. This rotation is so fast that any blanket of atmosphere tends to be stratified and rendered sterile so far as the development of life is concerned.) The earth's lazy rotation of about a thousand miles an hour at the equator was just enough to allow a night which was not long enough to permit one side to become too cold, and a day that was not too long to allow the other side to become too hot.

It was thus in Pre-Cambrian time, in the shallow sea adjacent to some primordial continental mass, with the sunlight sifting down through the waters, that the first life began. Some say that the genesis resulted from an electrical impulse from atmosphere to water, or a cosmic impulse from space, or a magnetic impulse from within the earth. Whatever it was, it was then and there that life was created which later developed into the higher forms we know today. These microscopic singular-cell forms of life were capable of all the functions of life of any form: they could reproduce; they possessed a kind of metabolism, for they could ingest minerals and other matter from water and keep life going; and they had what biologists call irritability—that is, reaction to stimuli.

From these simple unicellular forms, higher life developed. The first animals could hardly have lived anywhere but in the water, for the water supported them, gave them mobility, and protected them; life on land would have been too harsh. These small forms of life multiplied rapidly for millions of years in the warm coastal seas, and their bodies floated on the surface of the calm waters after they died, forming some sort of fermentation. This fermentation undoubtedly gave off carbon dioxide gas, which supplemented some that had already been created by the electrical transformation of methane and ozone.

Over millions of years an appreciable amount of carbon dioxide accumulated in the earth's lower atmosphere. It was then that the original photosynthesis took place. Possibly a billion and a half years ago, some of this tiny life began to exhibit some of the green coloring within itself which was chlorophyll, the catalyst needed for this essential function.

Photosynthesis is the well-known process by which carbon dioxide and water are united by a complex chemical reaction which captures solar energy, in the presence of chlorophyll, to form the simple food material necessary for all forms of higher life. It was thus that primitive plants began to make food, and primitive animals lived upon it. But the making of food was not the only miracle in the photosynthetic function. A unique and vitally necessary by-product was released through the process: free oxygen, or O_2, that element so necessary in the life of man today. Over great periods of time, perhaps three or four hundred million years, free oxygen was built up in the atmosphere to about the 21 per cent it is today. The creation of life had begun, and the conditions for higher life had been established. The development from this point on is another story, with which most of us are already familiar.

SEA LIFE OF TODAY

The waters of the great oceans are in an indefinable way enhanced by the varieties of life they contain. Indeed, a wide scope of life exists there, ranging from tiny single-cell animals to huge ninety-foot whales and giant squid with grasping tentacles measuring forty feet in length. A great many different kinds of jellyfish, sponges, crustaceans, mollusks, fishes, and mammals persist in the waters of the oceans of the world. And all is not yet known about the inhabitants of the deep; in fact, oceanographers estimate that we should know twice as much as we do about the life in our oceans. The small life was discussed in part earlier. Here we will deal mainly with the larger forms.

Plants of the sea range from small algae to large seaweed masses, such as exist in the calm parts of the oceans of the tropics. There is also an abundance of seaweed and sea grasses growing in the waters near the shores of the oceans. Although more is known about the plant life than about the animal life, much still remains to be learned about the potentialities of this plant life, particularly if it is to be domesticated and "farmed" by future generations as a potential source of food for man.

It is known that sea life exists almost everywhere, including the Arctic Ocean, and at all depths, including the deepest portion of the Mariana Trench; even at these black and high-pressure depths, the occupants of the bathyscaphe *Trieste,* in their seven-mile descent in 1960, noted certain varieties of fish. It is not to be assumed, however, that all the oceans of the world are teeming with life, for there are places which are virtually barren. These are usually areas lacking in the mineral nutrients and microscopic sea life mentioned earlier, and their location varies with the movement of the plankton.

The dearth of knowledge about marine life has encouraged many fabulous tales about ocean creatures. All of us have heard of sea serpents and other sea monsters. There are numerous accounts of ships disappearing without a trace at sea, and these disappearances are made to order for storytellers. Although no satisfactory evidence has been produced confirming the existence of giant sea serpents and hideous sea monsters, most of the ocean depths of the world are still not explored.

Not all tales about the giant creatures of the oceans should be dismissed. Some of the toothless or hump-backed whales of the Arctic regions are more than eighty-five feet in length and about thirty-five feet in circumference, and certain varieties of blue whales are reported to reach one hundred feet in length. They are surely among the largest creatures of all times.

For years tales about giant squid were brought home by seamen, who described a huge cone-shaped sea creature with large eyes, often about a foot in diameter, and great number of long, tentacle-like arms, some of them about forty feet in length, extending from the larger end or head of a body which appeared to be at least sixteen feet long. These ferocious creatures were reported to have grasped their victims in those long arms, much like the well-known octopus, pulled them in, and devoured them. Credence was given to these tales when scars from the suction cups on these long tentacles were found on whales, which had probably experienced a fierce battle with the grasping creatures. Now the existence of the giant squid seems to be an established fact, and damage which was often blamed on the octopus is now attributed to the giant squid, for the octopus does not reach such gigantic size. In fact, the giant squid is recognized as possibly the largest animal without a backbone on the face of the earth. Fortunately, its habitat is generally far down in the ocean, and it is not known to frequent shore areas.

Let us look more in detail first at the plants of the sea. A great many parts of the ocean contain billions and billions of plankton floating near the surface, moved about by tides and currents and waves. Much of this is phytoplankton—plant life—and is made up of algae existing in an astronomical multiple of billions and forming what is known by oceanologists as "pastures in the sea"; some, forming shells, are known as diatoms and comprise part of the ooze of the ocean's bottom. Algae are the basic food of the sea. They exist, of course, mainly where there is an abundance of mineral nutrients in the oceans, and these areas occur where there is upwelling of water from beneath. This upwelling is permanent in some places, but more often it is shifting, making the "pastures of the sea" somewhat of an elusive phenomenon.

Although algae is the most important, it is by no means the only plant life produced in the oceans. A great many varieties of seaweed exist, and there are even sea grasses and sea lettuce.

Seaweed is the most common and much of it is free-floating; consequently, seaweed may be found in many calm parts of the ocean, including the Sargasso Sea, where a great amount of it is amassed, but more frequently it is found near the oceanic approaches to continents. Seaweed may be of many colors, but most of it has the basic power of photosynthesis and produces the rudimentary food upon which other sea life feeds. In fact, seaweed has been eaten by humans with relish in many parts of the world, including the Orient, and has even been prepared as a soup in North America. It is reputed to be high in many of the vitamins needed by man, and studies are being made for its ultimate cultivation.

Sea grasses are also common plants of the ocean. The leaves appear to resemble those of land grass, but they are considerably taller, growing fixed to the sea floor on the shallow continental shelves. They grow side by side with rooted seaweed and help form the feeding ground for small fishes along these continental shelves, which in turn attract bigger fish and make such areas as the Grand Banks and the North Sea excellent fishing grounds. On the Grand Banks, oceanic currents bring in mineral nutrients, which aid the growth of the sea plants there. Along with sea grass, a plant known as sea lettuce usually grows, whose ruffled leaves resemble somewhat the leaves of land lettuce.

The creatures which live upon such plants are, of course, the sea animals. This animal life also lives upon itself—that is, some species devour others in their struggle for survival. It was noted earlier that part of the plankton upon which larger sea animals feed is made up of microscopic animals, which also eat the microscopic plant life of the oceans. These microscopic animals are usually protozoans, which feed on the small plant life and bacteria abundant in many parts of the oceans. As part of plankton, protozoans form a food for many creatures of the deep, including many of the giant whales of the world. Some protozoans form shells which, when shed, fall to the sea floor to become part of the ooze. Some make shells of glasslike silica, while others make shells of lime. The lime shells form many of the large limestone deposits, some of which appear eventually as limestone on land.

Going from the smaller of the sea animals to the larger, we come next to the sponges. Some of the protozoans in the early days developed little flagella or whiplike extensions which could propel them about and give them direction. Apparently, as sea life evolved, many of these single-cell animals with flagella were joined together to form an organism which resembles our present-day sponge. The arrangement of the cells is such that there is ample room for passage of water through all parts of the sponge, and the flagella of the outer cells are pointed out into these spaces or corridors to whip the water along. These cells, as part of the sponge organism, work together systematically in an intricate circulation system throughout the sponge, so that food and other valuable matter in the water can be brought to all parts of the organism. The dead sponge, which we use in our regular cleaning work, traps water and holds it in its complex system of passages.

Another simple creature of the deep is the jellyfish, which has a few cells that specialize in long tentacles extending from a mass of united cells which form the body; the tentacles are used for locomotion. In this manner the jellyfish is able to move about and expose most parts of its cellular mass to contact with the water, so that cells can obtain life-giving materials.

The coral, about which we spoke earlier as building up the island atolls in the Pacific, is in truth an animal very similar to the jellyfish. This animal, however, takes lime from the ocean water and builds a protective shell around itself so that it may not be attacked by larger sea creatures. It then extends its jellyfishlike portion outside the shell to trap other animals, retreating back into its shell when a larger creature approaches. These corals build shell upon shell in intricate patterns, and because some need to be near the surface, they construct a mass beneath themselves and, with a rising ocean, form such land masses as islands.

Similar in character to the corals are the echinoderms of the sea. Instead of the lime-hard coating of the coral polyp, echinoderms develop a prickly outer skin to ward off the attacks of larger sea life. The starfish is the most common of this type of sea animal, but this family also includes porcupine-like creatures known as sea cucumbers. The starfish, however, is the most typical. Its softer part, which it uses for feeding, lies underneath, and it simply spreads over the top of a victim to devour it.

Just as the earthworm represents an advance toward a higher stage of land existence, so does the sea worm represent an advance in the development of marine life. The earthworm represents the joining together of a number of organisms in ringed metameres, each metamere specialized, to form the larger organism. The sea worm is similar in every respect.

Still more complex is a very large group of animals called the crustaceans. They include such familiar species as the shrimp, the crab, and the lobster. The individual member of this group of sea animals has a rather complex set of internal organs and is usually surrounded on the outside by a hard exoskeleton of plasticlike chitinous material. These animals apparently have segmented bodies, somewhat like the sea worms, but they are much more diversified and complex. Segmentation, which practically disappears in higher animals, is beginning to disappear in these creatures. They have, in general, legs or tentacles or other appendages extending out from many of the segments, and they have well-developed light-perceptive organs which for all intents and purposes are eyes.

The complex inner development of these animals includes a digestive system and a circulation system of sorts for delivering nutrients to the cells throughout the body. Their "blood," however, is very different from that of higher animals. The tails of these creatures often make tasty seafood, since they are less differentiated, being farther removed from the front end of the animal, and hence represent a series of reasonably undifferentiated segments, which are masses of cells and in many cases edible. The portion of the shrimp which is eaten is, of course, the tail, and the best part and greatest concentration of meat in the lobster is in the tail. A small portion of specialized cells at the front end of these animals acts as a brain.

Crabs and shrimp are by far the most numerous of the crustaceans, and they live in many kinds of habitats. Some large crabs may live on land, and shrimp tend to travel in schools in the sea, often near shore. A type of domestication called shrimp farming has been performed in Japan with some degree of success.

The crustaceans include many land animals in addition to those found in the oceans. Those living on land are familiar to us as the many varieties of insects (ants, roaches, etc.), scorpions, and centipedes. Like their brothers in the ocean, these land crustaceans have the apparent segmentation and a complex set of inner organs, including a heart and a breathing apparatus. Those living on land breathe through small tubes leading into their bodies (the forerunner of lungs), and those in the ocean breathe through gills. Although the exoskeleton is not so apparent in the centipedes and scorpions, it is still there. The crusty outer shells of the insects are most obvious. In fact, many scientists believe that if any creature on earth were to survive man, should he destroy himself through atomic warfare and its devastating fallout poisonings, it would be the insects—at least on the land. It is apparent that their exoskeletons give them considerably more protection against radioactive fallout than anything inherently possessed by higher land animals.

Somewhat similar to the crustaceans, but yet more highly developed, is a group of sea animals known as the mollusks. This group includes again many sea animals which are familiar to us, such as the well-known oyster, the clam, the sea snail, the conch, and the scallop. Like the crustaceans, the mollusks are found throughout the oceans and in all climates, including the Arctic and the tropics. The shell of one of the sea snails is used commonly as a horn and is employed traditionally in plays concerning seafaring men.

Some of the mollusks are almost microscopically small; others grow to extremely large size, particularly the squid, as we have seen; fortunately they usually live far out from shore. Most of the other mollusks are found closer to land, including many varieties of the octopus. Also, like the crustaceans, some mollusks such as the land snail live on land. They are found in the Arctic and in the high mountains, as well as in the tropics and in extremely low places.

In many ways, the mollusks are similar to the crustaceans. They have complex inner organs, including a digestive system, a breathing apparatus, a heart and circulatory system, a brain, and light-sensitive organs which serve as eyes. Like the crustaceans, the breathing apparatus of the sea mollusks is the gill. The brain, however, in general is more highly developed, and many mollusks have a rasping tongue.

The mollusks have an exoskeleton also, like the crustaceans, but this skeleton is usually of much harder material, witness the two hard shells of the bivalve members of this group, such as the oysters and the clams. This exoskeleton is extant in all members of this group, including the squid, whose cone-shaped body looks fleshy and actually is so to the touch. This outer flesh, however, is just a mantle over an exoskeleton which lies beneath, protecting the inner organs. Although the squid and the octopus, with their long grasping tentacles, seem very different from the slow snail and the peaceful oyster, they nevertheless are of the same group. The tendency toward the development of tentacles is shown among some of the smaller of the mollusks, such as the tropical scallop and sea slug.

The economic value of the mollusks need not be stressed, for one has only to think of the oyster; oysters are not only good for eating but they produce pearls, and their shells are excellent for producing lime.

Now we come to the best and widest known of the seas' creatures, the fishes. Certain sea life developed an inner skeleton of bone, including a backbone, which inherited segmentation from more primitive creatures. These bony creatures became the fishes. Like the lower sea life before them, the fishes have gills, a heart, a brain, a circulatory system, a digestive system, and eyes. They are cold-blooded like their predecessors and are distinguished by their backbone and inner skeleton. They come in a great variety of sizes and shapes. Most of them have scales on their outer skin for protection, and some of them display brilliant colors.

The range in size among fishes is almost as great as among the mollusks, ranging from the tiny anchovy and the sardine to the large manta and the shark. The geographical range of fishes is as great as that of the mollusks. Even though the larger of the mollusks—the squid and the octopus—inhabit the deep ocean, most of the mollusks live close to the shore. Fish, on the other hand, are found all over the ocean, but largely in the upper layer, where sunlight and nutrients and plankton are found, as well as near the shore, where plant life is abundant. There are fish in the warmest of tropical waters and in the coldest of Arctic and Antarctic waters, not necessarily restricted to the upper zone, for many of them inhabit the ocean depths.

There is such a variety of fishes that we will not attempt to mention all of them. Looking first at some of the larger, let us examine the manta. This fish does not have a rounded and tapering body, like most of the fish we know, but is flat, with what appear to be huge extensions of its flesh from either side of its body which look almost like wings. From its head two horns extend on either side of a huge mouth, and from its posterior extends a huge tail-like organ which is reputed to have great strength and sting in it. The spread of the manta's "wings" is often as much as twenty feet, and its horns, which have earned the name "devilfish" for it, have often ripped holes in the bottom of small craft.

Although sharks come in many sizes, most of us are familiar with the larger ones, those approaching ten to twelve feet in length. Many sharks are not dangerous, but some are man-eaters. The most dangerous ones are the tiger shark, the blue shark, and the hammerhead shark. Unlike most other fish, sharks do not have regular scales but rather a multiplicity of small pointed spines projecting from their skin which smooth back toward the tail of the body. In fact, the shark's teeth are merely large spines, extremely sharp, projecting in the mouth from the jaw bone. These can be even more destructive than ordinary teeth. These fish generally roam far out in the ocean and usually live in the warmer portions.

Another dangerous fish, and one which inhabits the low latitude portions of the oceans, is the barracuda. It is smaller than the shark—about half its size, in general—and has genuine scales, like other fish, and genuine teeth which are extremely sharp. The barracuda seems to be found in greater numbers in the low latitude oceans and feeds voraciously on other sea life as does the shark.

Among the less dangerous fishes are the swordfish, with its horny projection extending outward from above its mouth; the sawfish, which has spines on the sides of its anterior projection;

the tuna; the sea bass, which is found in all climatic realms of the ocean; and the sea cat, which is also widely distributed. And among the many varieties let us not forget to note a few of the fishes which inhabit the black, deep depths of the ocean, among which are the headlight fish, which actually has a light-giving organ between its eyes; the lucifer fish, which also has a "light bulb" as well as long ferocious-looking teeth; and the hatchet fish, whose body expands in the front so that the entire fish somewhat resembles a hatchet. All of these fish, including the sea bass and the sea cat, run from less than a foot to several feet in length.

Some fish run in schools—that is, a great many of them travel together in the oceans in search of food. Among these are the mackerel, menhaden, herring, and sardine. These fish are chased as schools by fishermen well out into the ocean and are caught in nets. The mackerel and the sardine are well known to the dinner table, and the menhaden (sometimes called the porgy) are caught by net in great numbers and processed for their oil to make several useful products, including fertilizer. An unusual member of the herring family is the tarpon, which often grows to seven feet in length and offers considerable challenge to sport fishermen. Flying fish are those which can swim at great speeds and then use their spread fins as gliders after they leap from the water.

The salmon and cod are well known in the higher latitudes of the ocean. The salmon have an unusual life cycle and marked homing instincts. They swim up streams that are tributary to the higher latitude portions of the oceans in great numbers to cold inland pools, where they lay their eggs and die. The young fish swim out of the streams and live in the ocean until it comes their time to swim upstream again and lay their eggs and die. They return to the very place where they were born and, of course, are caught en route in great numbers.

Sea reptiles make up an appreciable number of the inhabitants of the oceans. They have backbones, like the fishes, and are cold-blooded. Although reptiles represent a higher species than the amphibians—those animals which crawled out of the sea and established backboned life on land—and logically should all be land animals, many of them are still found in the sea. Since a great many reptiles do inhabit the oceans, it has been assumed that some reptiles found life on land too difficult and too competitive and returned to the sea, where they became readapted after generations. Inasmuch as an age of reptiles (the Jurassic and Triassic periods of the Mesozoic Era) produced giants such as the Brontosaurus and Tyrannosaurus, it may well be that certain members of the reptile family did find it more convenient to return to the sea rather than compete with these giants on land. The descendants of those reptiles that did return to the sea, ostensibly during that era, are the reptiles of the oceans today. Among them are the sea serpents, the sea lizard or iguana, the sea crocodile, and the sea turtles.

From ancient times, man has reported sea serpents of tremendous size. Information from the logs of many ships may be cited which describes long sea snakes, some of them reported as being more than a hundred feet long and possibly ten feet in diameter. Most of these reports describe a huge sea snake which swims with its head out of water and portions of its body rising above the water like scallops behind it. Some of the reports even describe attacks by these serpents. There have been, however, no actual photographs taken of such monsters. The sea snakes or serpents that have been reliably reported were not more than several feet in length, and most of them were not dangerous. There are, however, a few poisonous sea snakes and, contrary to popular belief, they can bite under water. Sea serpents, like other oceanic reptiles, are inhabitants of the warmer oceans.

A cousin to the large land lizard known as the iguana is the sea lizard or sea iguana. These reptiles grow to four or five feet in length, like their relatives on land, and are reportedly as harmless. The sea iguana lives on other sea life and sea plants, as does the sea serpent.

The sea crocodile is the most ferocious of the sea reptiles, sometimes growing to twelve feet in length. Like semimarine crocodiles, these sea crocodiles have the same powerful tails, scaly bodies, and huge, powerful jaws with sharp teeth. They devour other animals of the sea and will attack man. Sea turtles, too, look much like land turtles, but they also often grow to a huge size, sometimes more than three feet across.

Last but not least of the creatures which inhabit the deep oceans of the world are the sea mammals, warm-blooded creatures akin to the higher animals living on land. They represent the highest form of life in the oceans. Included among them are the porpoise, the whale, the walrus, the sea lion, the sea elephant, the seal, the sea otter, and the sea cow. All are warm-blooded animals that have lungs instead of gills, yet they are able to sustain themselves under water for great lengths of time. In all cases these animals must surface occasionally to exhale and inhale air. In the case of the whale, the exhaling is done dramatically through a hole in the head, out of which water blows along with the exhaling air, forming the familiar spout usually associated with the whale. These animals have organs similar to the mammals on land, the external ones of which are adapted to life in the sea.

Numerous varieties of whale exist, the largest of which are the blue and the rorqual whales, which inhabit the high latitudes of the oceans and grow to lengths of eighty-five to a hundred feet or more. The sperm whale is probably best known, with its large, square head containing a huge storage space for oil. Other varieties are the humpback whale, which inhabits the more temperate oceans, and the toothless whale, which inhabits colder portions of the oceans. This last whale, one of the largest creatures of all time, is surprisingly the eater of one of the smallest creatures of all time, the plankton. The toothless whale is equipped with strainers across its mouth which sift the plankton into its stomach.

It is difficult to tell whether the sea mammals represent the return to the sea of some of the higher life on land—as was apparently the case with the sea reptiles—or whether these higher animals represent a culmination of evolution in the ocean, just as man represents a culmination of the evolution process on land. Evidence to date seems to point to the hypothesis that these warm-blooded mammals of the sea represent a line of evolution which was strictly oceanologic, rather than a return to the sea by mammals of the land. (This might also redeem many of the sea reptiles from the stigma of retreat to the sea and give them the dignity of a stage in an oceanary evolution process.)

Many scientists believe that the porpoise (sometimes referred to as dolphin) represents a stage in oceanologic evolution comparable to that of man on land. It has been learned in recent years that the porpoise has a brain as large, if not larger, than man's and just as complex. It has also been discovered that the porpoise possesses a high intelligence and, in spite of the lack of an articulate tongue, has developed within the limits of its vocal processes a rather complex language. Certainly it represents a high development of life.

SELECTED REFERENCES

Ahrens, L. H., and others (eds.). *Physics and Chemistry of the Earth.* 5 vols. New York: Pergamon Press, 1956.

Bigelow, Henry B., and W. T. Edmondson. *Wind Waves at Sea, Breakers and Surf.* U.S. Hydrographic Office publ. no. 602. Washington, D.C.: Government Printing Office, 1947.

Carritt, D. E. (chairman). *Desalination Research and the Water Problem.* Publication 901. Washington, D.C.: National Academy of Sciences, National Research Council, 1962.

Coker, Robert E. *This Great and Wide Sea.* Chapel Hill: University of North Carolina Press, 1947.

Defant, Albert. *Ebb and Flow: The Tides of Earth, Air, and Water.* Ann Arbor: University of Michigan Press, 1958.

Dietz, Robert S. "Marine Profile of Equilibrium: A Critical Appraisal." *Geological Society of America Bulletin.* Baltimore, Md. August, 1963.

Douglas, John Scott. *The Story of the Oceans.* New York: Dodd, Mead & Co., 1952.

Ellis, Cecil B., and members of the staff of Nuclear Development Associates. *Fresh Water from the Ocean, for Cities, Industry, and Irrigation.* Sponsored by the Conservation Foundation. New York: Ronald Press Co., 1954.

Hamilton, Edwin L. *Sunken Islands of the Mid-Pacific Mountains.* New York: Geological Society of America, 1956.

Hardy, Alister C. *The Open Sea. Vol. II: The World of Plankton.* Boston: Houghton Mifflin Co., 1959.

Igelsrud, Iver, and others. *The Distribution of Phosphates in the Sea Water of the Northeast Pacific.* Seattle: University of Washington Press, 1936.

Iselin, Columbus O'Donnell. *A Study of the Circulation of the Western North Atlantic*. Contribution no. 108 from the Woods Hole Oceanographic Institution. Cambridge and Woods Hole, Mass.: Massachusetts Institute of Technology and Woods Hole Oceanographic Institution, 1936.

La Fond, E. C. *Processing Oceanographic Data*. Publ. no. 614. Washington, D.C.: U.S. Navy Hydrographic Office, 1951.

Ley, Willy. *The Days of Creation*. New York: Modern Age Books, 1941.

Marmer, Harry. *The Sea*. New York: Random House, 1941.

———. *The Tide*. New York: Random House, 1943.

Neumann, Gerhard. *On the Dynamics of Wind-Driven Ocean Currents*. New York: New York University Press, 1955.

Oceanography, 1960–1970. 9 vols. Report of the Committee on Oceanography, National Academy of Sciences, National Research Council, Washington, D.C., 1960–61.

Papers in Marine Biology and Oceanography. Dedicated to Henry B. Bigelow by his former students and associates on the occasion of the twenty-fifth anniversary of the founding of the Woods Hole Oceanographic Institution. New York: Pergamon Publishing Co., Inc., 1955.

Pierson, Willard J., Jr., and others. *Practical Methods for Observing and Forecasting Ocean Waves by Means of Wave Spectra and Statistics*. Publ. no. 603. Washington, D.C.: U.S. Navy Hydrographic Office, 1955.

Riley, Gordon A. *Oxygen, Phosphate, and Nitrate in the Atlantic Ocean*. New Haven: Bingham Oceanographic Laboratory, 1951. (Yale University. Peabody Museum of Natural History. Bingham Oceanographic Collection. Bulletin. Vol 13, article 1.)

Rossby, Carl-Gustaf. *Dynamics of Steady Ocean Currents in the Light of Experimental Fluid Mechanics*. Contribution no. 115 from the Woods Hole Oceanographic Institution. Cambridge and Woods Hole, Massachusetts: Massachusetts Institute of Technology and Woods Hole Oceanographic Institution, 1936.

Shepard, Francis P. *The Earth Beneath the Sea*. Baltimore: Johns Hopkins Press, 1959.

———. *Submarine Geology*. 2nd ed. New York: Harper & Row, Publishers, 1963.

Stewart, Harris. *The Global Sea*. Princeton, N.J.: D. Van Nostrand Co., Inc., 1962.

Stommel, Henry. *The Gulf Stream*. Berkeley: University of California Press, 1958.

Sverdrup, Harald U., and others. *The Oceans: Their Physics, Chemistry, and General Biology*. New York: Prentice-Hall, 1942.

Thompson, Henry D. *Fundamentals of Earth Science*. 2nd ed. New York: Appleton-Century-Crofts, Inc., 1960.

U.S. Coast and Geodetic Survey. *Hydrographic Manual*. Rev. (1961) ed. Washington, D.C.: Government Printing Office, 1961.

U.S. Coast and Geodetic Survey. *Manual of Harmonic Analysis and Prediction of Tides* by Paul Schureman. Spec. publ. no. 98. Rev. (1940) ed. Washington, D.C.: Government Printing Office, 1941.

U.S. Hydrographic Office. *References on the Physical Oceanography of the Western Pacific Ocean*. Publ. no. 238. Washington, D.C.: Government Printing Office, 1953.

———. *World Atlas of Sea Surface Temperatures*. 2nd ed., 1944. Washington, D.C.: Hydrographic Office, U.S. Navy, 1948.

U.S. Navy. *Marine Climatic Atlas of the World. Vol. I: North Atlantic Ocean; Vol. II: North Pacific Ocean.* Published by direction of the Chief of Naval Operations. Washington, D.C.: Government Printing Office, 1955–56.

Vaughan, Thomas W., and others. *International Aspects of Oceanography, Oceanographic Data and Provisions for Oceanographic Research*. Washington, D.C.: National Academy of Sciences, 1937.

Veatch, Arthur C., and R. A. Smith. *Atlantic Submarine Valleys of the United States and the Congo Submarine Valley*. Special papers no. 7. New York: Geological Society of America, 1939.

Walford, Lionel A. *Fishery Resources*. Washington, D.C.: Public Affairs Press, 1957.

Whipple, Fred L. *Earth, Moon and Planets*. Rev. ed. Cambridge: Harvard University Press, 1963.

Wiegel, Robert L. *Waves, Tides, Currents, and Beaches: Glossary of Terms and List of Standard Symbols*. Berkeley: University of California Council on Wave Research, The Engineering Foundation, 1953.

Chapter 5 / The Wind Blows Free

Far more independent of the earth than any of the phenomena dealt with so far is the atmosphere—the air we breathe, the master artist of the sky, our protector from the harshness of space. The wind, the rain, and the heat or cold we experience are all aspects of this atmosphere. It is the maker of weather and climate, and most of us know how rapidly and drastically weather can change. The wind, which is atmosphere in motion, tends to play a leading role in our changing weather. It appears to be controlled very little by the earth and hence is said to "blow free." It should be noted, however, that the wind, like other aspects of the atmosphere, is not entirely free of the earth. Nor is the atmosphere as a whole free from the influences of space; it, too, appears to be a part of the great over-all unity in nature.

Weather and climate are influenced by the sun and other heavenly bodies. An even closer relationship will be demonstrated between climate and vegetation throughout the world. Soils will be seen to be intimately affected by both climate and vegetation, and there will be demonstrated a remarkable relationship between animal habitat and vegetation, soils, and climate. Man, too—or especially man—will be observed in a close relationship with all the natural phenomena, especially climate and vegetation. The cultures of mankind, as well as his means of making a living, will be related to these factors.

Many of these relationships are immediately apparent. The lives of people in the dry parts of the world are intricately affected by their climate. The sparsity of vegetation in these areas requires adjustments; the dearth of water requires conservation and economical use, together with the most favorable use of land.

We see this in the intensive irrigation agriculture in the Sonoran Desert of western North America, the irrigated river bottoms of the coastal plain of Peru, the irrigation agriculture in Iraq and Egypt, the nomadic pastoralism in Arabia and parts of central Asia, and the practice of cattle ranging in the dry parts of eastern South America.

Even more dramatic is the adjustment to climate that has to be made by natives of the polar lands of the northern hemisphere. In Scandinavia, for example, the Laplanders practice nomadic pastoralism by following the reindeer herds in their yearly migrations ahead of the frigid Arctic winters. The Eskimos of North America are well known for their adjustments to climate in their hunting habits and the structures they build. Even with modern equipment, the present-day Eskimo still has to stop on the trail in winter and set up crude temporary housing, similar to his original igloo, to weather out storms.

Although apparently complex, weather and climate may be reduced to several simple concepts. These concepts will be examined, and the climate throughout the world will be described in this and the following chapters. First, let us look at the nature of our atmosphere, whose variations comprise climate.

Layers of Atmosphere

Most of us are acquainted only with the layer of atmosphere closest to the earth's surface—that is, the "troposphere," the lower six to ten miles of atmosphere. The air we breathe is found on the earth's surface only up to about ten thousand feet. Those who have climbed mountains and breathed the air near ten thousand feet have realized that the nature of the atmosphere has changed; it has become lighter, or, as we often call it, "rarefied."

We read about experimental and military aircraft flying much higher than the thirty thousand feet ascended by commercial planes. Many of these craft have gone into what is described as the "stratosphere." Then there are the astronauts who have penetrated an outer layer of the atmosphere known as the "ionosphere." Our atmosphere occurs in these layers which function not only to give us breathing air but also to protect the earth's surface and its inhabitants against the harshness of space.

Recalling from Chapter 1 some of these harsh aspects, there are the extremely low temperatures characteristic of outer space (more than 400 degrees below zero Fahrenheit), the many cosmic particles, and the many harmful impulses, called "rays," traveling not only from our sun but from all neighboring stars in the universe. We know that our sun gives off dangerous ultraviolet and infrared rays which are filtered out by our atmosphere so that no harmful effects reach the earth's surface. We also know that many charged particles are thrown off from the sun and travel to us in great quantities, especially during years of high sunspot activity. The outer atmosphere filters out most of these particles, allowing only enough to get through to the earth's surface to be beneficial. We know that our atmosphere also carries clouds that bring rain, snow, and other forms of precipitation. And we know that atmosphere in motion constitutes the winds that move cool air onto warm lands and warm air onto cool lands.

In Chapter 4, we noted that the oceans of the world function as a great moderator of the earth. It is through the medium of the atmosphere that the effects of the ocean are felt in our climate. The atmosphere absorbs the ocean's influences and becomes more temperate. In fact, our climate is the condition of our atmosphere. So also is our weather. The difference between weather and climate, however, is simple: weather is day-to-day variation in the condition of the atmosphere at a given place; climate is the over-all long-range average of weather conditions at that place. For example, the place where we live may experience storms, calms, heat, and cold at different times within the year; yet the climate may be considered subtropical because the over-all average of temperatures is mild and the over-all occurrence of storms and cold is not frequent. On the other hand, a similar area may be considered middle latitude because of lower average temperatures.

Most of all, we are aware of the effects of our weather and

climate upon us and our livelihood. We experience discomfort when our weather becomes warm and humid, and we experience exhilaration when a "cold" front brings clear skies and cool, dry conditions. Some people, especially agriculturists, are keenly interested in the amount of precipitation; in a sense all of us are concerned with this, for it is on agriculture that our complex society ultimately depends.

Let us look now at the layers making up our atmosphere. The one closest to the earth contains the air we breathe and is known as the **troposphere.** This layer extends six to ten miles in height from the earth's surface. Within this layer, all of the air movement and all of the changes in weather and climate that we experience take place. This is where the surface winds travel and where the high counter winds, known as jet streams, move at great speeds. Here is where clouds are formed and where precipitation in the form of rain, snow, hail, and sleet takes shape and falls to earth. This is the layer which is warmed by the sun—not directly but rather by the sun's heat reflected from the earth. This is where the changes in temperatures that we experience occur; this is the life-preserving layer of the atmosphere. Here is where free oxygen is found.

It is important that we examine the composition of this layer which is so vital to us. Actually, free oxygen comprises only about 21 per cent of the troposphere. This, however, is enough to sustain life as we know it. The greatest portion of the troposphere, approximately 78 per cent, is made up of a gas called nitrogen. The abundance of nitrogen is not without significance, since it is taken from the troposphere by certain plants and transferred into nitrogenous materials which concentrate in plant roots, which in turn enrich the soil. The remaining 1 per cent of the troposphere is composed of carbon dioxide, water vapor, dust particles, and other extraneous materials.

Although this proportion of gases is reasonably constant throughout the troposphere, its density varies with height. In short, the particles of the gas mixture making up the troposphere are closer together near the surface of the earth and farther apart near the upper part of the troposphere. Consequently, we are aware of a sense of rarity in the air as we ascend to heights more than a mile and a half above sea level.

Above the troposphere is another layer which seals it over like a cap. This is known as the **stratosphere,** and extends from about ten to fifty miles. In this layer there is little or no air movement; it acts more or less as a restrainer on the air fluctuations within the troposphere. This layer is made up of a familiar form of oxyen known as ozone (O_3). It is an anatropic form of oxygen, not like free oxygen, and is harmful to us except in small doses. This material from time to time seeps down in small quantities to the surface and has a beneficial effect.

One of the main functions of the stratosphere is to filter out the harmful ultraviolet and infrared rays of the sun. Part of the stratosphere is extremely warm, and sometimes that portion is called the "thermosphere." This explains some of the heat problems experienced by astronauts when reentering the earth's atmosphere.

From about fifty to six hundred miles up is the layer of atmosphere known as the **ionosphere.** This layer is made up of very thinly dispersed and highly unstable ions of atmosphere, negatively charged. It is this layer that captures many of the particles sent by the sun and other astronomic bodies toward earth. Most of these incoming particles are positively charged and are stopped by the negatively charged particles in the ionosphere. As noted in Chapter 1, this phenomenon is responsible for the Northern Lights and the Southern Lights, when magnetic force brings charged particles through the ionosphere near the magnetic poles. This is somewhat like the gas mixture which lights up a neon sign. Some of the particles get through the ionosphere, however, but only in amounts to be beneficial to us, rather than harmful.

The lower end of this layer forms a ceiling or lid upon which radio waves are bounced. Radio waves sent from transmitters on earth, particularly short waves, depend upon this ionosphere layer. These waves rise to this layer and bounce back and forth against it until they are picked up by another distant station on earth. When sunspot activity is extremely violent and many particles are thrown into the ionosphere, this layer becomes disturbed and discontinuity appears along the lidlike bottom of the layer. Radio communications on earth are then seriously affected.

Research workers of the Radio Corporation of America, the U.S. Environmental Science Services Administration, and similar organizations in England have made a serious study of this layer to try to remedy this interruption of radio signals, which can sometimes have serious consequences. Their research found the amazing unity between these disturbances and sunspot activity.

The magnetic fields of plants and humans were found to be affected by this phenomenon and, surprisingly enough, by concomitant gravitational shifts within the earth and by earthquake phenomena. It was also discovered that our atmosphere has bulges similar to those in the ocean—that is, it also has tides that are influenced by the moon and the sun. The bulges in all three of the major layers of the atmosphere occur when the sun and moon are pulling together, exactly like the influence on the sea. Moreover, all of this seems to be tied in closely with fluctuations in earth's magnetism and is thus at peak force during high sunspot activity.

Perhaps eventually the simple denominator of all these phenomena may be shown to be magnetic force or associated cosmic impulses, which we know are tied directly with activity on the sun and to the relative positions of other astronomical bodies. If this were the case, it would be possible for the full unity of these associated phenomena to be understood, and then prediction of the less benevolent aspects of these phenomena could possibly be made and practical control exercised. The same forces that bring about the results from sunspot activity might reasonably also bring about the larger atmospheric waves and the greater disruption of the ionosphere just noted. The more one looks at nature, the more a unity seems to become apparent.

Beyond the six-hundred-mile limit of the ionosphere, some meteorologists identify another layer of the atmosphere which carries magnetic currents. This is estimated as extending more than a thousand miles into space and has been discussed in Chapters 1 and 2 with relation to magnetic forces in the Van Allen belts. Beyond about a thousand miles, the atmosphere is dissipated, and the coldness and blackness of space take over. Indeed, the blackness of space takes over in a practical sense somewhere in the ionosphere. All of this atmosphere is held to the earth, of course, by earth's gravitational pull.

Looking now at the troposphere, let us observe the forces which bring about movement within this layer. Basically, one concept is involved: differential heating by the sun over the earth's surface. We noted that the portion of the troposphere closest to the earth is heated not directly by the sun but by the sun's energy waves being reflected back as heat. In Chapter 4 we noted that water heats slower than land, simply because the sun's energy can penetrate farther into water and dissipate farther, whereas its energy is concentrated directly at the surface of land and reflected immediately back into the atmosphere. Consequently, the atmosphere above land masses will heat much more quickly than the atmosphere above ocean masses. In the same manner, open areas are heated faster than forested areas, which absorb much of the solar energy; and plains in general are heated faster than mountains, partly because the plains receive the sun's rays more directly.

Paramount among all the reasons for unequal distribution of heat on earth, of course, is the fact that the portions of the earth which catch the rays of the sun directly—that is, at right angles—receive the most heat, and areas receiving the sun's rays at lesser angles receive considerably less heat. This means that the waistline of the world—the equatorial areas—receives more of the direct rays of the sun than do the higher latitudes, where the sun's rays are dissipated at angles. Consequently, the equatorial areas, or lower latitudes, receive most of the sun's energy, and the higher latitudes experience a deficiency. In fact, it was noted in the *National Council for Social Studies Yearbook* in 1959 that in both the northern and southern hemispheres more heat energy is received from the sun than is lost by radiation in that part of the world from the equator north or south to nearly 35 degrees in latitude. Conversely, from about 35 degrees to the poles in the northern and southern hemispheres, more heat is lost by radiation than is received from the sun.

Thus latitudinal differentiation, as well as that created by land and sea differences and land configuration and cover, are responsible for unequal world heat. These differences have to be equalized by some means so that solar energy can be more evenly distributed. The means, of course, is air movement. We noted in Chapter 4 that ocean currents effect some of this equalization, but we shall see that the main work is done by movements of the atmosphere.

Wind Movements

The movement of air over the earth is referred to as wind. There are more winds than just the surface movements, however. There are high counter movements aloft, traveling at high speeds, known as "jet streams." For the moment, let us recognize that there are vertical movements of air as well as lateral movements. These, too, tend to equalize solar heating within the troposphere, as heating occurs at the surface of the earth and some mechanism has to exist for the transfer of part of this heat to higher altitudes. On an average, the cooling within the troposphere, with increased height, is about 3 degrees for every thousand feet of ascent.

Naturally, air moving laterally is forced up to go over mountain ranges and hence can bring warm air to higher altitudes, but the general transference of air to higher altitudes is largely by means of convection, which is essentially light-weight ascension of air. Basically, air that is warmed becomes light in weight and is then pushed up by other air that is cooler, carrying warmth to higher altitudes. Two basic principles are good to keep in mind at this point: warm air tends to rise; cool air tends to fall to earth.

It is essentially the unequal buildup of solar energy over the earth's surfaces, as noted, that causes the wind systems of the world. If there were little or no rotation of the earth, if the earth revolved around the sun at a very slow speed, and if the earth's axis were not at an angle from the sun, the air movement on the earth's surface would be simple. The area of the heat buildup in both hemispheres would receive air from the areas of deficiency in solar energy (Fig. 10), as the cool air from the higher latitudes pushed toward the equator, forcing aloft the lighter, warm air in the equatorial regions. It in turn would heat the upper regions of the troposphere and travel poleward aloft in each hemisphere. After being cooled aloft, this air would come to earth again in the higher latitudes to replace the air that had moved toward the equator. There would thus be a simple circular rotation of air extending from equator to pole in each hemisphere within the limits of the

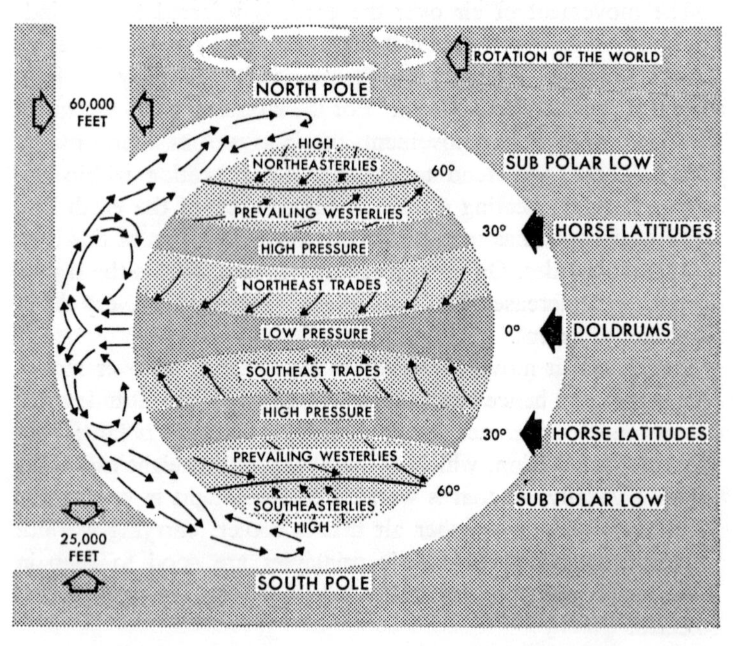

Fig. 10. Generalized air currents and pressure belts of the earth.

troposphere. This, in general and in overall view, actually is the case, with understandable variations, which will be explained. Differences in the heating of land and sea, as well as plains and mountains and open places and forested areas, would, of course, cause variations in this, but the general overall pattern would be the circular movement.

As we know, our earth rotates from west to east about a thousand miles an hour at the equator. Since the atmosphere is, to a certain extent, a relatively free agent, there is naturally a tendency for deflection of this air. This deflection is subject to Ferrel's law. It explains why the cool air from the higher latitudes in the northern hemisphere, moving over the surface southward, is deflected to the right—that is, westward. Consequently, this produces a northeast wind, and many of us have heard of these winds, which move across the low-latitude seas and are called the "northeast trade winds." (Winds are named for the direction from which they come.) In the southern hemisphere they are the "southeast trade winds," as cool air moving from the higher latitudes northward toward the equatorial regions in the southern hemisphere is deflected to the left and hence blows from the southeast to the northwest (Fig. 10).

When these winds reach the equatorial region, they too are warmed by excessive solar heating in that area and are forced to rise. This area is known as the "doldrums." (Besides doldrums, this belt is sometimes referred to as the intertropical front, the tropical low, or equatorial calm.) Even in the doldrums, the general masses of air tend to be deflected to the westward as they rise, due to the rotation of the earth. This leaves a certain deficiency of air in the very middle of this intertropical front, and some of the air moving in with the trade winds is forced to move eastward as a countercurrent to replace this air. These movements are known as the equatorial westerly winds.

The warm air that rises in the equatorial region is restricted in its vertical ascent by the limits of the troposphere, which we noted as not higher than ten miles. Thus, this warmed air ascends to nearly ten miles and then is forced to move laterally, because of the lid placed upon it by the stratosphere. Consequently, it moves northward underneath this ceiling in the northern hemisphere to replace the air from the higher latitudes that has moved southward, and it moves underneath the stratosphere southward in the southern hemisphere to replace the cool high latitude air that has moved northward over the surface to the equatorial region.

This air movement is also deflected, by the force of Ferrel's law, to the right in the northern hemisphere and to the left in the southern hemisphere. It would move aloft in tight curves were it not that it places a block in its own way. In brief, in deflecting to the right, for example, these masses of air tend to throw off air to the right, which piles up in great mounds reaching to the earth's surface over the oceans, about two thousand miles north and south of the equator, where great upwellings of cool ocean water occur on the western side of continents from the deflection of ocean currents in that area, as described in Chapter 4.

Thus, great mounds of air reaching from the stratosphere to the earth's surface are built up over the oceans near the western sides of continents about 30 degrees north and south of the equator. They actually unite to form a belt of descending air several hundred miles wide at this latitude in each hemisphere. These are known as persistent high-pressure areas, over the oceans, and are often referred to as "tropical highs." These highs are accentuated specifically off the western coast of North America in the vicinity of Baja California, the western coast of South America near northern Chile and southern Peru, the northwestern coast of Africa near the Rio de Oro coast, the coast of southwest Africa in the vicinity of the province of Southwest Africa, and off the entire western coast of Australia. All the coastal areas in the respective vicinities, it should be noted, are deserts.

Returning to the high northward and southward movement of air from the equatorial regions, we can see that the tendency to deflect to the right in tight curls is blocked by these permanent high-pressure mounds. Consequently, these high-up winds cannot deflect farther to the right in tight curls but are forced to become westerly winds aloft—that is, blowing from west to east. They move in a ribbonlike manner at great speeds, two hundred to four hundred miles an hour, between the latitudes 30 and 50 degrees in both hemispheres. These are the jet streams, familiar to pilots who fly higher than five miles. Not all of the air moving poleward aloft, however, is caught in these streams. Some of it continues to move poleward in almost a straight line, in spite of Coriolis force, as a counter action to the violently eastward-moving subtropical jet streams. Finally, this air reaches the polar regions and comes down as cold polar highs.

The oceanic high-pressure cells, or permanent parts of the tropical highs, blow air over the ocean surface in a clockwise manner in the northern hemisphere and in a counterclockwise manner in the southern hemisphere. They vary in size with the seasons, engulfing entire oceans in the summer seasons and regressing to smaller size during the winter seasons. In fact, they encroach considerably upon the surrounding land areas during the summers.

Until about forty years ago, the concepts about climate on our planet were based on very scanty observations made by one Matthew F. Maury more than a century ago. The wind systems of the world were poorly understood, and there was no realization of jet streams and their relation to surface climate. It was not until about 1930 that a Norwegian meteorologist named Vilhelm Bjerknes suggested that the movements of the upper troposphere were an integral part of the climate at the surface. With improved aircraft, more observations aloft were taken in the 1930's and, with greater acceleration during World War II, they increased to respectable volume in the 1940's. Added to these data were observations in the 1950's and 1960's until the present additional picture of the wind systems of the world was constructed.

Some of the air which descends in the high-pressure belts at 30 degrees latitude does not reach the intertropical front through the trade winds; it travels northward and eastward. In fact, a good amount of the air from the tropical high belt moves in this manner across the surface of the earth. We noted earlier that the subtropical jet stream races from west to east between latitudes 30 and 50. In doing so it helps drag this lower surface air from west to east. This air, however, was already headed that way by the force of Ferrel's law, deflecting to the right in the northern hemisphere and to the left in the southern hemisphere.

This movement of surface air on the poleward side of the tropical high belt is often felt as far north or south of the equator as 55 to 65 degrees latitude. This portion of the world in both hemispheres is known as the middle latitudes. All areas from this belt to the equator are low latitudes and all to the poles are high latitudes. It must be remembered, too, that in the latitudes between 35 degrees and 55 to 65 degrees north or south, the boundary between too much and too little solar energy is crossed, and from thence to the poles there is a deficiency in solar heat.

The middle latitudes (or the zone of the prevailing westerlies) are in between the warm low latitudes and the cold high latitudes. At about 55 to 65 degrees north or south latitude, the prevailing westerlies are met by cold polar air from the northeast, which tends to push up this westerly air and create an appreciable belt of low pressure. This is often referred to as the "subpolar front" or the "subpolar low" and is considered a part of the middle latitudes. Poleward of this subpolar low in both hemispheres are the "polar easterlies" of the high latitudes —that is, air moving from northeast to southwest over the surface of the earth—and, in the vicinity of the poles, there are the cold, heavy "polar highs" (Fig. 10).

Air descending from higher altitudes to the surface tends to get warmer and dryer. Conversely, ascending air is cooling and wetting air and tends to bring precipitation. It is for this reason that belts of the earth such as the doldrums at the equator and the subpolar low between 55 and 65 degrees in either hemisphere are usually areas of considerable precipitation, whereas areas under the influence of tropical highs, or more particularly the centers of the belts in the vicinity of cold oceanic upwellings, tend to be dry.

A narrow belt between about 35 and 40 degrees in both hemispheres is something of a transition zone. It is largely in the middle latitudes, as frost is known in this belt, but at the same time it is fed by tropical high air during the summer. This narrow belt is known as the "subtropics." Its precipitation comes when the air in this belt moves from west to east during the winter. Consequently, this subtropical belt tends to be dry in summer and wet in winter. Being so close to the tropics, it has a mild climate. In general, this subtropical belt has some of the more favorable climates in the world, for this is the type of climate that characterizes the Mediterranean and Southern California.

It has been noted that the true middle latitudes are largely poleward of 40 degrees and hence are in an area which has a deficiency of solar heat. It might also be observed that the direction of the prevailing westerlies here tends to bring warming air to these latitudes, and they are, on the average, moderate. Let us hasten to note, however, that these latitudes are moderate only in the sense of an average and are in no sense "temperate," as they are so often characterized. This zone is often visited by cold blasts from the Arctic. In the southern hemisphere it is known as the terrible "Roaring Forties." It must be noted, too, that in this prevailing westerly belt, the westerly concept is merely the general drift of the air. In short, the weather systems in this belt tend to move from west to east.

This does not mean that the wind is continuously from the west, for it tends to blow from every direction. When the cold arrives in the northern hemisphere, there is a clockwise circulation of air. Following each polar blast there tends to be a counterclockwise circulation. These traveling highs and lows, as they are often called, move from west to east along with the general atmospheric movement in the so-called prevailing westerlies. The line dividing a high and a low is commonly referred to as a "front."

At the extreme top and bottom of the world lie the polar

highs. In these areas, much of the air that rose in the tropics and that which went aloft at the subpolar low descends to earth as a mound of cold, still, heavy air. As this mound piles up, other air tends to move out from it along its periphery, and this is deflected to the right by the force of Ferrel's law; hence it blows from the northeast to the southwest in both hemispheres, forming the belt alluded to before as the polar easterlies.

Whereas the polar highs tend to be cold and calm, the polar easterlies tend to be windy and raw. Moreover, it must not be considered that these areas are in any sense undisturbed, for even the polar highs are not always calm. Often storms which are born near the edge of the polar realm roar across the polar highs, with strong winds whipping up the bitter cold air. Both the polar easterlies and the polar-high belts are quite inhospitable, yet since they are both influenced by high pressure they do not have much precipitation. The popular concept seems to be that it is always snowing in these regions and that there is much precipitation. This is not the case; less than ten inches of precipitation fall annually at those latitudes.

This polar belt often ejects those large masses of cold air alluded to earlier, which visit the middle latitudes or the zone of prevailing westerlies and cause storms. Essentially this is what happens. The mound of cold air in the polar-high region tends to get too large, being continuously fed, and the movements of polar easterlies do not drain off the air fast enough. As the mound of air gets too large, pieces of air break off from the edge of the mound, much like drops of water would break from a mound of water held together by surface tension on a curved or sloping piece of glass. Just as the drops of water break away and roll down the glass, so do these masses of air break from the polar-high mound and roll down the surface of the globe. These separated parcels, sometimes as high as the troposphere and extending to the ground, are often a thousand or more miles wide.

As the disengaged masses move southward in the northern hemisphere or northward in the southern hemisphere, they break through the subpolar low and move into the prevailing westerlies. Here they are caught in the general drift of air from west to east and tend to have the same directive movement. In the middle latitudes these are known as "highs." Around the tapering backs of these highs, air tends to curl in a counterclockwise fashion as the highs plow along. These back eddies grow large, about a thousand miles in diameter, and are known as "lows."

Thus we have the pattern of weather in the prevailing westerlies or the true middle latitudes. These polar emanations come about once a week. The reason is that once a piece has been spun off from the polar high, the mound has to recuperate to regain its mass before giving off another parcel. This pulsation requires about six or seven days. Consequently, the middle latitudes are visited, particularly in winter, by a high about once every week. This high brings cool, clear skies and dry weather, because it is cool descending air, which is drying air. Being about a thousand miles in width, it usually takes three or four days for one of these highs to move over any given area.

As just indicated, a high is followed by a low, which is essentially the warmer air which the high plowed into, rising and cooling. This low travels from west to east immediately behind the high and takes about three days to pass over any given spot. Thus, we have a six- or seven-day or weekly cycle of weather in the middle latitudes. We have a clear, calm, and cool period of the high, and then this is followed by the usually overcast and wet period of the low. The low is generally wet because the air is ascending, and it is the rising of the air that causes it to cool and lose its capacity to hold moisture and thus precipitate.

According to such authorities on climate and man as Ellsworth Huntington and Clarence A. Mills, the weekly cycles of highs and lows play important roles in people's health, longevity, success, and emotional stability. Although smaller and less potent than the larger cycles of climate and magnetism dealt with in Chapter 2, these weekly weather cycles are supposed to exert critical influences upon us. The benign period is reputed to be the high, with its cool, dry air and its clear skies and high atmospheric pressure. The malignant period is the low, with its damp and relatively warm air, its precipitation and overcast skies, and its low atmospheric pressure. During highs, it has been demonstrated, people pull through operations better, feel better, succeed in any venture they undertake better than other times, and they are emotionally stable. On the other hand, during lows more accidents and other tragedies happen, many things one tries become "flops" and more people than usual become emotionally unstrung. In fact, according to E. R. Dewey of the Foundation for the Study of Cycles, business is generally better during anticyclones.

The storminess of the middle latitudes is usually associated with the zone of contact between the polar emissions and the warm air moving from the southwest in the prevailing westerlies movement, along the line of contact. This line of contact is called a cold front. Here the contrast of air is so drastic that disruption occurs, and such violent manifestations of nature as strong winds and even tornadoes occur. For this reason, this belt is sometimes referred to as the stormy westerlies. It should be noted, though, that it is this contact at the cold fronts and the movement of air from lower latitudes upward in lows that bring the moisture and precipitation, and ultimately an abundance in agriculture, to much of the middle latitudes.

This affluence of precipitation, however, depends upon proximity to water bodies, for if air is moving poleward over nothing but dry land it does not have enough moisture to precipitate much, even if carried aloft by a storm or a low-pressure cell. The eastern portion of North America owes its abundant year-round precipitation to the fact that the Gulf of Mexico is just to the south. Southern China owes the ampleness of its rain to the bend of the Asiatic coast, exposing the China Sea just to the south. Where these reservoirs of moisture are shut out, middle-latitude deserts occur, as in central Asia and west-central North America.

One other type of surface wind movement must be taken into consideration: the "monsoons." These are essentially winds which blow at a given place from one direction half the year and from the opposite direction the other half of the year. Generally, this is associated with the movement of air in summer from the sea to the much-warmed land and in winter from the much-cooled land to the relatively mild sea.

There are many monsoon winds, large and small, throughout the world, as many places have this type of reversing wind system. Many of them occur as the result of that differential seasonal heating of land and sea. The largest one in the world, the classical one, however, does not occur in this manner, and must be given special attention here. It is the monsoon of Asia which blows inward across India and southeast Asia during the summer and outward across India and southeast Asia during the winter. Its inward-blowing summer winds are said to be forced over the Himalayan Mountains as they move toward hot central Asia and thus bring the monsoon rains of India and southeast Asia. We shall see that the heating of land and water has only limited influence on the Asian monsoons and that air masses do not actually move over the Himalayas.

According to the long-held belief, first advanced by Matthew Maury more than a hundred years ago, the inward draft of air from the south into Asia was caused by the development of a large low-pressure center in west-central Asia due to land heating. According to this theory, air would move in from the Indian Ocean across the Himalayas, dumping torrential rain on India, and then would move over the Tibetan plateau and westward across the Asian plains to the low-pressure center in southwest Asia in a counterclockwise fashion. Conversely, the old theory reported, a large high-pressure center would build up in central Asia in winter, and air would be forced out from this center in a clockwise fashion, crossing the Himalayas and going down across India, bringing a dry winter, to move finally into the tropical low farther south.

We now know that this is not the case. In essence, the high subtropical jet stream migrates to the south of the Himalayas in winter, pushing with it the tropical high which brings dryness to the Indian peninsula. The rise in surface pressure results in winds that move away from the land and appear to come from the northeast.

In summer, however, the high jet stream migrates to the north of the Himalayas and the Tibetan plateau, and the tropical low or doldrums belt moves up onto the Indian peninsula. This alone would bring a great deal of rain to India in the summer, but another influence is present which brings additional rain and accounts for the torrential downpours experienced during this season. In essence, the equatorial westerlies—the eastward-moving air current which compensates for the westward deflection of air into the tropical low—has a free movement during this season, with no sector of the tropical high to discourage it, and so a far-flung influence is noted. These equatorial westerlies that cross the Atlantic Ocean now move all the way across Africa north of the equator and cross the northern part of the Indian Ocean to the southern part of Asia, where, now moisture-laden, they are forced to rise as they approach the Himalayas. Here they are chilled as they ascend, dump torrents of extra water on India, and die in the mountains. Hence the monsoon of Asia is largely an effect of the high subtropical jet stream, the tropical low, and the equatorial westerlies (Maps 6 and 7).

With the exception of the monsoons and the subtropics, all that has been said so far about the banded characteristics of our wind systems and climate tends to imply that these bands are fixed and perfectly stable. This would be the case were it not for seasonal changes. In Chapter 1 we learned that the direct rays of the sun do not strike on the equator continuously throughout the year. Due to the 23½-degree tilt of the earth's axis with relation to the axis of the sun, the direct rays of the sun strike the equator only during the period of the equinoxes in March and September.

We learned that the earth in its yearly revolution around the sun exposes itself to the direct rays of the sun as far as 23½ degrees south latitude in December and to the direct rays of the sun as far north as 23½ degrees north latitude in June. Thus, the area of maximum heating of the sun, sometimes referred to as the heat equator, migrates to 23½ degrees north latitude in June, crosses back across the mathematical equator in September, and migrates to 23½ degrees south latitude in December. This accounts for the seasons as we know them. This movement of the heat equator carries along with it, at a great lag, the migration of the doldrums, or tropical-low rain belt. All other belts, including the tropical high, move correspondingly north in the summer of the northern hemisphere and south in the summer of the southern hemisphere (Maps 6 and 7).

Inasmuch as the actual rain belt of the tropics is at least 20 degrees wide, some portions of it are always over a narrow belt of 5 degrees on either side of the equator, which we know as the true equatorial calms or doldrum belt. The migrating peripheral portions bring summer rains to the wet and dry belts of the zone of trade winds, between 5 and 25 degrees in either hemisphere, usually in two peaks, only to the extent that a portion of the tropical rain belt passes over the area. In short, the summer rain period in the trade winds belts diminishes with increased distances from the equator.

This wet and dry belt in both hemispheres, then, has considerable summer rain near its equatorial edge and very little summer rain near its poleward edge. The tropical-high belt poleward of the trade winds belt correspondingly moves toward the poles in summer and toward the equator in winter. The area allotted to it between 25 and 35 degrees north latitude is flexible, but in general that area is always under drying high pressure (Maps 6 and 7).

The transitional nature of the subtropics has been noted: a dry summer when the tropical high is over it, a rainy winter when the storm systems of the prevailing westerlies of the middle latitudes are over it. Correspondingly, the entire system of the winds of the prevailing westerlies moves poleward in summer, discouraging the systematic blasts of polar air which are characteristic of that belt in winter.

Without the rhythmic force of the polar emissions, the oceanic highs spoken of earlier tend to drift in upon the eastern parts of the continents in summer in this zone of the prevailing westerlies. Much of the thundershower precipitation in that portion of the continents in the summer is the result of this oceanic influence, which overcomes at this season the general drift of the prevailing westerlies. Even the subpolar low—the polar easterlies—and the polar high move poleward slightly during the summer in both hemispheres, and the polar highs accordingly contract. The reverse, of course, is true in the winter in both hemispheres, where the polar highs are tremendously large and potent and send devastating polar outbreaks which dip down into the zone of the westerlies all the way into the subtropics and occasionally even into the poleward edge of the tropics.

SELECTED REFERENCES

Beer, Arthur (ed.). *Vistas in Astronomy.* 5 vols. New York: Pergamon Press, 1955–1962.

Bjerknes, Vilhelm. *The Oceanic Influence on Climate.* Chicago: New Science Library, 1929.

Boerker, Richard H. D. *Behold Our Green Mansions: A Book about American Forests.* Chapel Hill: University of North Carolina Press, 1945.

Carnegie Institution of Washington. I. *Ionospheric Research at College, Alaska, July 1941–June 1946,* by S. L. Seaton, H. H. Wells, and L. V. Berkner. II. *Auroral Research at College, Alaska, 1941–1944,* by S. L. Seaton and C. W. Malich. Washington, D.C.: Carnegie Institution of Washington, 1947.

———. *Ionospheric Research at Watheroo Observatory, Western Australia, June 1938–June 1946,* by L. V. Berkner and H. H. Wells. Washington, D.C.: Carnegie Institution of Washington, 1948.

Clayton, Henry H. *Solar Activity and Weather Changes.* Misc. Coll., Vol. 78, No. 4. Washington, D.C.: Smithsonian Institution, 1936.

———. *Solar Relations to Weather and Life.* 2 vols. Canton, Mass.: Clayton Weather Service, 1943.

Cressey, George B. *Asia's Lands and Peoples.* 3rd ed. New York: McGraw-Hill Book Co., 1963.

Defant, Albert. *Ebb and Flow: The Tides of Earth, Air, and Water.* Ann Arbor: University of Michigan Press, 1958.

Douglas, John Scott. *The Story of the Oceans.* New York: Dodd, Mead & Co., 1952.

Edgeworth, Kenneth E. *The Earth, the Planets, and the Stars.* New York: Macmillan Co., 1961.

Flick, F. J. *The Forests of Continental Latin America.* Washington, D.C.: Government Printing Office, 1952.

Franklin Institute. *Earth Satellites as Research Vehicles.* Monograph no. 2, proceedings of the symposium held April 18, 1956, at The Franklin Institute in Philadelphia. Philadelphia: Franklin Institute, 1956.

Hapgood, Charles. *Earth's Shifting Crust.* New York: Pantheon Books, 1958.

Huntington, Ellsworth. *Civilization and Climate.* New Haven: Yale University Press, 1924.

———. *Mainsprings of Civilization.* New York: John Wiley and Sons, 1945.

Iselin, Columbus O'Donnell. *A Study of the Circulation of the Western North Atlantic.* Contribution no. 108 from the Woods Hole Oceanographic Institution. Cambridge and Woods Hole, Mass.: Massachusetts Institute of Technology and Woods Hole Oceanographic Institution, 1936.

King-Hele, Desmond. *Satellites and Scientific Research.* 2nd ed. New York: Dover Publications, 1960.

Kuiper, Gerard P. (ed.). *The Atmospheres of the Earth and Planets.* Rev. ed. Chicago: University of Chicago Press, 1952.

——— and Barbara M. Middlehurst (eds.). *The Solar System.* 4 vols. *Vol. I: The Sun; Vol. II: The Earth As a Planet.* Chicago: University of Chicago Press, 1953–1963.

Leonard, Carroll M., and Vladimir L. Maleev. *Heat Power Fundamentals.* 2nd ed. New York: Pitman Publishing Corp., 1956.

Lillard, Richard G. *The Great Forest.* New York: Alfred A. Knopf, 1947.

Mills, Clarence A. *Climate Makes the Man.* New York: Harper & Brothers, 1942.

Minnaert, Marcellus. *The Nature of Light and Colour in the Open Air.* London: Bell, 1940; New York: Dover Publications, 1954.

Simak, Clifford D. *The Solar System: Our New Front Yard.* New York: St. Martin's Press, 1962.

Statesman's Yearbook. London: Macmillan Co., yearly.

Sverdrup, Harald U., and others. *The Oceans, Their Physics, Chemistry, and General Biology.* New York: Prentice-Hall, 1942.

Thomas, William L., Jr., and others (eds.). *Man's Role in Changing the Face of the Earth.* Chicago: University of Chicago Press, 1956.

Toynbee, Arnold J. *A Study of History,* Vols. I–IV. London: Oxford University Press, 1956.

Tugwell, Rexford G. *The Stricken Land: The Story of Puerto Rico.* New York: Doubleday & Co., 1946.

Unstead, J. F. *A World Survey.* London: University of London Press, 1962.

U.S. Foreign Commerce Department. *Our World Trade.* Washington, D.C.: Chamber of Commerce of the United States, quarterly.

U.S. Hydrographic Office. *References on the Physical Oceanography of the Western Pacific Ocean.* Publ. no. 238. Washington, D.C.: Government Printing Office, 1953.

U.S. Hydrographic Office. *World Atlas of Sea Surface Temperatures.* 2nd ed. 1944. Washington, D.C.: Hydrographic Office, U.S. Navy, 1948

U.S. Naval Observatory. Nautical Almanac Office. *The American Ephemeris and Nautical Almanac for the Years 1964 & 1965.* Washington, D.C.: Government Printing Office, 1964.

U.S. Navy. *Marine Climatic Atlas of the World. Vol. I: North Atlantic Ocean; Vol. II: North Pacific Ocean.* Published by direction of the Chief of Naval Operations. Washington, D.C.: Government Printing Office, 1955–56.

Van Valkenburg, Samuel, and Ellsworth Huntington. *Europe.* 2nd ed. with Colbert C. Held. New York: John Wiley & Sons, 1952.

World Almanac. New York: New York World Telegram, yearly.

Yearbook of Agriculture: Climate and Man. Washington, D.C.: Government Printing Office, 1941.

Yearbook of Agriculture: Grass. Washington, D.C.: Government Printing Office, 1948.

PART TWO

Chapter 6 / The Ways of the World

A variation in conditions within any climatic region brings us to a basic concept in our study of environmental science, which we will examine before taking up systematically the climates of the world. That concept is, essentially, that the stage of development—or "occupance," as it is sometimes called—of a given region signifies only what that region is now, not what it could be, which lies solely in the region's potential. In general, it may be said that people occupying any given area will tend to progress through certain common stages as they adjust to a region in the course of using the land.

All people start out with a primitive hunting-gathering-agricultural type of occupance. As they develop, they tend to make better use of the land. If the region is humid, there will be a tendency toward some sort of fixed agriculture; if the region is semi-arid or arid, a pastoral adjustment will be made. The attitude of the people occupying the area, however, enters into the picture as soon as they climb out of the primitive stage. If they have no taboos against using all the potentials of the land, then the next general stage will be a fine differentiation in land use, whereby each part of the area is generally utilized to best advantage. Thus, minerals will be exploited, either shipped out of the area or processed within it.

The processing of materials within the region and their manufacture into finished products will be effected largly in the succeeding stage, which depends upon the region's accessibility to major world trade routes. A region's proximity to these routes largely influences its development. Today the major transportation lanes both on the sea and across the land are oriented generally from west to east at about 20 to 50 degrees latitude;

the largest deviation from this pattern is the trade route through the Mediterranean and Red Seas to India, eastward across the Indian Ocean to Singapore and Australia, then extending northeastward to rejoin the main stream of travel in the mid-Pacific Ocean at Hawaii. Along the major routes stretch most of the steamship lanes, across both the Atlantic and the Pacific; and along this same east-west axis across North America go most of the railroad and major highway routes. Likewise, most of the transportation routes—road, rail, and canal—across Europe are east-west and at about this same latitude. Even the Trans-Siberian Railroad and what highway connections there are across Asia are at the same latitude.

It is not surprising, then, to find that most of the regions of the world which have reached a high stage of development in land use—a stage where industry and diversified agriculture are practiced—are within this latitudinal belt and not too far from these lanes of commerce. Nor is it surprising that the Amazon Basin in South America still remains generally in a primitive stage of growth, with native Indians practicing hunting and gathering and a crude migratory type of subsistence agriculture. On the other hand, that portion of the Malay Peninsula near Singapore, the adjacent island of Java, and the northern portion of Sumatra have developed a rather intensive, diversified agriculture representing a much higher stage of occupance. Both regions are in the rainy low latitudes and thus have the same basic physical characteristics. The difference is that the Malay region is along a prime transportation route, the southerly one just mentioned.

In similar fashion, the high development in the Sonoran Desert region in northwestern Mexico may be attributed largely to its proximity to the major routes across North America. On the other hand, the extremely primitive hunting culture of the peoples in the Kalahari Desert in southwestern Africa may be explained by their remoteness. Both the Sonoran and Kalahari deserts display essentially the same physical conditions, the difference again being essentially in their respective proximity to lanes of commerce.

Some areas remain rather primitive in spite of being near arteries of transportation. The Guiana Highlands, for example, are primitive although they are near a line of dip from the east-west-oriented commerce lanes of the world. This dip runs south to embrace the Panama Canal and then joins the east-west flow in the Pacific around Hawaii. Although the Guiana Highlands are not too far from this particular southern route, they still remain backward, largely because of the forbidding jungles and rain forests surrounding them, which serve to isolate them from the major flows of human commerce and ideas.

We are, of course, speaking of the present-day Anglo-Saxon ideas which dominate so much of the world today; other concepts of occupance in the past have left their mark, but we must deal with what is extant. We must also realize that much of the Far East is even today still under a rice-growing land system where attitudes are oriented toward a subsistence agriculture. We recognize, too, that the old-world dry lands are different from physically similar lands in the west.

Throughout history, various attitudes toward the land have dominated the world, of which at least sixteen have been described by Arnold Toynbee. Among these were the old Minoan and the Hellenic concepts; the Hellenic idea ascended to its cultural grandeur in the Greek intellectuals about 500 B.C. and was changed and adopted in the Roman Empire before the birth of Christ. Most of these ideas have either died out, declined, or become part of another culture; only a half-dozen different ones persist on any large scale today. These systems are: the Anglo-Saxon concept, the Indo-Oriental concept, the old-world dry-land concept, the Shangri-La concept, the new-world equestrian concept, and the prime-original concept.

The Anglo-Saxon Concept

The Anglo-Saxon is by far the most widespread system that has ever influenced the earth, affecting at present most of the populated areas of the world. It originated in western Europe and is centered on the British Isles. It dominates all of Europe, including Russia, as well as all of the continent of North America. It is also predominant in Australia and in most of central and south Africa, with the exception of the Congo Basin. Its influence is seen even in Japan and Malaysia, in the Orient.

One of its basic characteristics is a preoccupation with commerce—that is, the development of a highly efficient system of world commerce whereby numerous products are exchanged over excellently maintained routes. Another salient characteristic is preoccupation with mechanization; it is machine conscious. Another is an extremely acute time consciousness; everything is reckoned by the clock. Still another characteristic is a puritanical, almost hypocritical attitude toward life.

Whatever merit this Anglo-Saxon concept has, and whether or not it is in a decline, it is dominant today, and stages of development within regions throughout the world now to be discussed will be judged by the materialistic standards of this system. Its emphasis on transportation and commerce requires the best use of land throughout the world, and thus it is fitting that it should be a geographical standard for judging regions.

The Indo-Oriental Concept

The Indo-Oriental system is characterized by a preoccupation with the growing of rice, largely on a subsistence basis, and with the veneration of the family. The family is not only a social unit but also an economic unit, for the growing and harvesting of rice. This preoccupation with the family, and the growing of rice strictly for the family, has led to some degree of isolation or inbreeding. Roads are not built; there is very little need for them. There is no commerce, since everybody grows everything he needs for himself. Manufacturing does not develop, because again the home and the village are self-sufficient units. The river valleys, which are the best for flooding in the growing of rice, become thickly populated, whereas the interstream areas are left empty and without roads.

The landscape of an Indo-Oriental area, therefore, looks

vastly different from that of an Anglo-Saxon area. Whereas the western landscape would have roads and other transportation and communication media in evidence throughout the countryside, the Oriental landscape lacks this completely. While the western area would have an even distribution of farms throughout the arable part of the land, the Oriental setting has a dense development of farms in the river valleys and emptiness in the interstream areas. The western landscape would have towns and industrial centers; the Oriental scene has villages and no industrial centers.

This landscape predominates throughout much of the Orient—all of China and India, as well as much of southeastern Asia and the East Indies. Although a certain amount of industrialization has been effected in India, due to the influence of the Anglo-Saxon culture, the basic theme of the Indian landscape still remains Indo-Oriental. Likewise, the efforts to industrialize China have met with considerable difficulty for the same reason, and apparently the basic warp and woof of the Chinese landscape still remains Indo-Oriental.

The Old-World Dry-Land Concept

The old-world dry-land system still persists throughout the arid portions of Africa and Asia. This includes North Africa, the Arabian peninsula, most of the Middle East, and most of central Asia. This concept is based in general on nomadism—that is, the practice of grazing livestock by following the stock from pasture to pasture. This activity, practiced from the earliest times, has a definite significance for the system. There is a lack of fixed homes; people who move from time to time, following the herds, develop no concept of a permanent abode. Correspondingly, these people have developed an odd concept of property: personal real estate or property has no meaning to them. Land is a domain for those who find and hold it, and it is their domain only so long as it provides pasture; then it can go to anyone. Harshness is a common thing in these areas, and it is reflected in many ways, even in the religions. Although irrigation areas like the Nile have been greatly influenced by the Anglo-Saxon idea, and areas in Asia have been influenced by the Soviet production attitude, most of these dry lands are still marked by nomadism.

THE SHANGRI-LA CONCEPT

The Shangri-La idea is dominant largely on the Tibetan plateau in Asia and in other isolated places throughout the world. This concept is not based so much on the use of land but rather is largely preoccupied with religion: the individual exists for God, and worldly comforts take a secondary place. The pursuit of this idea is so assiduous in Tibet that many of the known rich minerals on the Tibetan plateau are not mined. It is even reflected in active resistance to the influence of any other idea. For example, the wheel has not been used in Tibet, although its existence and use are known, simply because it might be the harbinger of other influences. Not even the political dominance of the Red Chinese has been able to alter the warp and woof of the Shangri-La idea on the Tibetan plateau.

THE NEW-WORLD EQUESTRIAN CONCEPT

The new-world equestrian system is limited largely to South America and predominates on most of that continent, with the exception of the Guiana Highland areas and the Amazon Basin. This concept originated in the equestrian (cattle-growing) land use of Old Spain and was brought to South America by Spanish settlers in the eighteenth and nineteenth centuries. Spain itself has now adopted the Anglo-Saxon idea, as has all of Europe, but vestiges of its old "horseback" system still persist in South America.

The most outstanding facet of this attitude is, of course, preoccupation with the raising of cattle. This is carried on so persistently that often good land capable of abundant agriculture, which has a much greater population-carrying capacity than pastoralism, is used for cattle grazing. Concomitant with this is the concept of large estates. This has led to a tenant-farming system which is barely above serfdom and an unenlightened concept of independence on the part of most of the people who live on the land. Little stress is placed on individual initiative; contests for power seem to be more normal in this society. In short, people do not develop as self-reliant individuals, able to move to a new frontier and pioneer new land. Consequently, in all of South America, in spite of millions of square miles of unused but good land, there has been only imperfect and spotty development.

Manufacturing has a difficult time increasing on any large scale in these areas, for although a concept of commerce and industry is extant, a remnant from the commerce and industry of Old Spain, the concept of big industry seems to be inadequate. The attitude of many Latin American manufacturers is the old one of making a few items to sell at a high price to a select clientele rather than mass-producing them to sell to many people at a lower price. In spite of all of this, however, the Anglo-Saxon idea has influenced areas within this region; note, for example, the large industrial regions of Buenos Aires and Rio de Janeiro, as well as the almost complete Anglo-Saxonization of Mexico.

The Prime-Original Concept

It might be questionable to call the last concept, the prime-original, a single idea at all, but for convenience we do so, since it takes up the remainder of the world. This system is found wherever there is inhospitable land or where there has remained a primitive way of living. It might be said that all systems start out with a primitive stage, but these particular areas have resisted change; consequently they will probably remain as such.

Although the prime-original system may be found in all isolated places, its usual homes are tropical rain forests and jungles, inhospitable deserts, high rugged mountains, and areas of the world gripped by ice. Included are such areas as the central desert of western Australia, the Tierra del Fuego land of South America, the Kalahari Desert of southwest Africa, the Amazon Basin, the Congo Basin, the highlands of the East Indies, the Guiana Highlands of South America, and the frigid lands of the Eskimos of North America and Greenland, and some of the Arctic tribes of Siberia. The characteristics of the natives vary throughout, as does the character of the land, but the primitive original approach to living is common; all of these people have a hunting and gathering type of culture, assisted by a small amount of crude subsistence agriculture, very often migratory.

It might be said that most of these people are still in the Stone Age, for they have to spend all their time obtaining the bare necessities of life from an unyielding environment. Tribal social organization and a system of communal property seem to be common among all, enforced by the severity of the environment. From the bushmen of Australia to the Indians of the South American rain forest to the Eskimos in the bare Arctic tundras, the concept of communal property—and communal marital relations—seems to persist.

In spite of the entrance of other concepts, particularly the Anglo-Saxon idea, natives in these areas vehemently resist the injection of the Anglo-Saxon pattern; they would rather retreat farther into the inhospitable land than accept new ideas. As Ellsworth Huntington once wrote, "The primitive native of both the southlands and the northlands will have little to do with Anglo-Saxon influence. Perhaps it is because he has little use for the puritanical aspects of that culture, which must appear ridiculous to him who is daily in a life-death struggle with nature."

Stages of Anglo-Saxon Development

It may be said that a region is affected largely by its physical characteristics—climate, soil, and other resources, as well as the concepts influencing it, and its relationship to transportation arteries. On this basis we will examine the geographical locations of the world. We will take a climatic belt which comprises a number of physically separated regions with a common geographical complex—climate, vegetation, soil, and a breed of native animals. We will then look at the separate regions within this similar physical pattern and see how they differ on the basis of cultural influence and the effects of the tentacles of world transportation. We can then observe how these regions compare with one another and study, in this way, the potential of many undeveloped areas. An arbitrary yardstick must be used, however: the stages of normal development of the Anglo-Saxon system. This development has been touched upon before, but it is necessary to observe it in a little more detail at this time.

The first, of course, is the **primitive stage,** the prime-original level, and bears a similarity to all primitive cultures past and present.

The second level of development is what is known as a **subsistence stage.** People now become fixed to the land and sedentary—that is, agriculture in one place becomes common. Also, in this period, the family becomes the predominant social unit, even to a point where it becomes isolated from other families and completely independent. There is, however, in this stage a resemblance to order, for the people are generally occupied in the tilling of the land. If subsistence tilling of the land is not possible because of aridity, then the comparable stage is an orderly sort of pastoralism. In the old world it was nomadic but whatever it becomes, it is orderly.

The third normal development is the **commercial stage,** where the various subsistence areas of agriculture begin trading goods with one another or subsistent pastoralists begin trading with one another. This leads to the development of lines of transportation and communication, and also the raising of commercial crops on farms and the breeding of cattle for market in areas of pastoralism. In short, the whole complex of narrow subsistence living vanishes, and a broadening area of commerce, transportation, travel, and variety is entered upon. The concept of individual rights and property and money becomes paramount at this stage, and a new class, the commercial, rises in society. Mining of usable minerals takes place, and the exploitation of forest, fishery, and game resources occurs. The family, which was the prime unit in the earlier stage, loses importance, and new concepts of commercial units rise, sometimes taking the form of nationalism. In short, other influences begin to take hold of the individual.

The fourth step is a dramatic refinement of the third stage and is called the **industrial stage.** During this period the materials that were mined and the crops that were sold for cash begin to be processed within the region rather than being sent out for sale. Thus, manufacturing develops, which leads to intensification of commerce; it also leads to further intensification of agriculture. Whereas, in the third stage, cash crop agriculture superseded subsistence agriculture, in the fourth stage an intensified and specialized crop agriculture supersedes the general cash crop agriculture. In other words, while in the third stage a farmer raised wheat, in the fourth he would probably raise asparagus or celery or maintain orchards and vineyards, all of them intensively cultivated. Even the areas where pastoralism was previously practiced would now exhibit specialized ranching or even stock farming. Areas formerly devoted to lumbering would now become areas with intensified tree crops, and special conservation methods would be introduced in such activities as the fishing industry to assure a permanent supply of fish.

The final stage, reached by some parts of the world, is known as the **climax stage.** Specialization of land use is carried to a point where every piece of land is used to its best possible advantage, as in parts of Europe and the northeastern United States. Vast urbanization characterizes this final development. Family control and much of the social control characteristic of rural life tend to break down, often accompanied by a religious and moral decline and a constant growth of population. Concepts of belonging become rare, and anything related to pride is considered ridiculous. According to many experts, this stage in the development of land is to be avoided.

SELECTED REFERENCES

Adams, Nicholson B. *The Heritage of Spain: Introduction to Spanish Civilization*. Rev. ed. New York: Holt, Rinehart & Winston, 1959.

Bowman, J. *The New World*. New York: World Bank Co., 1928.

Butwell, Richard. *Southeast Asia Today—and Tomorrow*. Rev. ed. New York: Frederick A. Praeger, Publisher, 1964.

Cressey, George B. *Asia's Lands and Peoples*. 3rd ed. New York: McGraw-Hill Book Co., 1963.

Cumberland, Kenneth B. *Southwest Pacific, A Geography of Australia, New Zealand, and Their Pacific Island Neighborhoods*. New York: McGraw-Hill Book Co., 1956.

Duffy, James, and Robert A. Manners. *Africa Speaks*. Princeton, N.J.: D. Van Nostrand Co., 1961.

Durant, Will. *The Story of Philosophy*. London: Oxford University Press, 1952.

Freeman, Otis W. (ed.). *Geography of the Pacific*. New York: John Wiley & Sons, 1951.

Gottman, Jean. *A Geography of Europe*. 3rd ed. New York: Henry Holt & Co., 1954.

Huntington, Ellsworth. *Civilization and Climate*. New Haven: Yale University Press, 1924.

———. *Mainsprings of Civilization*. New York: John Wiley & Sons, 1945.

James, Preston E. *One World Divided*. New York: Blaisdell Publishing Co., 1964.

Kimble, George H. T. *Tropical Africa*. 2 vols. New York: Twentieth Century Fund, 1960.

Mills, Clarence A. *Climate Makes the Man*. New York: Macmillan Co., 1946.

Morley, Sylvanus G. *The Ancient Maya*. 3rd ed. revised by George W. Brainerd. Stanford: Stanford University Press, 1956.

Semple, Ellen. *Influences of Geographic Environment*. New York: Henry Holt & Co., 1911.

Chapter 7 / THE CLIMATE BELTS

Returning to climate: reduced to the simplest terms, differential heating over the face of the earth by the sun causes variations in weather. It has been explained how the sun's heat is greatest around the equator and least in the polar regions. The average temperature in equatorial land regions is in the upper 80 degrees Fahrenheit. Average temperatures in the polar regions are close to the freezing point, 32 degrees Fahrenheit, or well below.

We have noted that, because of the tilt of the earth's axis and its yearly revolution around the sun, we have seasons. We have also found that land heats faster in summer than water and cools faster in winter. Consequently, in winter in each hemisphere the larger land masses become extremely cold, exceeding the average cold of the polar regions. Conversely, the larger land masses in each hemisphere become extremely warm in summer, particularly the areas remote from the oceans, and temperatures rise to heights even greater than the average in equatorial regions.

Differential heating by the sun also causes air movements, often called winds, over the surface of our world. These air movements bring precipitation to all the land areas of the world and are responsible for the devastating storms, tornadoes, and hurricanes which occur.

It is the rain-giving aspect of these movements that is all important. If it were not for lateral air circulating throughout the world, the land masses would remain dry. These air movements pick up water from the oceans, for air has a capacity to absorb moisture and carry it within itself; this water is dumped on land later, when the capacity of the air to carry it is changed. Thus, through the wind systems of the world the oceans provide the water to make green the land, which in turn returns water to the oceans by rivers and underground seepage.

In some places this conveyance of water results in a great amount of precipitation upon the land, causing floods or nurturing the growth of great forests. Such is the case in areas like the upper Amazon Basin of South America, where well over 180 inches of rainfall are dumped yearly. Still greater rainfall is experienced in areas where occasional winds force air to rise against high mountains, as in northeastern India, where the monsoons drop more than 400 inches of rain annually upon the land.

On the other hand, many areas of the world have too little rainfall for normal agricultural methods—less than 15 inches of precipitation annually, or even less than 10. In the low latitudes, where temperatures and evaporation rates are high, fewer than 25 inches of rain almost precludes normal farming. In the middle and higher latitudes, where temperatures are lower and evaporation is less, less than 15 inches will exclude regular agriculture. In all such areas, irrigation and substitute agriculture methods (dry farming, planting farther apart, etc.) have to be introduced.

The air movements of the world and their relation to large water bodies are therefore extremely important in ascertaining the climate in any part of the world. The two basic principles were noted earlier: warming air is dry air; and cooling air is wet air. In short, air that is moving from higher to lower latitudes or from higher to lower altitudes is drying air. Air that is moving from lower to higher latitudes or from lower to higher altitudes is wetting air and hence will be likely to bring precipitation. If a large body of water is nearby, this air will bring abundant rain; if it is not, it will bring only slight precipitation in spite of its movement.

Principal Zones

There are three main climate belts: the low latitudes (tropical), the middle latitudes (stormy or prevailing westerlies), and the high latitudes (polar). Basically, the low latitudes extend from the equator to nearly 35 degrees latitude, covering that area of the earth which is practically frost free. The middle latitudes extend from about 35 to about 65 degrees, including a portion of that part of the earth which has frost and a definite winter but also has enough summer so that conventional agriculture can be practiced. The high latitudes comprise those areas above 65 degrees, where winters are long and severe and summers are so short and mild that normal agriculture cannot be practiced; it includes the areas of the polar easterly winds and the polar highs. The slight variation from the limits of these zones given earlier is due to the greater refinement of the treatment in this chapter.

Within each of these belts, as noted earlier, are several minor belts, based largely on wind direction and precipitation. Let us define these roughly by latitude.

Characteristics of the Low Latitudes. In the low latitudes we recognize, first, a belt of **rainy low latitudes,** which extends about 5 degrees from the equator. This is where air is always rising, due to excessive sun heat, and where the air is fed by the trade winds from higher latitudes, with the result that torrential rain is dumped daily throughout the belt. This belt is variously called the doldrums, the intertropical front, the tropical low, or the equatorial calm, and it is always hot and wet (Fig. 11).

The next belt within the low latitudes extends from about 5 to about 25 degrees and is known as the **wet and dry low latitudes.** This area gets precipitation in the summer time, when the rainy low latitudes move slightly northward with the seasonal change. The rest of the year this belt receives the trade winds, which blow from northeast to southwest in the northern hemisphere (and southeast to northwest in the southern

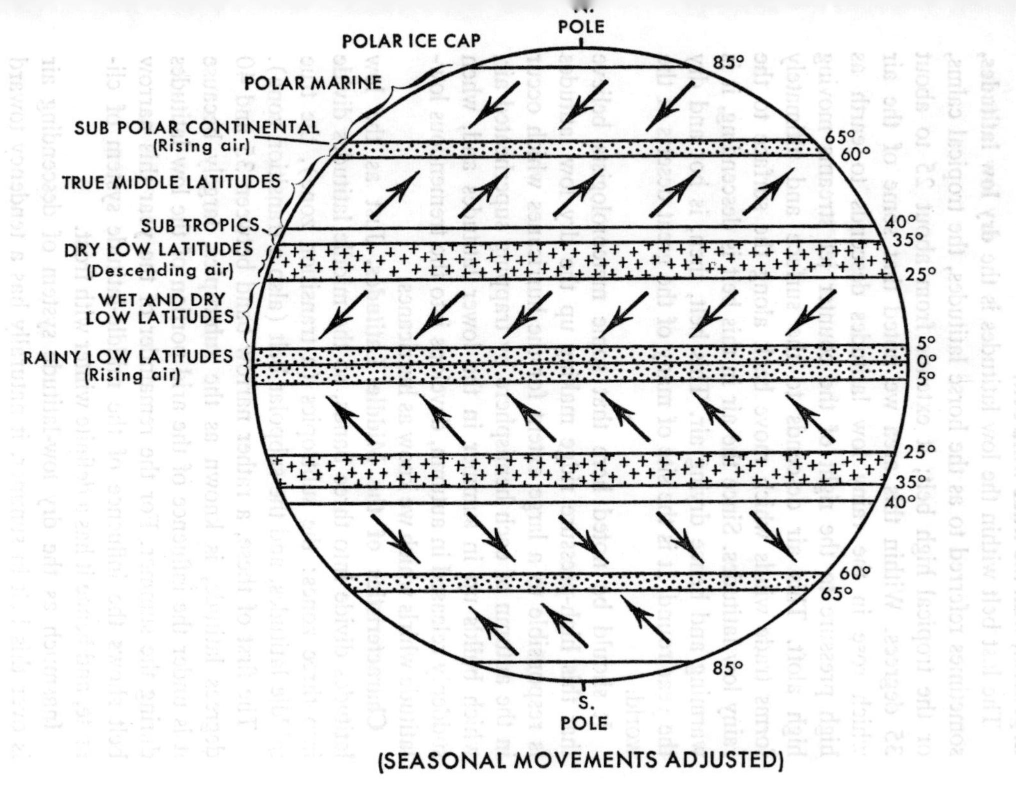

Fig. 11. Generalized climate belts.

hemisphere), and, moving from higher to lower latitudes, are drying winds. Consequently, winter in this belt is the dry period. Year-round warmth, summer rain, and winter dryness, then, are the characteristics of this belt, which corresponds, in general, with the trade wind belt.

The last belt within the low latitudes is the **dry low latitudes,** sometimes referred to as the horse latitudes, the tropical calms, or the tropical high belt; it extends from about 25 to about 35 degrees. Within this area we noted that some of the air which rose in the rainy low latitudes descends to earth as high pressure to the right of the counter jet streams moving high aloft. This air descends to the surface and ultimately forms trade winds which move back along the surface to the rainy low latitudes. Since the air in this belt is descending, it is warming and hence drying air. This belt, then, is hot and dry the year round. It is the site of many of the great deserts of the world.

It should be noted here that some meteorologists believe that this high-pressure ridge making up the dry low latitudes is responsible to a large extent for the hurricanes which occur in the autumn of each hemisphere by trapping superheated air, which builds up in summer in the lower latitudes and, when suddenly released in autumn, develops into the tremendous low-latitude whirls which we know as hurricanes.

Characteristics of the Middle Latitudes. Just as the low latitudes divide into three bands, so the middle latitudes divide into three zones: the subtropics (a transition zone), the true middle latitudes, and the subpolar belt (also a transition zone).

The first of these, a rather narrow band between 35 and 40 degrees latitude, is known as the **subtropics,** largely because it is under the influence of the arid portion of the low latitudes during the summer. For the remainder of the year this narrow belt shows the influence of the middle-latitude system of climate, and hence it has a definite winter with frost.

Inasmuch as the dry low-latitude system of descending air is over this belt in summer, it naturally has a tendency toward dryness at that season; the stormy middle-latitude wind system which covers the belt in winter brings rainfall. The belt is characterized, then, by a mild climate, with winter rains and a tendency toward summer drought. The Mediterranean region, with a climate extolled all over the world, lies within this belt.

All of the subtropical belt, however, is not characterized so clearly. Part of it gets very little precipitation, even in winter, and hence is very dry. These portions lie remote from water bodies. Still other parts of the realm have abundant precipitation the year round, 40 to 50 inches annually, enough for prosperous agriculture. Such portions get precipitation even in summer, in spite of the presence of the dry low-latitude wind system. These areas usually lie on the eastern edge of continents and come under the influence of oceanic air movements during the summer. This circulation brings moist air inland, and precipitation is generated by small convection currents developing over portions of the land, causing thundershowers. Such areas as the southeastern portion of the United States have this kind of climate—the mildness of the subtropics plus year-round abundant precipitation.

The next belt of middle latitudes, lying between 40 and 60 degrees, is often referred to as the **true middle latitudes** or, sometimes, as the zone of the prevailing westerly winds (Fig. 11). Here, some of the air that descended in the dry low latitudes moves northward and, being twisted to the right by the force of Ferrel's law, drifts to the north and to the east, making a general movement of air from the southwest to the northeast.

As was noted earlier, we should not assume that the wind is always from the west in this zone. Because of various disturbances known as highs or "anticyclones"—all referring to polar blasts—local winds in this belt can come from any direction. The general movement of the large highs, which we noted are on an average about a thousand miles in diameter, is of course from west to east, traveling a distance of about three to four thousand miles in a week. Snow and subzero temperatures are common in this belt in winter, and enough warmth for good corn-growing in summer. Most portions of the belt get ample precipitation, fairly evenly distributed, and some parts even get abundant precipitation.

The reason for this variance of wind direction, which is often very beneficial, is that this belt is almost regularly bombarded by those cold blasts of air from the Arctic air mass. The cold air which builds up in the polar zone, we observed, having been carried aloft from the low latitudes, comes to earth as a huge mound over the polar region. Like any mound which is continuously fed, it has to lose some of its mass at its periphery. Consequently, large parcels of cold air break off from this polar air mass at regular weekly intervals.

These thousand-mile-wide blasts of cold air, we remember, are referred to as cold fronts because of their steep front side. As they plow into the warmer prevailing-westerly air, they force it to rise; it cools as it rises, thus precipitating in a violent manner. It is this phenomenon which characterizes the passing of the fronts—squalls and storms, bringing violent rains in spring, autumn, and summer and snow squalls in winter.

Within each succeeding mound of air, after its front has passed over a given area, there is a movement of its own—that is, the air within this mound tends to move downward and outward in a clockwise fashion in the northern hemisphere and counterclockwise in the southern hemisphere, according to Ferrel's law. This is the true high or anticyclone. This phenomenon brings northwesterly winds, which are cold, and, because they are coming from higher latitudes and higher altitudes, they are drying winds and the skies are clear. So, after the passing of the squall line or the cold front, there is a high period with clear skies for several days, cold in winter and cool in summer.

As the high passes, which usually takes about three days over a given area, it is followed by what we referred to before as a low. These lows are known as "cyclones" and constitute air moving upward in a counterclockwise fashion (clockwise in the southern hemisphere). The low, which usually follows the high, is about as big as the high—that is, about a thousand miles in width, and it too takes about three days to pass over a given area. Consequently, most places in the zone of prevailing westerlies or true middle latitudes are normally visited by a high and a low in succession in the course of a week.

The low is caused by warm and moist prevailing-westerly air, which has been pushed aside by the high, moving around to the back, and, because the back side is sloping, tending to curl around with a counterclockwise motion. As this air moves, it is forced aloft, cooled by higher altitudes, and forced to precipitate. Consequently, the period of a low over a given area is characterized by overcast skies and long sessions of precipitation. During the summer, this precipitation comes as a long steady rain; in the winter, as a continuous big snowfall. After the low has passed, another high usually moves in.

This succession of highs and lows is normally very regular in winter in the true middle latitudes. In summer in many places the recession of the polar air mass diminishes the frequency of highs, and for a time the oceanic air mass, thwarting the westerlies, takes over in this belt. This air drift, too, brings in moisture, but the precipitation then is by convectional thunderstorms, due to super or differential heating of the land by the sun.

Parts of this belt, however, are relieved of the violence of summer thundershowers. They are the portions on the western side of continents, where the oceanic drift takes over almost completely during the summer. By natural good fortune, these areas are also bathed by mild oceanic currents, such as the North Atlantic current (Gulf Stream) in the North Atlantic Ocean. Air from over these mild currents is brought inland during the summer and, with a slight rise in air forced by the land mass, precipitation occurs in gentle showers. In winter, these coasts are visited in succession by highs and lows, but the extreme cold of winter highs is ameliorated somewhat by the influence of the mild oceanic currents just off the coast.

Such coasts are characterized, then, by abundant precipitation the year round, with a definite winter and a definite summer, but with the extremes of both seasons ameliorated by the presence of mild currents in the adjacent ocean and by the general movement of weather systems from west to east. Such areas are familiar to us. Most of western Europe has this sort of climate, as does the northwestern portion of the coast of North America, the southeastern end of Australia, and all of New Zealand.

The remainder of this prevailing westerly or true middle-latitude belt is subject to the violent changes characteristic of a succession of cyclonic storms and the violence of summer thundershowers, the latter of which, when overdeveloped, carry a partial vacuum and become tornadoes. In general, these regions get abundant precipitation throughout the year, as most of the belt gets more than 40 inches of rain annually in any given place, but areas remote from water bodies naturally get less, such as the west-central portion of North America and the central portions of Asia. Most of the humid eastern portion of North America falls within this belt, as does central Europe and most of eastern Asia.

The upper middle latitudes, or **subpolar belt,** is a rather narrow strip between 60 and 65 degrees latitude. It is a transitional zone between the acceptable conditions of the middle latitudes and the inhospitable conditions of the high latitudes. For a time in summer, this belt is influenced by the middle-latitude system of weather, but during its cold winter season it is dominated by the polar system. The function of this zone, basically, is more than transitional; it is the buffer between the high latitudes and the true middle latitudes—a zone of continuous battle. Here, except for a few short months in summer, relatively warm prevailing westerly air meets the steady movement of cold polar air, flowing from the distant polar air mass and causing a clash along the climate front.

Besides giving off blasts of air, the polar air mass generates a steady flow of air in the form of cold winds. These winds meet the relatively warm winds of the prevailing westerlies in this subpolar transition belt, and the cold air, being heavier, pushes under and forces the less cool air aloft, causing precipitation. After precipitation, this forced-up air joins the other air to move northward and feed the distant polar-high air mass. The southward-moving surface polar air, after forcing the prevailing-westerly air aloft, is generally caught within the polar bursts or highs and is carried with them into the middle latitudes. Because of air being forced up and because of the precipitation, this belt is often referred to as the "subpolar low." The precipitation in the belt is usually enough to nurture the great northern woods found in these latitudes.

Characteristics of the High Latitudes. The next major band is the high latitudes. It includes the belts of polar easterlies and the cold polar highs (Fig. 11).

The belt we have called the **polar easterlies** is better known climatically as the "polar marine" belt. It lies between 65 and 85 degrees latitude, and its more amenable parts often lie on the westward or lee coasts of land masses, giving rise to the term polar marine. Here the steady flow of cold air emanating from the polar high flows generally toward the subpolar low. Since it is moving southward in the northern hemisphere, it is deflected to the right and becomes a wind from the northeast, hence the name polar easterlies. These winds are extremely cold, carrying subzero temperatures most of the year. Consequently, they keep the areas over which they pass frozen far into the subsoil most of the year.

Although the winds are moving from a higher to a lower latitude, they are too cold to be affected much by what little change in latitude they experience in that part of the world. Only for a brief month or two in summer does the belt of the polar easterlies get any relief from these icy winds, when the subpolar low swings slightly northward. At that time some precipitation accompanies the subpolar low, and a brief warm period comes simultaneously with the Midnight Sun, for these areas are above the respective Arctic or Antarctic circles. This period is not warm enough or long enough, however, to melt the subsoil, which is deeply frozen during most of the year by the polar easterlies. Consequently, the subsoil in this belt is always frozen, and the topsoil, which melts during the summer, is then usually squashy and poorly drained.

This poor drainage and the inhospitable conditions in general exclude tree seedlings, and hence this area of the world is covered by vegetation known as the "tundra." These are short grasses, mosses, and hearty shrubs such as willows. In general, this zone is unsuitable for normal agriculture and is an uninviting part of the world.

The most inhospitable portion, however, is that belt poleward of 85 degrees latitude. This is the zone of **polar highs** or the polar-continental belt—or the polar icecap—where it is always cold and the ground is always frozen. Here the air which has risen in the equatorial or rainy low-latitude zone, or that which rose in the subpolar low, has come to earth as a cold heavy mound. This polar-high belt is persistent the year round and is continuously fed from air movements aloft. As we noted, it gives off air from its great mass, in the form of polar emissions or highs, and gives off a steady flow of surface winds in the form of the polar easterlies.

But the big mound itself is ever present, and it is so cold that it keeps everything below it frozen. In winter its influence is even more potent than at other times of the year, as it spreads to join high-pressure mounds which build up over the northern portion of Asia and North America, and the air masses it throws off are then more virile than ever. The polar emanations penetrate all the way down to the subtropics and sometimes into the tropics in winter; but always the polar high is the most forbidding zone of continuous year-round inhospitality.

Altitudes

While speaking of zones of climate, we have been referring largely to the areas which are reasonably low lying in elevation. Mountainous areas lying above four thousand feet naturally put themselves into climatic zones one belt higher in latitude than contiguous regions, while areas above nine thousand feet in elevation put themselves in a zone about two belts closer to the pole than their actual physical location. Thus, places above ten thousand feet in the Alps or in the Himalayas, or even in the Rockies, are in reality in a polar climate.

In the low latitudes, areas above twelve thousand feet are in this type of climate, such as the Altiplano in the high Andes in Peru and Bolivia. In the low latitudes, however, the zone between about four and ten thousand feet is ideal; temperatures have been altered to a point where they are equitable, and these are the delightful portions of the low latitudes. Such places as Mexico City, at eight thousand feet, and Quito, Ecuador, at nine thousand feet, are good examples.

Geographic Regions

We have seen the general alignment of climates throughout the world. Before going specifically into subbelts, it would be expedient here to note the manner in which the areas within those subbelts are separated for treatment. As must be apparent now, each of these subbelts extends all the way around the world, embracing its own span of latitude. Moreover, because the climate is the same around the world within each subbelt, the vegetation, soil, and native animal life also tend to be the same.

This pattern persists because climate has a large influence on the type of native vegetation cover that develops in an area. A hot, wet climate will develop a broadleaf rain forest, whereas a cool, semidry climate will engender grassland. The type of soil developed will depend principally upon the climate and the vegetation. For example, the incessant rains of a hot, wet climate will sap the soil material of its nutrients and leave a sticky clay as soil, whereas the dryness of the semi-arid climate and humus-forming potential of grass will develop a rich black soil in the grassland. Native animal life in the rain forest will of course be arboreal (in the trees), and in the grassland it will naturally be comprised largely of ground-walking herbivorous animals.

Each subbelt, then, tends to be uniform around the world in at least four geographic factors: climate, native vegetation, native animal life, and soils. The specific areas within these subbelts differ, however, in several other physical geographic factors. They may be physically separated, as the Congo Basin is from the Philippines in the rainy low latitudes; or they may have different shapes and relations to water bodies, as the narrow coastal strip of the Malabar coast of West India has from the sprawling, inland Amazon Basin in the same subbelt. Also, they may differ in land form, as a low, poorly drained basin differs from a sloping, well-drained coastal plain. They may also be different from one another in geological structure and mineral wealth. These differing physical features are the main causes for the division of the subbelts into separate geographic regions, such as the Amazon Basin or the Malabar coast. (The nature and distribution of factors not related to climate were, of course, treated in earlier chapters in this book.)

But, in spite of their physical differences, the regions within a given subbelt should tend to have the same type of land use, since climate and vegetation tend to influence strongly the way man uses the land. They differ greatly in land use, however, on the basis of the culture influencing the region and on the stage of occupance which the region has reached. These factors, discussed at length in the previous chapters, are the bases upon which the geographic regions within each subbelt can be compared with one another, change evaluated, and potential ascertained.

SELECTED REFERENCES

Clarke, George L. *Elements of Ecology*. New York: John Wiley and Sons, 1954.

Dale, Tom, and Vernon G. Carter. *Topsoil and Civilization*. Norman: University of Oklahoma Press, 1955.

Delorit, Richard J., and Henry L. Ahlgren. *Crop Production*. 2nd ed. New York: Prentice-Hall, 1959.

Freeman, Otis W. (ed.). *Geography of the Pacific*. New York: John Wiley and Sons, 1951.

Ginsburg, Norton S., Brian J. L. Berry, and Bert F. Hoselitz. *Atlas of Economic Development*. Chicago: University of Chicago Press, 1961.

Graham, Edward H. *The Land and Wildlife*. New York: Oxford University Press, 1947.

Great Britain Board of Trade. *Statistical Abstracts of the British Empire*. London: British Board of Trade, yearly.

International Yearbook of Agricultural Statistics. Rome: International Institute of Agriculture, yearly.

Israelsen, Orson W., and Vaughn E. Hansen. *Irrigation Principles and Practices.* 3rd ed. New York: John Wiley and Sons, 1962.

Meinig, Donald W. *On the Margins of the Good Earth.* London: John Murray, Publishers, 1963.

Millar, Charles E. *Soil Fertility.* New York: John Wiley and Sons, 1955.

New International Year Book. New York: Funk & Wagnalls Co., yearly.

Panshin, Alex J., and others. *Forest Products.* 2nd ed. New York: McGraw-Hill Book Co., 1962.

Thoman, Richard S. *The Geography of Economic Activity.* New York: McGraw-Hill Book Co., 1962.

Tugwell, Rexford G. *The Stricken Land.* New York: Doubleday and Co., 1946.

Unstead, John F. *A World Survey.* London: University of London Press, 1962.

Van Royen, William. *Agricultural Resources of the World.* New York: Prentice-Hall, 1954.

——— and others. *Mineral Resources of the World.* New York: Prentice-Hall, 1952.

Waksman, Selman A. *Soil Microbiology.* New York: John Wiley and Sons, 1952.

Wechsler, David. *The Range of Human Capacities.* 2nd ed. Baltimore: Williams and Wilkins Co., 1952.

Weigert, Hans W., and others (eds.). *New Compass of the World.* New York: Macmillan Co., 1953.

Yearbook of Agriculture: Grass. Washington, D.C.: Government Printing Office, 1948.

Yearbook of Agriculture: Soils and Man. Washington, D.C.: Government Printing Office, 1939.

Ziegler, P. Thomas. *The Meat We Eat.* Danville, Ill.: Interstate Printers and Publishers, 1962.

Chapter 8 / The Warm and the Hot

As the title implies, this chapter deals with the low latitudes, to see where they are and how people deal with them. The climate belts included are the rainy low latitudes, the wet and dry low latitudes, the dry low latitudes, and the low-latitude highlands.

The Rainy Low Latitudes

Take first the rainy low latitudes, the belt around the world near the equator, which gets rain practically every day throughout the year and is always hot. Such areas are: the Amazon basin of South America; the eastern coast of Central America and all of Panama (called the "Mosquito Coasts" after local Indian tribes); the Congo basin and the Ivory Coast of Central Africa; the eastern part of the island of Madagascar; the Malabar coast of India; and the Burma-Malay area, the Philippines, and the East Indies (collectively called Islandic Asia). Also included is the east coast of Brazil, a narrow strip stretching southward from the city of Pará nearly to the city of Rio de Janeiro (Map 8).

The presence of the Amazon and Congo basins in this belt is easily understood, as well as most of Islandic Asia. Areas as far poleward, however, as the Mosquito Coasts of Central America, the east coast of Brazil, the Burmese and Philippine portions of Islandic Asia, and east Madagascar seem to be out of the realm of continuous coverage by any portion of the doldrums belt. These areas should have summer rain and winter dryness. The reason for the deviation is orographic rainfall (caused by topography)—that is, they get their winter rainfall when the trade winds are forced aloft over mountains and dump precipitation on the windward side of the mountains.

In the case of Central America, the northeast trades are forced over the mountains of Central America to drop rain on the eastern slopes and the eastern coast. As for the east coast of Brazil, the southeastern trade winds are forced over the eastern mountains of Brazil and drop precipitation during the winter along that eastern coast. The same is true for the eastern part of Madagascar.

On the Burma coast in southern Asia, the counterequatorial air currents, or equatorial westerlies, are drawn northward in winter and move inland off the warm Indian Ocean over the hills of southeast Asia, leaving rain along the Burma coast when forced even to a slight rise. The same is true for the Philippines, which also get extra precipitation for a part of the winter when air blowing out of a high-pressure system over Asia moves across them from a northeasterly direction to enter a small low which has developed over the western part of Australia.

All these regions are "blessed" with an abundance of rainfall and warm to hot temperatures throughout the year. This, of course, allows for continuous growth of vegetation and a constant green forest. These forests are so thick that the branches of their tall trees, most of them more than 150 feet in height, interlock and close out light. Consequently, underbrush in the areas between streams is uncommon in these woodlands, which are widely known as "rain forests," and they should not be confused with jungles, which have an additional lower level of vegetation. Except for the dense undergrowth near stream edges, these forests are easy to walk through. Since almost any tree can grow well under these warm, moist conditions, a great variety of trees is found here, including the all-important rubber tree and such valuable tropical hardwoods as teak and ebony. Hardly any pure stands of any kind of tree are found in these forests. They are widely separated, and this sometimes makes selective lumbering difficult.

In spite of the abundance of warmth, these regions have in

general not produced the successful agriculture that it would seem they should. This is partially because of the soil which develops under these conditions. With rainfall every day and high temperatures, the water which reaches the ground through the canopy of trees percolates into the soil and dissolves out valuable mineral substances, carrying them to lower strata. Such soils are considered leached and have little crop-producing value, unless artificially fertilized. At the same time, this type of vegetation tends to discourage clearing, for when an area in the forest is cleared the climate encourages a riotous regrowth of scrub vegetation, and considerable effort has to be expended in keeping it back. In addition, a hot and wet climate the year round is not always considered the most conducive to human achievement. Consequently, much of this belt remains in a primitive type of cultural development. In most areas of the Amazon and Congo basins the natives live much as they did thousands of years ago. They settle in little thatched villages along streams where they make a clearing and grow crude crops of bananas and yams. They are in a subsistence stage of occupance. Wild game is not abundant in the rain forest, for land animals are practically absent. This may be surprising, but this is not the belt of the lion and the tiger and the cougar, which are land animals. It is the belt of arboreal animals: monkeys and reptiles.

The diet of natives living in this belt is low in animal protein, for practically the only protein they get is from the fish they catch in streams. Because of the poor soil and the encroachment of the forest, a native village is usually abandoned at least once in every generation and a new village established; consequently, their crude farming is often referred to as migratory agriculture. All in all, it is a primitive type of life, with most effort expended in gaining a living from a forest which yields it meagerly.

In some areas—Central America, the East Indies, the Philippines, the Burma coast, the Malabar coast, and the east coast of Brazil—plantations have exploited the climatic benefits with varying degrees of success. Large outside investments have set up extensive farms which are operated as self-contained units; such crops as rubber, bananas, and spices have been produced on a large scale. In the case of the Philippines and the east coast of Brazil, sugar and cacao (cocoa) may be added to the list.

On the island of Java in the East Indies, small spice farms have developed, individually owned, owing partially to a special type of volcanic soil which could not be leached even by devastating tropical rains. A similar type of spice farming has evolved on the eastern coast of Madagascar, even without the benefit of the rich volcanic soil. It is such places as Madagascar that offer hope for the future development of these regions, which still lie in a primitive subsistence stage because of remoteness and the drawbacks inherent in the rainy low-latitude belt.

The Wet and Dry Low Latitudes

The wet and dry low latitudes of the world (Map 9) embrace such regions as the Brazilian plateau (including the São Francisco Basin, the Mato Grosso plateau, the Brazilian campos, São Paulo area, and the Minas Gerais uplands), the Orinoco Basin in Venezuela, most of Central America and the West Indies Islands, the Sudan belts stretching almost all the way across Africa north of the Congo Basin and the Angola belts across southern Africa south of the Congo Basin, Oceania, east Africa to west Madagascar, and northern Australia. Over these regions, the trade winds blow in winter and bring dryness, while the migration of the rain belt brings rain in summer. Eastern India and southeast Asia belong in this group as well, but their summer rainfall is exceptionally violent and abundant because of the Asian monsoon.

The amount of rain received in most of these regions is suitable for prosperous agriculture, but it varies throughout the zone, those portions of the belt closest to the equator get more rain. All of this belt, however, has the year-round warm temperatures characteristic of the low latitudes.

In the portions closest to the equator, or closest to the rain forest, the natural vegetation is jungle, owing to the abundance of rainfall (usually nearly 100 inches a year). The jungle differs from the rain forest in that it has a riotous growth of underbrush as well as tall trees. During the dry period the trees in this belt lose their leaves, which allows sunshine to get to the ground. Thus there is a growth of underbush—and hence the character of the jungle, which is infinitely more impassable than the rain forest. On account of underbrush, the jungle allows the development of native land animals, including such menacing ones as lions and jaguars.

Farther poleward within this belt, the rainfall is less and the jungle gives way to a type of vegetation known as the "savanna," where there are a few scattered trees among a ground cover of tall grass. Animals indigenous to this type of area, in addition to the beasts of prey, are horselike or deerlike creatures such as the zebra and the wildebeest.

Still farther poleward, the summer rainfall is even less and the trees give way to grassland. All of these regions have the temperatures characteristic of the warm latitudes, and even the grassland has enough precipitation to carry on normal subsistence agriculture. In the case of the grasslands, especially toward the poleward edge, dry commercial farming sometimes has to be practiced, which means a regular system of following the ground and planting the individual crop seeds farther apart and deeper. Near the poleward edge, the rainfall is too slight for agriculture, and some form of pastoralism has to be pursued. In place of the savanna portion in some sectors of the world—parts of the Brazilian plateau, for example—there develops a scrub forest, which is much more difficult to deal with and much more difficult to utilize than the savanna.

The truly monsoon regions of India and southeast Asia are considerably farther poleward than is normal for wet and dry low-latitude regions. However, they have in summer the abundant rainfall and native jungle vegetation typical of the equatorward portions of the wet and dry belt and its characteristic winter dryness. The summer rainfall here is torrential, due largely to the monsoons described earlier and only partially to the migration of the rain belt.

Abundant summer rainfall tends to deplete the soil in these

areas as well as in the rain forest regions already examined. Almost all of the mineral matter eventually becomes leached from the soil except aluminum and iron. The iron becomes oxidized in the warm temperatures of these latitudes, and hence the soils appear red. The soils in the portion of this belt which are grassland are richer and darker, however, for grass roots tend to put fertility back into the soil.

Let us look specifically at regions within this belt. The great bulk of **the Brazilian plateau** is covered by scrub forest and is known as the Mato Grosso. It is largely undeveloped and has a hunting and gathering economy. Native Indians live in thatched-hut villages much like the Indians in the Amazon basin and practice a crude type of primitive agriculture. They have more wild game to hunt than the Indians in the Amazon and their diet has more protein.

The southern portion of the Brazilian plateau is largely a savanna or grassland and is sometimes referred to as a Brazilian *campos*. Here the soil is good and the precipitation is enough for prosperous agriculture; yet the area is practically unused. The paucity of the soil might well discourage colonization in the Mato Grosso, but the grass-enriched soil of the *campos* should not discourage colonization or movement on the frontier. Except for occasional cattle ranging, however, most of the region is yet unused. It is either in an incipient commercial stage or a prime-original stage, and the new-world equestrian attitude is in full sway.

It might be reiterated here that the culture of much of Latin America is equestrian and is such that movement on a frontier is not a part of it. This becomes rather clear when it is noted that there has been frontier movement in very few places in all of Latin America. Where it has occurred, such as in southern Argentina, it has been brought about by people outside the Latin American culture. Consequently, it appears that a cultural block, rather than a natural impediment, has deterred the development of part of this area.

Although the three remaining regions of the Brazilian plateau —the São Francisco basin, the São Paulo coffee lands, and the

Minas Gerais uplands—have a wet and dry low-latitude climatic regime and are depicted on that map, they will be discussed later under low-latitude highlands. In effect, these regions barely qualify as highlands, but their support of the bulk of Brazil's population shows many of the characteristics of other low-latitude highlands.

A significant region is **the Orinoco basin** of northern South America, which has much summer rain and extreme winter dryness, almost like the monsoon regions. Here the summer rains are so abundant that the Orinoco River overflows its entire basin, and the dryness of the winter is so severe and scorching that only tough grasses can survive. Consequently, the Orinoco basin has remained in a stage of cattle ranging and is not likely to move forward until dams and other control projects harness the river.

In **the Tehuantepec jungle** of Central America and Mexico, the native Indians live in primitive fashion and in a prime-original hunting and gathering culture, much like those on the Mato Grosso. Some banana plantations adorn the coastal areas and rivers. In **the Caribbean plantation region** or West Indian islands, plantation agriculture—the growing of sugar cane and coffee—is fairly widespread. On **the Yucatán peninsula,** owing to unusual underground drainage in the underlying limestone, the plantation crop is sisal, a hemp fiber that is particularly adapted to those conditions.

Sudan and Angola

In Africa **the belts** of jungle and savanna and grassland on either side of the equatorial Congo basin represent neat zones across the western half of the continent, with the northern and southern hemispheres being nearly counterparts of one another. A belt in **east Africa and west Madagascar** is also very similar. These areas on the main continent have not developed very far, largely because they are squeezed in between the rain forest on one side and rather inhospitable deserts on the other. Besides, the precipitous nature of much of the African coastal area has not allowed easy development. In the jungle belts (the Sudan agricultural area and the Congo jungle) the natives live by a primitive migratory agriculture much like the natives in the Amazon basin, and the Sudan pastoral land on the north and the Angola savanna on the south are still largely in a migratory agriculture and hunting stage. (An extra deterrent to the development of these regions has been the deadly tsetse fly, which causes sleeping sickness, particularly in the Angola savanna.) Where subsistence-stage agriculture is practiced in these areas, kaffir corn and millet and other small grains are prominent.

In the grassland portions of these belts, pastoralism is practiced with considerable success. It is basically nomadic, although the range of migration is not wide because of the abundance of grass. The shepherds, however, follow and live with the herds they tend. In western Madagascar the raising of cattle is featured and is developed to a reasonably high degree, well into the commercial stage, with definite tracts for each shepherd, some areas even being fenced.

Many of **the islands of Oceania** have a wet and dry low-latitude climate. Some of them are still in a subsistence-agriculture stage of development, but many are in a semicommercial stage, with plantations. Copra, spice, and sugarcane are among the crops.

In **the region of northern Australia** the belt known as the Australian jungle is largely undeveloped. The prime-original aborigines who first inhabited the area have diminished greatly in number, and the Anglo-Saxon settlers have developed the area only to a limited extent. Some American adventurers have established a few rice plantations in the jungles, but the region, by and large, remains in its primitive stage. The grassland on the southern side, known as the Australian pastoral, is used somewhat in cattle ranging and should be considered to be in the commercial stage of occupance.

Eastern India, on the other hand, with abundant summer rainfall and uniform warm temperatures all year round, has one of the densest populations in the world. A variety of crops is grown by plantation or small farm methods, and subsistence agriculture is practiced in remote areas by millions of people in supporting this extremely dense population. The basic agricultural crop, both for export or for consumption within the region, is rice, for which summer rainfall and winter dryness are ideal.

Cash crops in India include cotton, spices, jute, and tea. The lower Ganges subregion, which is densely populated, is an example of a certain potential capacity of these wet and dry low-latitude regions. It is in the manufacturing stage, with steel and other industries near Calcutta and a certain amount of commercial crop production throughout. The Deccan cotton subregion nearby is in the commercial stage, its principal crop being high-quality cotton grown in the rich unleached lava soils of the plateau. The Deccan rice subregion, India's main famine area, although exhibiting some commercial production, must be considered in the subsistence stage, for its teeming millions can barely raise enough rice to feed themselves.

The southeast Asia region known as the Indochina hills has the abundant summer rainfall that is characteristic of India and has a similar Indo-Oriental rice-producing culture, yet it is underpopulated compared with India. Many reasons have been postulated to explain this, the most common one being that the terrain is different. In India much of the land is river bottom, flood plain, or flat-topped plateau, all areas of flat or gently sloping land necessary for the cultivation of rice. Southeast Asia, on the other hand, has a rather hilly terrain, and only the river valleys are suitable for rice growing. Here the population concentrates, and the interstream areas are left to the jungle and its animals. Expansion of the rice-growing areas of southeast Asia in recent years has kept ahead of the growth of the population, and thus the region is a surplus producer of rice. For this reason, such overpopulated areas as China to the north look hungrily at southeast Asia and its surpluses.

The Dry Low Latitudes

The dry low-latitude belt of climate around the world (Map 10) is the part of the world where some of the air which rose in the rainy low latitudes comes back to the surface as a high-pressure belt. Largely this is a deflection of air moving poleward aloft, building up a high-pressure ridge from that air which has been cooled aloft and is descending to the ground. Consequently, these areas have clear, sunny skies and very dry conditions.

It should be remembered also that these regions all face the western side of continents adjacent to areas where cold oceanic water wells up. This tends to concentrate the tropical high-pressure ridge on the western side of continents and also localizes the dry low-latitude regions toward the western side of continents in their respective belts on either side of the equator. On the eastern side of the continents, this effect decreases, and oceanic air masses or monsoon effects bring precipitation to these latitudes. Consequently, the location of these areas is to the west.

The dry low latitudes are composed of the following regions: the Sonoran Desert, the Peruvian Desert, the Atacama Desert, the Sahara and Arabian Deserts, the Kalahari Desert, and the Australian Desert. All are characterized by the most extreme dryness, none of them receiving as much as ten inches of rain annually and some of them not having rain for years at a time. What vegetation there is consists of drought-resistant plants such as cacti and greasewood. Only in a few places are plants entirely missing, but the individual plant forms everywhere are a considerable distance apart. Agriculture cannot be carried on except by irrigation, and the irrigation has to be supplied by rivers that get their water outside these regions. Native animals are of the type that can survive with very little water and very little shelter—snakes and lizards and other desert creatures.

The Sonoran Desert region, in northwestern Mexico, includes the peninsula of Baja California and the adjacent areas on the opposite side of the Gulf of Baja California.

Among the scattered cacti and rocks of this wasteland, a number of streams which arise in the Sierra Madre Mountains in Central Mexico travel to the Gulf of Baja California, providing water for irrigation. This has permitted the development of irrigation agriculture in the river valleys, producing winter vegetables for North American markets and allowing for local processing of certain vegetable products. In marked contrast to this, the interstream areas and the islands of the Gulf of Baja California, as well as the peninsula itself, remain in an unspoiled state. In fact, the Indians on Tiburón Island in the Gulf are said to be among the most unaltered in the world. Yet in spite of that, the processing and recreational industries there, together with the specialized irrigation agriculture, have put the region in the fifth or climax stage of occupance (*see illustration section*).

The Peruvian Desert on the west coast of South America is very similar to the Sonoran. Here streams from the Andes Mountains travel across the dry coastal plains, providing water for irrigation, and again a high type of irrigation agriculture has developed—year-round growing and processing of sugarcane—so that it is essentially in a manufacturing stage.

Farther south, **the Atacama Desert** of northern Chile is so dry that streams from the Andes wither up before they get to the ocean, leaving large flats of mineral salts. For a while this provided the basis for a nitrate industry, but with the development of equipment which extracts nitrates from the air, even this business has dwindled, and the Atacama Desert is now one of the most desolate and primitive in the world.

The Sahara and Arabian Deserts of northern Africa are well known. Here, in a belt across northern Africa and eastward to include the Arabian Peninsula, is another extremely hostile desert. Traditionally, a subsistence nomadic pastoralism has been carried on here—tribes following their herds to wherever vegetation grows, moving frequently. The Nile, fed by the mountains in Ethiopia and by the rainy low latitudes, crosses this region and provides age-old irrigation. The production of long-staple Egyptian cotton in the Nile is well known.

The Arabian Peninsula part of the region is still very much in a nomadic pastoral subsistence stage, largely the result of Moslem influence. This great desert strip extends east to include the area of the Indus Valley in northwestern India, the Indian or Thar Desert. Here another stream, rising this time in the Himalayan Mountains, flows across the region, providing water for commercial-stage irrigation agriculture and the production of cotton as an export crop.

In southwestern Africa lies a desert little known to most of us, **the Kalahari Desert.** It borders a steep, inhospitable coast and has been only slightly penetrated by settlers—and then only from the east. In this desert live people still more primitive than the Indians on Tiburón Island or in the Sonoran Desert. They are the earliest aborigines of southern Africa, who were driven into this desert by the encroachment of European settlers from the south and Negro settlers from the north more than a century ago. The Kalahari is extremely dry, and these aborigines live by a prime-original hunting culture, without formal housing or well-developed weapons. Even their language is phenomenally backward, and the hardships of their existence allow little chance for indigenous development.

The Australian desert region that occupies much of western Australia is similar to the Kalahari in many respects. It is just as dry and inhospitable, and it is occupied only by natives, driven there by early settlers in the area. These Australian natives live very much like those in the Kalahari, except that they have at least one better-developed instrument—the boomerang—and their language is slightly more advanced. Occasionally, some cattle and sheep ranging is done in the Australian desert by European settlers, but only in the better parts; in general the region is in the prime-original stage.

The Low-Latitude Highlands

Since a mountainous habitat makes such a difference in the low latitudes, let us look at the low-latitude highlands of the world (Map 11). We shall not do this with the highlands of other portions of the world, for the difference between highland and lowland is not so great there and the highland regions blend more or less into the general regional characteristics of the middle and higher latitudes. But the highlands in the low latitudes are important, in many cases providing the only truly pleasant portions of the tropics. They include the highlands of Mexico, northwestern and eastern South America, East Africa, Ethiopia, Oceania, and the East Indies.

As noted before, most of the low latitudes are frost free, and temperatures are often high. This is particularly true in summer, when temperatures in the drier portions reach well above the hundred mark daily. (A good example is Yuma, Arizona, which lies within the Sonoran Desert.) Yet at elevations above four thousand feet in the low latitudes, temperatures are much more bearable, particularly to people who are accustomed to living in the middle latitudes. The rainfall schedule of any portion of the low-latitude highlands would naturally be substantially that of the belt in which it lies.

The low latitudes may be divided into three vertical zones according to temperature, and they have been so divided by Latin American geographers.

The lowest zone is that below four thousand feet in elevation and comprises all of the area with which we have been dealing so far. This is known as the *tierra caliente*, or "hot land," and takes in all the warm lowlands of the low latitudes.

From about four thousand to nine or ten thousand feet is an elevation belt known as the *tierra templada,* "temperate land." Here the elevation is high enough so that the extreme heat of the low latitudes disappears and one can feel comfortable. We noted before that the average temperature drops about 3 degrees for every thousand feet of ascent, so that if the sea-level temperature averages 85 degrees, the reading at four thousand feet would be about 73 degrees, which we all know is comfortable. Carrying this temperature up another four thousand feet to an elevation of about eight thousand, the average temperature drops to about 61 degrees, which is really comfortable. Moreover, this temperature does not vary much throughout the year, for variation anywhere in the low latitudes is small.

Above nine or ten thousand feet, the average temperature drops into the fifties, and this is too cool for real comfort. Thus from about ten thousand feet up to the very tops of the highlands the zone is known as the *tierra fría,* "cold land."

We have discussed the activities and the products of the *tierra caliente* in the low latitudes. Let us look now at the *tierra templada* and the *tierra fría*. In general, the *tierra templada* has a vegetation that resembles somewhat the middle latitude forest, and such crops as grain and potatoes are grown. In the *tierra fría* of ten thousand feet and beyond, the trees begin to resemble those of our great northern forest—that is, needlelike evergreen trees—and still higher the trees give out and pastureland similar to the tundra exists up to the snow-capped peaks of the mountains. Pastoral and lumbering activities are characteristic of the *tierra fría.*

In the valleys or basins of **the Mexican highlands** (the Mexican *llanos* and the Mexican *cordillera*) are grown many crops. Mexican agriculture is in general prosperous. Along the higher slopes in the *tierra fría,* lumber and pastoral activities are carried on, as well as mining, to supplement the Mexican agricultural economy. The regions may be considered in a manufacturing stage.

In the Guiana highlands of **northern South America,** the higher elevation is in the *tierra templada,* and it is a delightful area; but it is still in a prime-original culture because of inaccessibility, having jungles all around it.

In the Andean coffee region of South America, confined largely to Colombia, the areas of the *tierra templada* support an excellent development of fourth-stage agriculture and industry. Here Andean coffee is grown which is treasured throughout the world. And here such cities as Bogotá, about seven thousand feet in elevation, are delightful places to live.

Farther south in the high Andes there are very few flat places where people can live in the zone of the *tierra templada,* but there is a sizable intermountain plateau at eleven to twelve thousand feet in the *tierra fría.* This is the Altiplano of Peru and Bolivia. Some crude subsistence-stage agriculture is carried on here through the raising of root crops by the Indians, and extensive pastoralism is practiced, with the llama, a sure-footed goatlike creature, as the chief animal.

Here also lies a concentration of population unusually large for a *tierra fría* belt. This is where many of the money-paying ores of Peru and Bolivia are found. Copper and some gold and silver are mined; particularly important is tin, for this is one of the few areas in the world where an abundance of this metal is found. The region must be considered as in the commercial stage, for the ores are processed largely outside. At an elevation of nearly twelve thousand feet, the highest capital in the world is located, the city of La Paz, Bolivia.

Still another important highland area exists in eastern Africa, the **east African highlands.** It comprises a plateau extending from South Africa all the way across the equator northward to the Ethiopian highlands. This plateau ranges from about four to eight thousand feet, with peaks such as Kilimanjaro rising to more than eleven thousand feet. The temperatures are also equitable here, and the climate is suitable for growing a variety of crops. Here too is practiced the varied commercial-stage agriculture of south Africa, the plantation agriculture of middle Africa, and the subsistence pastoralism of the northern and other extremities of this highland. Mining and manufacturing are carried on in South Africa, particularly in the gold belt near Johannesburg and in the diamond area nearby.

The **highlands of Ethiopia,** known as the Abyssinian highlands, at the northern end of this plateau are some of the highest in Africa. Although nearly surrounded by inhospitable jungles and deserts, the portions of Ethiopia between four and nine thousand feet in elevation are delightful. Here a variety of subsistence-stage crops are grown, and in the *tierra fría* above nine thousand feet extensive pastoralism is practiced, as well as some lumbering. Although the development of Ethiopia has been more or less retarded by the isolation obdurated by the surrounding hostile lands, the current road-building and construction of dams—harnessing the power of Ethiopia's rivers, all of which break out of the mountains in canyons—will probably lead to a prosperous development of the *tierra templada* and *tierra fría* of these highlands. It is now largely in the subsistence stage but has the potential of soon rising out of it.

Also included within the low-latitude highlands are the **mountains of eastern South America,** specifically those in eastern

Brazil (shown on Map 9 as the Minas Gerais uplands, the São Francisco Basin, and the São Paulo coffee regions). They reach elevations of more than nine thousand feet and are oriented in a north-south direction, west of the rainy coastal belt along the eastern end of Brazil. Most of the flat or park lands of these highlands lie above four thousand feet and consequently within the *tierra templada,* although the São Francisco basin is slightly lower. At the southern end, these mountains reach the coast and form a beautiful setting for the city of Rio de Janeiro. Still farther south, at the tip of the highlands, is the city of São Paulo, to the west of which stretches the large São Paulo plateau, still part of the highlands, ranging from four to six thousand feet.

In these highlands lies the greater portion of the population of Brazil. At the northern end there persists a peculiar system of land use, largely because much of the area is held by big estates of the new-world equestrian culture. The basic economy, because of this culture of the settlers, is commercial-stage cattle raising, but the land, which is normally forested, has to be kept clear of trees for the raising of cattle. Consequently, tenant farmers are employed to clear and farm the land for a number of years until the soil wears out. Then they are moved to another spot and cattle is grazed on the area while the soil restores itself. The entire region is often called the São Francisco Basin because a river of this name flows northward across it. The block valley in which the river is located is dry, and a variety of crops are raised for outside markets under irrigation. The new-world equestrian land system is prevalent in the valley as elsewhere, and the entire region may be placed in the third or commercial stage.

In the middle portion of these highlands a great mining industry has developed, with the extraction of iron on a large scale and some mining of coal. This is the Minas Gerais highland. This is also where the famous Brazilian industrial diamonds are found. Permanent truck farming is carried on to supply the mining areas in this region, and stock farms are operated on a continuing basis. These mines supply the materials for the industrial-stage development of the entire region and especially for the city of Rio de Janeiro, with its nearby iron and steel centers.

The large high plateau in the vicinity of São Paulo is where the famous Brazilian coffee is grown, supplying a good portion of the world's coffee. Here the elevation, plus the wet and dry rainfall regime, makes possible the growing of fine coffee by the commercial-stage plantation method. It is here, as well as in the mining region immediately to the north, that some of the best-developed lands in the highlands of South America—indeed in the low-latitude highlands of the world—are to be found.

Another significant region of highlands in the low latitudes is in **the East Indies, or Island, highlands,** in the mountains of New Guinea, Borneo, Sumatra, Java, and Celebes, and in **Oceania** (*see illustration section*). The central parts of the larger islands are very mountainous, the peaks on New Guinea reaching well above ten thousand feet. In World War II the difficulty of crossing the Owen Stanley Mountains contributed largely to the defeat of the Japanese in that theater. Large sections of *tierra templada* exist in these mountains, and an appreciable area of level or park land may be found. The entire mountainous region of the East Indies, however, is in a prime-original stage of development, except for the upland parts of Java.

The same obstacles that held back development in such areas as the Guiana Highlands in South America have retarded development of the highlands in Oceania and in the East Indies. All these uplands are ringed by inhospitable jungles or rain forests, which has kept them isolated and has restricted their culture. The natives are still in a hunting and gathering stage of development. They live in villages by streams, much like the natives in the surrounding jungles. They hunt and gather nuts and fruits in the forest and catch fish from the streams. There is some crude gardening, consisting largely in the growing of a type of yam and some grain. Stone artifacts—knives and other tools—are employed. In short, much of this area is still in a modern counterpart of the stone age. During World War II, flyers who were forced to land in these highlands were surprised to learn that many of the natives had never seen a "civilized" man before.

SELECTED REFERENCES

Bates, Marston. *Where Winter Never Comes.* Rev. notes and sources. New York: Charles Scribner's Sons, 1963.

Butwell, Richard. *Southeast Asia Today—and Tomorrow.* Rev. ed. New York: Frederick A. Praeger, Publisher, 1964.

Carlson, Fred A. *Geography of Latin America.* 3rd ed. New York: Prentice-Hall, 1951.

Cressey, George B. *Asia's Lands and Peoples.* 3rd ed. New York: McGraw-Hill Book Co., 1963.

Cumberland, Kenneth B. *Southwest Pacific, A Geography of Australia, New Zealand, and Their Pacific Island Neighborhoods.* New York: McGraw-Hill Book Co., 1956.

Delorit, Richard J., and Henry L. Ahlgren. *Crop Production.* 2nd ed. New York: Prentice-Hall, 1959.

Dobby, Ernest H. G. *Southeast Asia.* 7th ed. London: University of London Press, 1964.

Duffy, James, and Robert A. Manners. *Africa Speaks.* Princeton, N.J.: D. Van Nostrand Co., 1961.

Flick, F. J. *The Forests of Continental Latin America.* Washington, D.C.: Government Printing Office, 1952.

Fraenkel, Gerd, and Lindley L. Stiles. *Today's World in Focus: Israel.* Boston: Ginn and Co., 1963.

Freeman, Otis W. (ed.). *Geography of the Pacific.* New York: John Wiley and Sons, 1951.

Ginsburg, Norton S., Brian J. L. Berry, and Bert F. Hoselitz. *Atlas of Economic Development.* Chicago: University of Chicago Press, 1961.

Great Britain Board of Trade. *Statistical Abstracts of the British Empire.* London: British Board of Trade, yearly.

Hager, Dorsey. *Practical Oil Geology.* 6th ed. New York: McGraw-Hill Book Co., 1951.

Hanna, Willard. *Bung Karno's Indonesia.* Rev. ed. New York: American Universities Field Staff, 1960.

International Yearbook of Agricultural Statistics. Rome: International Institute of Agriculture, yearly.

Israelsen, Orson W., and Vaughn E. Hansen. *Irrigation Principles and Practices.* 3rd ed. New York: John Wiley and Sons, 1962.

Kimble, George H. T. *Tropical Africa.* 2 vols. New York: Twentieth Century Fund, 1960.

Meinig, Donald W. *On the Margins of the Good Earth.* London: John Murray, Publishers, 1963.

Millar, Charles E. *Soil Fertility.* New York: John Wiley and Sons, 1955.

New International Year Book. New York: Funk and Wagnalls Co., yearly.

Panshin, Alex J., and others. *Forest Products.* 2nd ed. New York: McGraw-Hill Book Co., 1962.

Sauer, Carl O. *Agricultural Origins and Dispersals.* New York: American Geographical Society, 1952.

Sears, Paul B. *Deserts on the March.* 3rd rev. ed. Norman: University of Oklahoma Press, 1959.

Shepard, Ward. *Food or Famine: The Challenge of Erosion.* New York: Macmillan Co., 1945.

Thoman, Richard S. *The Geography of Economic Activity.* New York: McGraw-Hill Book Co., 1962.

Tugwell, Rexford G. *The Stricken Land.* New York: Doubleday and Co., 1946.

Unstead, John F. *A World Survey.* London: University of London Press, 1962.

Van Royen, William. *Agricultural Resources of the World.* New York: Prentice-Hall, 1954.

——— and others. *Mineral Resources of the World.* New York: Prentice-Hall, 1952.

Yearbook of Agriculture: Grass. Washington, D.C.: Government Printing Office, 1948.

Yearbook of Agriculture: Soils and Man. Washington, D.C.: Government Printing Office, 1939.

Ziegler, P. Thomas. *The Meat We Eat.* Danville, Ill.: Interstate Printers and Publishers, 1962.

Chapter 9 / The In-between Lands

Seldom is the influence of material development so noticeable in the differentiation of geographic regions as in the subtropical belt throughout the world. This belt, which we have called the "In-between Lands," is a transition zone. It is not tropical because it does have a definite winter and frost. However, its temperatures are sometimes rather warm, and its periods of cold are usually mild or of short duration.

There are several separate types of regions within this belt, and even they may be subdivided into distinct groups. One group of geographical regions, lying roughly between 35 and 40 degrees in both hemispheres, exists on the west coasts of the continents. They have a mild climate, like all subtropical areas, but they also have a distinctive characteristic of their own—winter rains and summer drought. These areas are called the "Mediterranean subtropics." Another group, known as the "dry subtropics," lies inland and away from all large bodies of water; it too has winter rain and summer dryness, but the rainfall here is so slight that the areas are designated as arid. Still another group, on the eastern coasts of the continents, is known as the "humid subtropics." It also exhibits the mild temperatures of the subtropics, but it is characterized by having an abundance of rain evenly distributed throughout the year, and wherever these regions occur, the land is rich and abundant.

For the sake of convenience, these three groups of subtropical regions will be dealt with separately. This is logical, since each of the subgroups definitely has common physical characteristics; hence they can be compared as to stage of material development, often referred to as occupance. As noted before, each stage implies a developmental step and a specific use of the land. It also implies the potential use of the land, which may be seen by comparison of regions of similar physical attributes. It recognizes that land use and regions are no respecters of political boundaries; hence it pays little attention to them, except when some political unit affects certain uses of the land, or when they are used for purposes of identification.

It should be said that in this book, in general, political boundaries and political control of areas are not considered. From the point of view of world comparative geography, political boundaries and national entities are man-made and have little to do with the unity within nature which includes man and his works. An area that might be a colonial possession of another country one year may become an independent country the next year. It may develop its own government, but the use of the land goes on, influenced only by the larger forces of nature and the powers of habit.

According to Arnold Toynbee, whatever nationalism may occur in the world usually takes place at a certain stage in the decline of a dominant culture, which he claims is the current stage of Anglo-Saxon culture. Other scholars, among them Ellsworth Huntington, equate even the stages of culture with forces emanating from the "great outside" and from the "mysterious within," such as climatic changes and earth magnetism. It is the stage of the development of a region, the alleged influences of space and the earth itself, and their effects upon our habitat with which we are concerned.

The Mediterranean Subtropics

The Mediterranean subtropical regions of the world are characterized by winter rain and summer drought (Map 12). Such a region exists on the southwestern coast of the United States—the entire coastal area of California south of San Francisco. The region does not extend far inland because it is blocked by the Sierra Nevada Mountains to the east. Another region within this realm is the Mediterranean itself, which embraces the entire coast of the Mediterranean Sea, as well as the adjacent west coast of the Iberian peninsula, and extends all around the southern side of the Black Sea. It includes the entire southern portion of the Italian peninsula, most of Greece, southern and eastern Spain, and southern France.

In the southern hemisphere, the Cape of Good Hope comprises a Mediterranean subtropical region, its inland area blocked somewhat by the rise of mountains just to the north and east. Also in the southern hemisphere, the central portion of Chile is another such region, the inland area of which is blocked by the Andes Mountains as was the inland area of the southern California region by the Sierra Nevadas. There is also the southern Australia Mediterranean subtropical region, which includes the entire southwestern tip of Australia adjacent to the city of Perth and extends eastward along the southern coast nearly to the other end of the island continent.

All five of these regions have the same type of climate—winter rain and summer drought, mild warm summers and pleasant rainy winters. They all have basically the same native vegetation—that is, Mediterranean scrub forest, with such trees as the cork and the olive, which are physiologically constructed to withstand the summer drought, as well as grapevines and citrus trees.

Ground-walking herbivorous animals were once indigenous to this region, and a fairly rich native soil was initially abundant. Consequently, a climax land-use stage in any of these regions might reasonably be expected to have vineyards and citrus groves utilizing the soil and physical setting best suited for each of them. Wheat fields planted in the fall and harvested in the spring would take advantage of the mild winter rains; winter vegetables would probably be grown also, excellently suited for commercial development; manufacturing plants and recreational development might take advantage of the warm summers and the mild winters. Such a stage has been reached in several of these regions.

One region in this stage is **Southern California,** where vineyards are planted on the well-drained middle slopes and citrus trees on the lower slopes and where ground water is abundant.

Winter vegetables are found in the bottom lands, for abundant moisture is present, and winter wheat is grown on the uplands, where only the periodic rains of winter are needed for perfect development.

In addition to this idealized specialization of crops on the most beneficial sites, industry of various types has developed in Southern California. Prominent has been the movie industry, taking advantage of the many cloudless days in summer. Recreation, the luxury industry, as well as a rather unique form of endeavor, the retirement industry, has developed to great proportions. It might be said that the area has grown to climax development partly because of its location in the Anglo-Saxon culture of North America. It has, to a certain extent, almost gone beyond climax—to a point where it could decline. Population increase has taxed the water resources severely in this region, exemplifying one of a number of forces that menace its stability.

Another problem which Southern California faces is urbanization. This malady is experienced by dwellers of all the large metropolitan areas in the Anglo-Saxon culture. As noted by Toynbee, Will Durant, and others, urbanization is a blessing only in the early part of the development of a culture. It provides people with benefits that could scarcely be obtained otherwise, such as medical help and specialized services. After a given point, however, the benefits of urbanization appear to be outweighed by the detrimental aspects, one of which is the decline of the moral fiber of the people.

Recent biological studies have indicated that urbanization induces a great many lethal maladies among humans and is responsible for a long list of mental disturbances. In short, overurbanization weakens a people physically, mentally, and morally. Its growth is insidious, but at the same time it is almost imperceptive; a society drops from a dominant position to a lesser place without knowing what has happened. Although this problem is raised with respect to Southern California and its large urban population, which has reached the climax stage in material development and occupance as far as Mediterranean subtropical regions are concerned, the problem is not strictly local. It is paramount throughout the realm of the Anglo-Saxon culture, a problem that has confronted other cultures which have risen and declined throughout history.

The Mediterranean region itself is faced with the same problems, perhaps even to the extent that it has gone beyond the stage of Southern California and has experienced some of the decline which follows climax occupance. Views vary as to when the Mediterranean region reached its climax, but most authorities agree that it is now in the post-climax decline. Such an occupance is merely an extension of the climax land use, but it experiences the decline in health, mentality, and morality resultant of an overdevelopment of the climax. This does not mean, of course, that the region will not long continue in this post-climax stage, for it can do that indefinitely.

In this post-climax stage, the land adjustments of the Mediterranean region itself are very similar to those in Southern California, with the growing of winter wheat, citrus fruit, grapes; and with such unique commercial crops as the cork oak and the olive. Its recreation industry has been developed to a high degree, but its manufacturing has settled to a selective type, such as the processing of olive oil.

The region is faced with the matter of conserving its soil and forestry resources, which up to and through the climax stage were wantonly exploited. After it curtails its riotous growth of population, it will probably settle down comfortably in the post-climax stage, which will portray the best use of the region, and continue in that indefinitely. The olive trees, the grapevines, and the citrus trees, which are ideally adjusted to the mild climate with its dry summers and wet winters, can go on producing indefinitely. The recreation industry can continue for ages to exploit the pleasant, warm, sunny summers on the blue Mediterranean. It can be a benign continuance.

The Mediterranean subtropical region of **central Chile** has reached the fourth or industrial stage of occupance. Here in a broad valley and coastal plain facing the Pacific, on the western side of the Andes Mountains, the bright summer suns and pleasant winter rains create the identical conditions extant in Southern California. Here is developed one of the best occupances in all South America. In fact, the landscape of the Mediterranean subtropical region of central Chile looks very much like Southern California, except that it lacks the large development of the movie industry and the recreation industry.

Winter wheat is grown in the higher well-drained areas, and there are vineyards on the hillsides, citrus groves on the lower slopes, and a variety of vegetable crops on the flat lowland areas. Even the higher slopes, approaching the mountains, are used for grazing, as they are in California. Moreover, considerable industry has grown up in Santiago, Chile's capital and major city, largely the processing of indigenous materials: the making of wines, the production of olive oil, the packing of meat. In the coastal city of Concepción, a considerable steel industry has been developed, exploiting Chile's iron resources and meager coal supply.

Chile does not have as large an area to draw on for a recreational industry as does Southern California, so this industry is still in an incipient stage. Remarkable also is the resemblance of central Chile to the Mediterranean region of Europe. It must be remembered, however, that the settlers who colonized and built Chile came from the same type of region back home. The entire coastal fringe of Spain is a Mediterranean region, and these settlers carried to Chile the material adjustments they had made to their environment in Europe.

The development of central Chile to a near-climax stage in the short time it has been settled by western man is understandable when taking into account the ideal situation of transplanting a culture to a comparable setting elsewhere. This, to a certain extent, was also the case in Southern California. Although the area is now a part of the United States, its early colonization was completely dominated by Spain; again, the Spanish were in an area that was like home to them. Even after California became a part of the United States, the Spanish influence, as far as the use of the land was concerned, prevailed. Consequently, the land use in Southern California and central Chile has had the advantage of development by people from a mature climax occupance elsewhere.

One problem confronted by Chile but not present in Southern California was the old Spanish concept of landholding. The new-world equestrian culture had its influence upon Chile. The use of the land principally as a pasture did not pose a problem, for the settlers knew of an alternate use, but the concept of individuals of an aristocratic class holding land in large parcels did have an effect. In fact, this is the one facet of the new-world equestrian culture which is extant throughout South America, and to a certain extent in Central America. (It has been mostly eliminated in Mexico.) It has been troublesome in Brazil, Argentina, Venezuela, Colombia—in fact, in all of the South American countries and some of those in Central America. Thus, Chile's problem has been to break up the larger estates. It has had some success in this, actually improving the land use of the region in the process.

The Mediterranean subtropical region of the **Cape of Good Hope** is in the third or commercial stage of occupance. The original settlers here were Dutch and English, who did not have the cultural background for development of this kind of region, and hence the development was relatively slow. Moreover, the settling of this region was at a later date (mid-nineteenth century). At present most of the region produces a cash grain crop of winter wheat, which is shipped elsewhere for processing and refinement.

The last Mediterranean subtropical region is **southern Australia**. Here again the settlers were English and the settlement was late. This region also is in the third or commercial stage of occupance, and, like the Cape of Good Hope, the most general land use is in the cash grain farming of wheat. The cities of Perth and Adelaide are well known as wheat ports. It might reasonably be expected that both the Cape of Good Hope region and the southern Australian region will pass ultimately into an industrial stage, when products produced in the region are also processed there, and that a diversification of land use suitable to the region will take place. This will foster the development of vineyards and citrus groves and other Mediterranean subtropical crops and, finally, the development of their own manufacturing and recreational industries. In short, these two regions have not yet reached their climax.

The Dry Subtropics

The dry subtropical regions of the world include the Orange River basin of South Africa, the Murray and Darling river basins in Australia, part of the Andean Foreland in western Argentina, the Great Basin of southwestern North America, the Spanish *meseta,* the Atlas region of North Africa, and the Asia Minor plateaus (Map 13). All of these regions have the same summer dryness which is the result of the horse latitudes being over them, and they have winter dryness largely because of being blocked from sources of moisture by mountains. In the case of the Andean Foreland, the Andes blocks the moisture from the westerly system of winter rain; the same is true in North America in the Great Basin, due to the blocking of winter rains by the Sierra Nevada Mountains. In South Africa and Australia the dryness results from sheer interior location, as it does in the plateaus of Asia Minor. In central Spain and in the Atlas region, mountains again block off the moisture.

The native vegetation throughout the dry subtropics is either grassland, steppe, or desert. Along streams a type of forest exists, featuring such trees as cottonwoods, which can tolerate long dry periods. As in all grasslands, the soil is good, and it is especially rich along river flood plains, where it often gets enough moisture seepage to support abundant forage crops—alfalfa, for example.

In all of these regions, the material occupance is a matter of development of pastoralism, and in some cases the development of supplemental irrigation agriculture and industry. In the **Great Basin area** of southwestern North America, which includes the Colorado Plateau, the southern Great Plains, and the Mexican Hacienda, the ranching industry is developed to a point where the regions are in a commercial stage of occupance.

Cattle are raised and shipped out of the region for final fattening and butchering.

In the **Andean Foreland** (Gran Chaco Western), however, irrigation agriculture supplements ranching, and wine grapes are grown, as well as garden vegetable crops, for the tables of such cities as Buenos Aires. This has led to a certain degree of process manufacturing (wine making, etc.) in cities such as Cordoba, and the region may be considered in the fourth or industrial stage of development, for the specialization of river bottom land for irrigation agriculture is commensurate with that stage (*see illustration section*).

In the **Orange River basin** (South African veld) of South Africa, the region is still in the third or commercial stage, for cattle are raised on ranches for sale outside the region. This is true also in the **Murray-Darling basins** in east-central Australia. Here sheep are raised on ranches and are marketed for outside processing. Some irrigation agriculture is practiced, using artesian wells, but this is merely to grow extra forage crops for the sheep. Manufacturing has not developed to any great degree within this region.

The **Spanish meseta,** the central plateau of Spain, might be considered in the fourth or industrial stage of development. Here cattle are raised on ranches, much as in the other regions, but these cattle are butchered and processed locally in such cities as Madrid. The region, of course, is the seat of the equestrian culture which gave rise to the new-world equestrian system (*see illustration section*).

The **Atlas region** of North Africa, whose mountains block off its own moisture, might be considered in the second or subsistence stage of material development; thus, cattle or other animals are raised within the region largely for local use. This area is still under the old-world dry-land culture; hence a subsistence type of pastoralism is practiced.

The same stage of development is prevalent to a large extent throughout the other overall region of the dry subtropics—the **Asia Minor plateaus,** which include the Iranian plains and plateaus and the central plateaus of Turkey, Iraq, and Afghanistan.

There are, of course, good examples of individual areas within this Asia Minor region which have gone into other stages, but in general it may be considered in the second stage. Notable examples of portions in another stage are those of the Tigris-Euphrates valley and the irrigated portions of Israel, which are in the third (commercial) or even the fourth (industrial) stage of development. Land specialization is practiced, with irrigation in the river valleys producing a wide variety of crops, including melons and dates. Although some of the crops, such as dates, are processed within the region, others are shipped out for sale. Isolated areas where oil is produced are different culturally from the rest of the region, but they represent only a small part of the total area of that part of the dry subtropics.

Humid Subtropics

The humid subtropical regions are agriculturally among the most productive of the world. Included among these regions are southeastern North America, east-central South America, southeastern Africa, eastern Australia, southern China, South Japan-South Korea, and the Upper Ganges-Brahmaputra basins (Map 14). These regions all have the mild climate of the subtropics with the gentle winter rains, but they also have summer rain which comes in the form of thundershowers. As explained earlier, the oceanic highs expand during the summer in each latitude and thus push moisture-laden air onto land facing east coasts; this air is triggered into convectional currents by the warm summer heating, and these currents develop into thunderstorms which bring abundant rain. Most of these regions have gone through the earlier stages of occupance and are in the fourth or manufacturing stage, where diversification of land use best suited for each part has taken place and where manufacturing or processing of materials is practiced.

The native vegetation in these regions is a normal mesophytic forest—broadleaf trees that shed their foliage once a year, such as oak, hickory, walnut, and maple—alongside occasional pure stands of needle-leaf pines that occupy sandy coastal areas where other trees cannot grow. The soil, while not as rich as in grassy areas, is nevertheless better than the forest soils of the low latitudes, inasmuch as it is not as leached: mineral nutrients still remain, and very rich alluvial soils often abound on river flood plains.

The first region of this group which we will look at, however, has passed beyond the fourth stage and is entering the fifth or climax stage of occupance. That region is **southeastern North America,** including the subregions known as southern pine, southern plantation, and Florida peninsula, which is essentially all of the southeastern portion of the United States south of the Ohio River, ranging from Florida northward to Washington, D.C., and westward across Tennessee, Kentucky, Alabama, Mississippi, Arkansas, Louisiana, and into Texas to include the cities of Dallas, Fort Worth, and the huge metropolitan area of Houston.

Within this region—which during its commercial stage was largely a producer of a single crop, cotton, that was sent outside for manufacturing—a variety of crops is produced today in a diversified agriculture, many of which are processed within the region. In addition to an abundance of precipitation well distributed throughout the year, the region also has a long growing season: more than two hundred days. This allows for a wide range of crops, so the tendency is for each section to produce what it best can, according to its topographical setting and soil composition. The region is now producing and processing peanuts, tobacco, lumber products, and many other articles of comment.

Recreation has developed to a high degree in Florida and other places, so the over-all region may be considered in the fifth stage. The subregions within this region indicate its diversification: the southern pine suggests the specialized production of pine products; the Florida peninsula produces citrus fruits and winter vegetables; while the southern plantation produces tobacco, cotton, peanuts, and so on.

East-central South America, an overall region composed of the Gran Chaco Eastern and Paraná pine subregions, includes the southern part of Brazil, much of Uruguay, and most of those portions of the Paraguay and Paraná River valleys which pass through Paraguay. Although exactly like southeastern North America as far as climate is concerned, and blessed with a fairly good soil, this region is still within the third or commercial stage of occupance. Owing to the influence of the new-world equestrian culture, much of the land within this region is still held in large estates. Also, the crops and other products of the area are sold commercially for processing outside the regions.

Uruguay and Paraguay are still largely cattle-producing countries, and most of the cattle is shipped for slaughter to such places as Buenos Aires. The city of Montevideo in Uruguay does some processing, but not to the extent that it would change the complex of the region. In southern Brazil there is some growing of the yerba maté plant, which furnishes a popular tea for South America, and in the river valleys of the Paraguay and Paraná rice is produced, but this is largely for internal consumption. To a limited extent, lumbering of pine is carried on also in southern Paraguay, giving the traditional name "Paraná pine" to that subregion. In general, however, the area is still largely cattle-producing, not even using its commercial agricultural potential. Accordingly, it can even be said to be in the lower portion of the commercial stage of occupance. The Gran Chaco Eastern, however, is still in a primitive stage, practically empty of population except for some Indians; only a few scattered herds of cattle range in this equestrian land. The potential of the region, of course, can be seen in the development of the southeastern North American region, and whenever the grasp of the new-world equestrian culture is released the future of this region will be assured.

Southeastern Africa (Natal Coast) is in the fourth or industrial stage of occupance. Its landscape appears like that of southeastern North America, although it lacks the recreation industry. Here a great variety of crops are grown on moderate-size farms, including cotton and corn. The city of Durban is a significant manufacturing center, and the region is one of the more prosperous ones in Africa.

The **eastern Australia** (Sydney-Brisbane) region resembles southeast Africa in most respects. It has a varied subtropical agriculture, adjusted to various sites within the region, including crops such as cotton, corn, and wheat. In addition to the processing of its own materials, the cities of Sydney and Brisbane also have steel industries based on local deposits of coal and iron. In general this is considered the most developed area of Australia. The recreation industry has also begun in this area, but not to the extent that it has in southeastern North America, so that the region, while not reaching its climax, is well on its way.

The **southern China** region, which includes the valley of the Si-Kiang and the valley of the Yangtze River with its three separate basins, is also in the fourth or industrial stage. Although the region embraces the Canton hills, where teeming millions live in a subsistence rice culture, the general pattern of agriculture is in a semicommercial stage; the Yangtze River valley produces cash crops of corn and wheat. Although it is not as extensive as in the other humid subtropical regions, there is enough commerce to consider this partially a commercial-crop area, which is somewhat unusual for a region with an Indo-Oriental culture. This, however, may now have been changed back to subsistence agriculture by the large increase in population in recent years in China.

Such cities as Hankow and Wuhan in southern China helped advance the region into its current industrial stage, although it must be considered the lower portion of that stage. In Hankow the steel industry has been developed from local coal and iron resources. All of this, of course, was prior to the lowering of the Bamboo Curtain. It is possible that now the region may have reverted largely to the second or subsistence stage, commensurate with the Indo-Oriental culture.

The **South Japan-South Korea** region may also be considered in the upper portion of the fourth or industrial stage. Japan's agriculture has always been intensive, with each plot of land suited to its best use, largely because of the lack of arable land in Japan. In addition to the growing of rice for local consumption, Japan produces a great variety of specialized crops for export, such as cucumber pickles and spices.

In spite of its defeat in World War II, Japan has come back

strong with its industry, both in processing its own materials for markets abroad and also in processing raw materials brought in for manufacture and reshipment before marketing. The South Korean portion lags behind Japan, owing partially to its struggle with North Korea and Red China, but crop specialization is taking place there also, along with a certain growth of industry in the city of Seoul.

The **Upper Ganges-Brahmaputra** region in India may be ranked in the commercial stage, although much rice is grown for subsistence to feed a very dense population. Jute, spices, and tea are among the commercial crops which elevate the region above the subsistence stage.

SELECTED REFERENCES

Adams, Nicholson B. *The Heritage of Spain: Introduction to Spanish Civilization*. Rev. ed. New York: Holt, Rinehart and Winston, 1959.

Ahlgren, Gilbert H. *Forage Crops*. 2nd ed. New York: McGraw-Hill Book Co., 1956.

Allen, Durward L. *Our Wildlife Legacy*. Rev. ed. New York: Funk & Wagnalls Co., 1962.

Allred, B. W. *Practical Grassland Management*. Danville, Ill.: Interstate Printers & Publishers, 1952.

Bowman, J. *The New World*. New York: World Bank Co., 1928.

Cressey, George B. *Asia's Lands and Peoples*. 3rd ed. New York: McGraw-Hill Book Co., 1963.

Cumberland, Kenneth B. *Southwest Pacific, A Geography of Australia, New Zealand, and Their Pacific Island Neighborhoods*. New York: McGraw-Hill Book Co., 1956.

Dice, Lee R. *The Biotic Provinces of North America*. Ann Arbor: University of Michigan Press, 1943.

Flick, F. J. *The Forests of Continental Latin America*. Washington, D.C.: Government Printing Office, 1952.

Geographical Journal. London: Royal Geographical Society, quarterly.

Gottmann, Jean. *A Geography of Europe*. 3rd ed. New York: Henry Holt & Co., 1954.

Great Britain Board of Trade. *Statistical Abstracts of the British Empire*. London: British Board of Trade, yearly.

Hoffman, George W., and others. *A Geography of Europe*. 2nd ed. New York: Ronald Press Co., 1961.

Israelsen, Orson W., and Vaughn E. Hansen. *Irrigation Principles and Practices*. 3rd ed. New York: John Wiley & Sons, 1962.

James, Preston E. *A Geography of Man*. 2nd ed. Boston: Ginn & Co., 1959.

Jenks, William F. (ed.). *Handbook of South American Geology, An Explanation of the Geologic Map of South America.* Memoir 65. New York: Geological Society of America, 1956.

Kaswell, Ernest R. *Textile Fibers, Yarns, and Fabrics.* New York: Reinhold Publishing Corp., 1953.

Kellogg, Charles E. *The Soils That Support Us.* New York: Macmillan Co., 1941.

Klages, K. H. W. *Ecological Crop Geography.* New York: Macmillan Co., 1942.

Meinig, Donald W. *On the Margins of the Good Earth.* London: John Murray, Publisher, 1963.

Millar, Charles E. *Soil Fertility.* New York: John Wiley & Sons, 1955.

Odum, Eugene P. and Howard T. *Fundamentals of Ecology.* 2nd ed. Philadelphia: W. B. Saunders Co., 1959.

Osborn, Fairfield. *Our Plundered Planet.* Boston: Little, Brown & Co., 1948.

Prescott, Samuel Cate, and Bernard E. Proctor. *Food Technology.* New York: McGraw-Hill Book Co., 1937.

Sauer, Carl O. *Agricultural Origins and Dispersals.* New York: American Geographical Society, 1952.

Schery, Robert W. *Plants for Man.* New York: Prentice-Hall, 1952.

Sears, Paul B. *Deserts on the March.* 3rd rev. ed. Norman: University of Oklahoma Press, 1959.

Sherman, Henry C. *Food Products.* 4th ed. New York: Macmillan Co., 1948.

Statesman's Yearbook. London: Macmillan Co., yearly.

Statistical Abstract of Latin America. Los Angeles: University of California, yearly.

Symonds, Percival M. *The Dynamics of Human Adjustment.* New York: Appleton-Century Co., 1946.

Thoman, Richard S. *The Geography of Economic Activity.* New York: McGraw-Hill Book Co., 1964.

Thomas, William L., and others (eds.). *Man's Role in Changing the Face of the Earth.* Chicago: University of Chicago Press, 1956.

Thorne, David W., and H. B. Peterson. *Irrigated Soils: Their Fertility and Management.* New York: McGraw-Hill Book Co., 1954.

Tolbert, T. J. *General Horticulture.* Philadelphia: Lea & Febiger, 1956.

Tressler, Donald K., and J. M. Lenron. *Marine Products of Commerce.* New York: Reinhold Publishing Corp., 1951.

Tugwell, Rexford G. *The Stricken Land.* New York: Doubleday & Co., 1946.

United Nations. *Trade Yearbook.* New York: United Nations, yearly.

U.S. Bureau of the Census. *Statistical Abstract of the United States.* Washington, D.C.: Government Printing Office, yearly.

U.S. Department of the Interior. *Mineral Yearbook.* Washington, D.C.: Government Printing Office, yearly.

U.S. Foreign Commerce Department. *Our World Trade.* Washington, D.C.: Chamber of Commerce of the United States, quarterly.

Unstead, J. F. *A World Survey*. London: University of London Press, 1962.
Van Cleef, Eugene. *Trade Centers and Trade Routes*. New York: D. Appleton Co., 1937.
Van Valkenburg, Samuel, and Ellsworth Huntington. *Europe*. 2nd ed. with Colbert C. Held. New York: John Wiley & Sons, 1952.

Chapter 10 / THE STORMY AND THE COLD

The remaining regions of the world are in the rest of the middle-latitude belt and in the high latitudes, and they are essentially either stormy or cold or both. Included are the true middle latitudes, the subpolar middle latitudes, and the two high-latitude belts, consisting of the polar marine (easterlies) and the polar continental (ice cap).

In the regions of true middle-latitude climate—between 40 and 60 degrees in either hemisphere—there is a marked winter and a marked summer; in fact, the winters are quite severe and the growing season is less than two hundred days. In general, precipitation is abundant the year round within most of these regions, with the exception of some areas in the interiors of continents where there is a tendency toward dryness. Considerable differences exist, however, between the kinds of climate within this belt, depending on whether the region is on an east coast, on a west coast, or in an interior location

THE TEMPERATE MARINE MIDDLE LATITUDES

Let us look first at the group of regions that lie on the west coasts of the continents. These areas are known as the "temperate marine middle latitudes" (Map 15) and include such regions as the American Pacific Northwest, the southern Chilean region in South America, the Tasmania-New Zealand region, and Western Europe.

Under the influence of the prevailing westerlies, with their cyclonic (highs and lows) storms, these regions get abundant precipitation throughout the year. Inasmuch as the weather systems move from west to east in these latitudes, and the regions face the west coasts and have uplands either to the west or south, the various winds moving off the oceans onto the land are forced to rise somewhat and bring considerable rain evenly distributed the year round. These weather systems are most active in the winter and bring about the long, slow rains typical of cyclonic precipitation. Moreover, with these winds and rains come the influence of the ocean, which in winter is considerably warmer than the land and in summer is appreciably cooler, hence ameliorating the normal extremes of winter and summer temperatures. Consequently, these regions are often referred to as temperate marine regions.

In the case of Western Europe, these westerly winds in winter bring air from off the warm North Atlantic current, which we spoke of in Chapter 5, moderating the climate of western Europe to such an extent that it is a very habitable place, in spite of latitudes around 50 degrees. In both summer and winter these regions get cyclonic rains, and, in addition, with the summer growth of the oceanic highs, they get some extra moisture from the clockwise motion of these highs, which produce rainfall when the moisture-laden air is forced to rise over the land mass.

Because of the temperance of the climate and the abundance in precipitation, the natural vegetation in the temperate marine middle latitudes tends to be a thick mesophytic forest containing a variety of trees, conifers, like the pine, hardwoods, which lose their leaves in the winter, and others. The largest trees in the world (more than three hundred feet high) grow in these regions, in California and Tasmania.

The **American Pacific Northwest region** takes in the western coast of North America from San Francisco northward to Anchorage in Alaska. It extends inland in general to the Rocky Mountains, which become the Alaska Range at the northern end. In the United States portion it extends inland only to the Cascade and Sierra Nevada ranges.

This region is largely in the fourth or industrial stage of occupance. Here land for agriculture is limited to such valleys as Puget Sound, the Willamette, and the Matanuska. Because of the hospitable temperateness of the marine climate, a great variety of crops is grown, most of them vegetables for canning or freezing. Tuber crops, which grow underground, are a speciality; they do well in this climate, for an abundance of sunshine is not characteristic in this region, owing to the fogs which are often brought off the ocean onto the land and to the number of overcast days commensurate with the slow rains accompanying cyclonic systems.

The lumbering industry, of course, is carried on extensively in this region because of the abundant growth of large trees; the dairy industry is prevalent, owing largely to the lush grass and the temperate climate. Cities such as Seattle, Tacoma, and San Francisco process a variety of materials from the region, including such dairy products as the canning of milk. The region has not, however, reached its full potential, for all parts of the land have not yet been fully utilized and the recreation industry has not been adequately developed, so we can say that it has not yet reached its climax and still has a bright future.

The **south Chilean region,** in this same climatic realm, may also be said to have a long future, for it is still in the commercial stage of development. Most of the items produced here—lumber, minerals, fish, and sheep—are sent out of the region for processing; the only city of any size within the region, Puerto Montt, is largely a shipping port for these products. All of the land has not yet been used to its best advantage for commercial production, so the region may be considered in the third stage of occupance, perhaps even in the lower part of that stage.

The **Tasmania-New Zealand region,** which includes the New Zealand islands and the island of Tasmania as well as a small portion of southern Australia near the city of Melbourne, might well be considered in the fourth stage, much like western North America. The region has specialized crop production, with a tendency for areas to be used to their best advantage, and it has considerable manufacturing; it also supports a considerable dairy industry on the north island of New Zealand and near the city of Melbourne in Australia. In addition to sheep grazing, for which the region is traditionally famous, a great variety of vegetable crops is grown, which are canned for shipment abroad.

The meat, vegetable, and lumber products are all processed within the region and the finished products are exported, including furniture. Cities such as Wellington and Dunedin in New Zealand are famous for their finished wool and wood products. The recreation industry has developed to a certain extent near Melbourne in Australia and at several places in New Zealand, but it is not enough to make a significant difference.

The **Western European region** has reached the fifth or climax stage of development. Although several composite small regions are shown on the map, the over-all region will be dealt with here as a whole. It includes the North Sea manufacturing region—embracing the Low Countries, West Germany, eastern England, and Scotland—the Celtic hills, the Norwegian "fields" region, the Aquitaine and Paris basins of France, the French Massif, and the Pyrenees and Cantabrian Mountains of northern Spain.

Specialization of agriculture, each to best advantage, is even more highly developed in Western Europe than in the American Pacific Northwest. Here crops, such as those grown in the Low Countries, are carefully situated and include all the varieties of garden vegetables and, in the case of Holland, flowers. The specialized wine grape areas on the Massif and in the French basins are well known, as are the potato-growing industry in northwestern Germany, the ever-present dairy industry in Great Britain and in the Norwegian "fields," and the intensive and diversified fisheries of the North Sea.

The raising of livestock has reached an extreme stage of specialization in this region, as exemplified by the bacon-producing combines of Denmark. Here hogs, fattened on farms where corn and dairy products are also produced, are alternately fed on the corn and milk, until eventually they yield a bacon which is perfectly striped in the pattern of fat and lean.

In addition to the great variety of industries which process its products, this region is dominated by a manufacturing complex, wherein many raw materials are imported and are manufactured, to be reshipped as finished products elsewhere. Consequently, the urban and manufacturing landscape is predominant.

Some of the manufacturing is of the heavy variety, such as the iron and steel industry in Great Britain, which was originally based on large reserves of coal from adjacent Wales, and the Ruhr industrial belt in southwestern Germany, which is also basically a large iron and steel center. Here coal and iron are brought to the surface out of deep mines and processed in a number of smaller cities in the long Ruhr Valley, including the city of Essen.

Still another center of manufacture is along the northern coast of Spain, which was the early seat of the famous Spanish steel industry. Here coal and iron are abundant, and a technique of producing fine steel has been passed down by tradition. Such cities as Bilbao, Santander, and Oviedo clang with the ring of steel.

Along with its intense specialization, which would naturally put this region into a climax stage, this part of the world also has a highly developed recreational industry, drawing upon much of the world for tourists, who bring in considerable wealth. In spite of the ravages of numerous wars, this region is still in the full bloom of the climax stage and shows no signs of going into a post-climax stage.

The Dry Continental Middle Latitudes

Looking now at the dry continental regions of the world, we find that they have all the characteristics of the true middle-latitude climate, including a severe winter, but lack abundant year-round rainfall. This is largely because of inland location, or lee location—eastward or southward of mountains in these latitudes, where the weather moves from west or northwest to east. By being in a lee location, the weather systems which drop abundant moisture on the windward side of uplands leave these lee sides dry. So the climatic characteristics of these regions, then, would comprise severely cold winters, dryness the year round, and, because of the lack of marine influence, hot summers. Regions in this group include the northern Great Plains, the lower Western Highlands, and the Columbia Plateau of North America; the Patagonian Plateau and Mountains of southern South America; and the over-all steppes and uplands of Asia (steppes are plains areas of short grass and semidesert) (Map 16).

The regions known as **the northern Great Plains, the lower Western Highlands, and the Columbia Plateau** of North America include much of the northwestern part of the Central Plains of North America and those highlands and intermountain plateaus which are located in the northwestern part of that area. The Columbia Plateau, as indicated in Chapter 3, was a result of a great outpouring of lava early in its geological history, and the soil derived from this lava is extremely rich.

Occasionally an appreciable amount of moisture-laden air is brought into these regions by the prevailing westerlies and, through convectional showers, there is enough rainfall to support in many places a lush grassland. Grass produces roots which, when the grass dies each year, add humus to the soil; and a new crop comes up each spring. This takes place year after year and tends to make the soil rich and black. These soils are in the class of the famous "chernozem" of European Russia, some of the best soil in the world. In the medium-high elevations of the mountainous parts, some forests result from precipitation from air forced to rise, but in higher portions (over ten thousand feet) the cold of elevation eliminates them.

Although considerable crop specialization has occurred in these regions, they must still be considered in the third or commercial stage of occupance, perhaps well in the upper part of that stage. In general, the regions may be labeled as cattle producing, with the cattle being raised on ranches and then being shipped east to the corn belt for fattening and final butchering in cities such as Chicago. This widespread cattle industry is what keeps these areas largely in the commercial stage.

There are, however, special crop enclaves within these regions that put them well into the top portion of the third stage, and these are the several irrigated sections. One is well known: the

Grand Coulee district of the Columbia Plateau, where the waters of the Columbia River have been raised to irrigate the area. These extremely rich soils yield respectable harvests of wheat and the vital sugar beet on modern, mechanized farms.

Irrigation throughout the Great Plains portion, such as along the Platte and other rivers, is often carried on to produce alfalfa for winter feed for cattle, but sometimes also to produce vegetables for shipment outside the region. Another bright spot within this area is a wheat-growing belt on the Columbia Plateau in eastern Washington where enough precipitation gets in past the mountains through the gap of the Columbia River to water its thirsty lava soils. A small recreation industry has developed in the lower Western Highlands (dude ranches), but not enough to lift the regions out of the commercial or third stage of occupance. Even the exploitation of the mineral wealth of that region has not yet effected this end. As mentioned in Chapter 3, many of the important hard-rock minerals are found in mountainous areas, and such is the case here; gold, copper, silver, iron, and other important minerals are mined and processed through the crude stages in the area, and most of the local cities are based on this processing (Denver, Butte, Pueblo), but higher fabrication of the products usually is done outside, in the industrial regions to the east. Eventually this region can develop its industrial capacity to a point where it can gloriously enter the next stage.

The **Patagonian Plateau and Mountains** of southern South America is another dry middle-latitude region, with climatic conditions, soil, and vegetation very like those in the northern plains and uplands of North America. This region too is in the commercial or third stage of occupance, but it has only recently arrived there. Prior to World War I, this region was in a subsistence or even a prime-original stage, occupied by Indians and only occasionally by Spanish settlers, who brought cattle into the area for occasional ranging. The broad wind-swept plateau was practically empty, for the new-world equestrian culture had no concept of how to deal with a land that is cold and forbidding in winter and hot in summer, with streams in deep valleys dissecting the plateau. It took the influx of Scottish and Welsh immigrants into Argentina to develop the region. They recognized here an area which could support good pastoral activities, particularly the raising of sheep, the art of which they had developed back home. Consequently, with this type of settlement, the region rapidly grew into the commercial stage, whereby sheep are grazed on the uplands in summer and brought down into the deep valleys—where the homes are and where winter forage crops are grown—when the cold winds sweep the plateau in winter. The sheep, of course, are shipped from this region to Buenos Aires or elsewhere for processing.

The last over-all region in this dry middle-latitude group is composed of **the steppes and uplands of central Asia,** which occupy an area extending eastward from the shores of the Caspian Sea into the edges of northern China, an area about three thousand miles across and nearly one thousand miles from south to north. It includes the subregions of the Kirghiz Steppes, the Tarim Basin (Hunza), the Gobi Desert, and the Tibetan plateau and uplands (embracing the Himalayas). It is a monstrous region of rolling plains, basins, plateaus, and high mountains, covered with short steppeland grass, desert shrubs, ice, and mountain meadows—an area of extremely cold and bitter winters and in many parts blistering hot summers, an area of grandeur and harshness (*see illustration section*). In spite of all the efforts of the Soviet Union and Red China, the greater part of this area is still within the subsistence stage of occupance. Nomadic pastoralism in the tradition of the old-world dry-lands culture is still the main land use. The yak, an extremely versatile and durable animal, is the principal herd beast of the region; it provides milk and meat, and its hides are used for shelter.

As with nomadic pastoralism elsewhere, the native Mongoloids of these areas are organized into tribes which follow the herds. Among these tribes is the Kirghiz, of whom most people have heard because of their ferocious fighting ability. Owing to the severe winters, these nomads cannot live in tents. Instead, they construct a very sturdy movable dwelling called a yurt, made of a framework of sticks covered by yak hides, which provides good warmth. Some irrigation agriculture is practiced along the shores of the Caspian Sea, where cotton is grown, and industry is carried on in the Kuznetsk basin, but the general occupance of the area is still subsistence: nomadic pastoralism.

The mountainous portion of the over-all region includes the Himalayas (the highest in the world) and several ranges of high mountains in north-central Asia, as well as some desert basins between ranges. With the exception of scattered industrial and mineral developments in the mountains and some irrigation agriculture in the desert basins, the bulk of even this part of the region is used in nomadic pastoralism. In Chapter 6, reference was made to the Shangri-La culture of the Tibetans and other mountain peoples, who ignore the development of their resources in their preoccupation with religion. Although development in all these areas is still somewhat shrouded in mystery, special cameras to photograph phenomena especially for the geographer are being carried in Gemini spacecraft, and with this new material on hand a more adequate geographic analysis can be made of these areas.

THE HUMID CONTINENTAL MIDDLE LATITUDES

This group of regions occupies a large portion of the northern hemisphere between 40 and 60 degrees, along the eastern part of the several continents, and including the central part of two. It includes also the eastern part of the only continent in the southern hemisphere extending to these latitudes. It is characterized by a definite winter, a definite summer, and abundant precipitation well distributed throughout the year—around 40 or 50 inches a year, which is plentiful for natural agriculture in these latitudes where evaporation is not great.

These regions are under the middle-latitude influence of cyclonic storms the year round, but most persistently in winter. In summer when the highs and lows (cyclones and anticyclones) break down, the regions receive moisture by a drift of air from the oceans or seas nearby in their east or south coast location, augmented by the expansion of the oceanic highs at that season. Inasmuch as the air moving around the oceanic highs is clockwise, the back side of the highs produces a flow of air from the southeast, which moves into these continental locations bringing moisture-laden air from the oceans. This is triggered into convectional currents and thundershowers by the summer heat in the continental locations.

The temperatures in these regions are more continental than marine, for the continental influence—with the extremes of summer and winter temperatures—is predominant. Consequently, these regions are sometimes referred to as the middle-latitude continental regions, although many of them do border partially on east coasts.

Regions included within this group are: The North American manufacturing and dairying region, the North American corn belt, the Appalachian and Ozark highlands, the American spring-wheat region, the Canadian shield region, the Rio La Plata region of South America, the North German plain region, the Soviet rye region, the Swedish manufacturing and Baltic dairy regions, the Alpine manufacturing region, the Ural manufacturing region, the Black Sea mir region, the Caucasus region, the Soviet spring-wheat region, the Altai-Sayan region, the Amur Valley region, the North China and North Korea region, and the Japan manufacturing and fishing region (Map 17).

In general, this entire area was originally covered with an abundant mixed middle-latitude forest, or mesophytic forest, with a great variety of deciduous trees, as well as an abundance of tall grasslands. The soils in the area in general are good, the best ones being in the localities which were originally the tall grasslands, where the dark chernozem soils develop. In addition, some parts of this realm were earlier covered with glacial til—rock pulverized by glaciation—or outwash plains and hence have a thick cover of mechanically disintegrated parent soil which is extremely rich in mineral matter, not having to lose it by the normal process of chemical breakdown of rocks. Some of the best agricultural lands in the world are in this group of regions.

Looking first at the **North American manufacturing and dairying region,** we find that it is located roughly between the Potomac River and the St. Lawrence River in eastern North America, spanning a distance of about seven hundred miles. It extends westward also for more than a thousand miles, in a generally narrowing strip, to the western end of the Great Lakes, which is almost to the middle of North America. It includes in a sort of crescent the urban complexes of New England and the mid-Atlantic areas, the St. Lawrence Valley, and the Great Lakes and adjacent manufacturing and dairying areas, pinching out beyond the western end of the Lakes. This over-all region includes the Atlantic manufacturing, Gulf of St. Lawrence, and Great Lakes manufacturing and dairying subregions.

This over-all region may well be considered in the fifth or climax stage of development. Its agriculture has gone into a stage of crop specialization, each crop situated where it fits best. The specialization covers a great variety of middle-latitude crops, including all the garden vegetables for canning and freezing, as well as selected kinds of tobacco, superior orchard fruits, and specialized dairying, producing a variety of milk and cheese items, as well as fresh milk for the many great industrial cities of this domain.

The highly developed manufacturing landscape in this region is almost continuous, for when traveling between Boston and Washington one is seldom outside a huge metropolitan area, and when traveling from New York westward to Chicago along the southern end of the Great Lakes one is seldom out of sight of a smokestack or an industrial plant. In Canada, the large industrial complexes of Toronto, Montreal, Halifax, St. John, and other cities are well known.

In addition to processing materials produced locally, or within the whole of North America, this region, like the European marine middle-latitude region, manufactures and processes materials from all over the world for reshipment to other parts of the world. Textile and steel industries are common in this region, as are chemical and electrical industries. The making of cheese, of course, is also important. The production of iron and steel is strong, based on coal reserves in Nova Scotia and the Appalachian Highlands and iron from northeastern Canada and the western part of the Great Lakes.

Some iron, however, is brought into this region for processing in the great steel centers of Halifax, Toronto, Pittsburgh, Cleveland, Philadelphia, Baltimore, the greater Chicago area, and elsewhere. Like the European middle-latitude marine region, this region also has a highly developed recreation industry, based largely upon the scenic aspects of the countryside, which has been made beautiful by the great continental glaciation in the geological past. All in all, this region is definitely in the climax stage of its development, with little or no indication of decline.

The next region is one of the best known in the world, the **North American corn belt.** It extends westward from the vicinity of the city of Columbus, Ohio, for about six hundred miles to the vicinity of Pierre, South Dakota. It reaches northward nearly to the southern end of the Great Lakes, where it contacts the North American manufacturing and dairying region, and southward roughly to the Ohio and Arkansas Rivers, where it contacts the southeastern North America humid subtropical region. Specifically, it includes western Ohio, most of Indiana, most of Illinois, all of Iowa, northern Illinois, eastern Nebraska, and eastern South Dakota.

This is an area of extensive glacial outwash or til plains: rock material taken from elsewhere and ground up by the great glaciers of the past was deposited here as a fine silt in great thicknesses—as rolling plains—over the entire area, leaving a mechanically disintegrated parent soil which has all of its original mineral nutrients on tap. Moreover, the native vegetation within this region was tall grassland, except for forests along the stream edges. This added to the richness of the soil, and as a result the corn belt is one of the finest agricultural areas in the world.

It is called the "corn belt" because of its peculiar characteristics for growing this crop. Corn needs rich soil and a warm, humid summer, both of which this region has in abundance. While corn is the principal crop, the region's agriculture is diversified and intensified, and there is local processing of materials. Consequently, the region is in the fourth or industrial stage of occupance. The type of farm found most frequently in the area is what is known as a stock farm, where crops are grown mainly to be fed to cattle which have been shipped in from the west for fattening. The farmer usually plants a variety of cattle-food crops (besides corn, this includes hay and oats) because of the fickleness of the summer rainfall, thus assuring that one or several of them will be successful. He then sells the cattle for processing within the region in the great packing and manufacturing centers at Des Moines, Indianapolis, Omaha, Chicago (considered a part of this area also, because of its proximity), and St. Louis.

The two upland regions, **the Appalachian and Ozark highlands,** with elevations ranging from two to about six thousand feet, were until recent years in a stage of subsistence agriculture, owing to isolation from outside influences because of their hilly terrain. Modern transformation has advanced them rapidly in a matter of several decades to practically the climax stage of occupance. Manufacturing, crop specialization, and the recreation industry are seen throughout these areas today, using the local labor market, local mineral wealth, the variety of terrain, and the beauty of the landscape. In some cases the advance has been almost too rapid, for it has left many pockets of poverty, where people have been shoved into an occupance with which they were not yet ready to cope and hence live in poverty unknown to their forefathers. In time, of course, they will make the adjustment.

The **American spring-wheat region** extends northward and westward from the western end of the Great Lakes almost to the Canadian Rocky Mountains, in a strip several hundred miles wide and about five hundred miles long. This region is also a part of the glacial til plains, with its rich soil, but it is too far north for the successful growing of corn. It is also on the dry side of the humid continental middle-latitude group, having only about

20 to 30 inches of precipitation a year, but this amount is effective because of the low evaporation in this northern latitude. The region, however, is ideal for the growing of spring wheat—that is, wheat planted in the spring and reaped in the fall—which flourishes in that amount of moisture and in those mild summers. (This is different from the wheat which was mentioned in the subtropical regions—wheat that is planted in the fall and harvested in the spring.) The wheat is grown on extensive farms with the use of mechanized equipment, which works easily over these gently rolling plains.

The region is in the third or commercial stage of occupance, where farming is done and crops are raised for processing outside the areas. Wheat that is grown here is processed in the North American manufacturing and dairying region, at cities such as Buffalo. This region may be said to be in the lower portion of the third stage, for it has not yet reached a stage of much diversification in the growing of cash crops. It is still largely planted in spring wheat, even if a variety of other crops can be grown in this area, such as flax and soy beans.

The Canadian shield region comprises the old Laurentian Hills (the region is shaped like a shield), which were scoured over by continental ice sheets during the last glaciation, leaving them barren of soil and cursed with a disarranged drainage system. Clothed with a cover of spruce, the region would probably be a wilderness left to the trapper of fur-bearing animals (which are the dominant fauna) were it not for the occurrence of a variety of strategic minerals here (see Chapter 4), including nickel and cobalt. On account of these minerals, the region is a prosperous mining area, with attendant lumbering activities. Since the real processing of the products of the mines is done in cities such as Toronto, outside the area, the region must be considered in the third or commercial stage of occupance.

The Rio La Plata region in South America takes in the most important part of the state of Argentina. The physical conditions in this region are comparable to those in the corn belt of North America, with rich soils, a plains type of topography, abundant precipitation the year round, and fairly warm summers. The region is in the fourth or manufacturing stage of development, just like the North American corn belt, but it might be considered in the lower portion of the fourth stage, considering that land diversification and intensification have not gone nearly as far here as in North America, largely owing to the influence of the new-world equestrian culture.

Whereas most of the available land in the corn belt is used in farms, principally the specialized stock farm, only a small portion of the potential farm land (around the city of Buenos Aires) is thus used in the Rio La Plata region. The remainder of the area is still kept for stock ranching; hence is not being put to the best productive uses for human consumption. Ranching lends itself to large estates, and the land is held that way. Even the manufacturing in this region, in places such as Buenos Aires and Rosario, is limited to industries processing raw materials, such as tanneries and meat packing plants.

It is difficult for industries to grow, in face of the equestrian distrust of mass production. For example, cattle raised on the ranches which cover a considerable portion of this region are brought into market and butchered in Buenos Aires, without the benefit of additional feeding on a stock farm; the corn and wheat grown on farms close to Buenos Aires are not used in stock feeding but are sold or processed directly into flour or corn meal. Consequently, the region has not advanced far into its present stage, and it still has a considerably bright future, if and when it is put to more productive uses.

The North German plain region occupies most of Germany and Poland north of the Alps and east of Hamburg and must be considered well into the fourth stage of occupance. Here again is a plains region of glacial outwash with rich soils. A great variety of crops is produced in this soil, notably the potato. Manufacturing on a large scale is carried on, including chemical products and steel manufactures. Recreation as an industry has made some inroads into the region.

The "black-bread belt," called **the Soviet rye region,** covers most of western Russia, and includes the vicinity of Moscow.

This region is much like the North German plain in that its soils are rich from glacial outwash, but it does not have the marine influence from the Atlantic which has some effect on the North German plain. Consequently, the severe cold of the long continental winters becomes dominant, and crops like wheat, which can be grown at other places, cannot be grown here. Instead, rye, oats, and potatoes are common in this region. The local bread is made from rye flour—hence the term "black bread."

This region must be considered also to be within the manufacturing stage, for some of its farm products are processed, and there is extensive manufacturing within the region. But this region should be considered in the lower portion of the fourth stage, because much of the farming within the region is of a subsistence type—the farm products are used largely right on the farm. In fact, many European peasants are subsistence farmers, consuming most of what they raise. The crops that are sold for market include rye, potatoes, and flax. The manufacture within the region includes the processing of raw materials, such as the making of flax into linen, as well as heavy steel industries in Moscow, and a variety of associated metallic industries.

The Swedish manufacturing and Baltic dairy regions include southern Sweden and southern Finland. Together they too must be considered in the fourth stage, for commercialization of agriculture, especially dairying, in both Finland and Sweden is well known, and there is a great variety of Swedish manufactures, including a world-renowned steel industry.

On the other hand, **the Alpine manufacturing region,** which includes the high Alps of northern Italy and Switzerland, the Carpathian Alps and the northern Alpine foreland, as well as the Hungarian and Romanian basins, might well be considered in the fifth or climax stage of development. Here again, land use is specialized to its best advantage, particularly in Italy, Switzerland, Rumania, and Hungary, where a great variety of grain, spices, and root crops is grown on the best possible sites; and the manufacturing industries are highly developed and versatile. There are, for example, electrical appliance industries in nothern Italy and precision gadget industries in Switzerland. The recreation industries have also developed on a large scale; the renowned facilities in the Alpine region are talked about all over the world.

The Ural manufacturing region likewise may be classified as in the climax stage. Owing partly to local minerals and coal, the region has developed a great variety of both heavy and light industries and exhibits specialization of land use. In addition, the recreation industry is fairly well developed in the area.

The Black Sea mir region is not highly developed (the Russian "mir" refers to the dominance of the rural village). It includes the Walachian plain of Rumania, which is also endowed with rich soil, as well as the plains areas all along the northern coast of the Black Sea. The latter area is likewise very lush in glacial outwash soil; although the glacier itself did not reach that far south, much rich material was transported there by water.

With soils practically as rich as the corn belt of North America, this region (sometimes part of it is called the Ukraine) does not produce a great abundance of surplus crops as does the corn belt. For one reason, the area is very densely populated, and much of what is grown has to be consumed within the region; however, a variety of grains, table vegetables, fruits, spices, and root crops, including potatoes and turnips, is grown for sale or manufacture. Manufacturing is prevalent throughout the region; hence it is in the fourth or manufacturing stage, but in the lower portion. The manufactures include those which process materials within the region and those which are based on certain local resources such as oil, iron, and coal.

The Caucasus region, the high mountains between the Black and Caspian Seas, may be considered in the fifth or climax stage, for the development of oil and hard-rock mineral resources, together with recreational facilities, has fostered manufacturing and land specialization in recent years. Like the Appalachian and Ozark highlands of North America, this rapid advancement from a subsistence stage has brought problems of adjustment which time will alter.

The Soviet spring-wheat region extends eastward from the vicinity of Moscow for more than a thousand miles around and beyond the Ural Mountains into central Asia. Whereas the region is several hundred miles wide in the western part, it narrows down continuously until it is a little more than a hundred miles wide in the vicinity of the Ural Mountains, finally pinching out entirely several hundred miles to the east. Like the American spring-wheat region, this belt has long cold winters, and the summers are too uncertain for the growing of many crops. It can, however, grow spring wheat during its short summer, and it is also blessed with good outwash soil. Consequently, this region is a commercial wheat-growing region, producing wheat on large farms for shipment and processing outside the region. It must be considered in the third or commercial stage of occupance.

Similar to the American spring-wheat region, there is little or no diversification of crops in this area, so it still has a potential of diversification within the commercial stage. One of the disadvantages within this region, however, is its east-west orientation. Whenever a bad climatic year is experienced here, it becomes a complete disaster. The northwest-southeast orientation of the American spring-wheat region, on the other hand, allows it a little more leeway, for one latitudinal location can meet disaster while other portions may remain prosperous.

The Altai and Sayan Mountains, which are rugged and beautiful, have tended to encourage isolation for their inhabitants and an attendant lack of advancement. Consequently, the region is largely in the subsistence stage, with subsistence agriculture and nomadic pastoralism widely in practice, together with a tribal social structure with all its colorful appurtenances. There is some manufacturing in the vicinity of Lake Baikal, but not enough to elevate the region above its current stage.

Extending eastward from and on the south side of the Altai-Sayan region, starting out as a very narrow band and expanding to several hundred miles in width as one moves eastward about six hundred miles to the Pacific Ocean, is the **Amur Valley** of eastern Asia. This region receives winter precipitation from cyclonic storms, similar to the rest of the regions, but it gets increasingly abundant summer precipitation from the drift of moisture-laden air from the Pacific, carried in by the movement of the summer monsoon winds. This drift, being forced to rise over the mountains to the west and north, triggers off into convection currents and thunderstorms over the hot plains in summer and brings abundant rainfall. The region does have hot summers, much like the American corn belt, because of its continental location. Consequently, its climate is very similar to that of the American corn belt, but the soils are not quite as rich. This region produces a great many cash and commercial grain crops, especially corn, and must be considered in the commercial stage, because the grains that are produced are processed outside this region.

The North China and North Korea region is where the products from the Amur Valley are processed. This region, which includes the northern portion of China and all of Manchuria and North Korea, has the same kind of climate as the Amur region and, in general, a rich alluvial soil. The region has large manufacturing in cities such as Mukden and Peking, both of which have large steel industries based on local supplies of coal and iron. Although the region may be considered in the fourth or manufacturing stage, it is in the lower portion of the stage. Some surplus crops are produced, but most of the agriculture within the region is consumed as subsistence crops. The dense subsistence farming along the Yellow River plain in northern China is well known, for whenever the Yellow River overflows many of the farmers are drowned and their crops ruined, resulting in famine. The matter of overpopulation could well keep this region indefinitely in the lower portion of stage four.

The Japan manufacturing and fishing region, comprising northern Japan, does not have as severe a climate as some others in this group, largely owing to its marine location. Because arable land is at a premium, crop specialization is assiduously practiced. Manufacturing is developed to a high degree, where raw materials are brought in, fabricated, and shipped out again for sale. The teeming population of the area long ago made necessary the exploitation of the fishing resources of the shallow adjacent seas, and the Japanese fishing industry is well known throughout the world. The region may be considered well advanced into the fourth stage.

THE SUBPOLAR MIDDLE LATITUDES

We come now to the climate between about 60 and 65 degrees latitude, where cold polar winds meet the warmer winds of the prevailing westerlies and a mass of frontal air is embroiled in a low-pressure belt of rising air all the way around the world at those latitudes. The regions here are sometimes called the subpolar taiga or the subpolar continental regions ("taiga" is a Russian word for the vast Siberian forest), and essentially occupy the belt of the subpolar low discussed in Chapters 6 and 7; they are the North American taiga, the Asian taiga, and the Scandinavian taiga.

These subpolar continental regions (Map 18) are characterized by sufficient rainfall to produce abundant forests, but the summer is not usually long or definite enough for successful agriculture. The areas are thus mostly quite wild, roamed by wild animals, and are sometimes referred to as the "great north woods." The trees are usually pine, fir, and spruce, all evergreen conifers. There is not the variety that is found in the tropical rain forests; consequently, they lend themselves easily to lumbering, since the individual species are found close together (*see illustration section*). The soil is not good, usually very acidic, and most of the area has a disarranged pattern of drainage left by glacial scouring; but these matters are not of much concern, since agriculture would not usually be successful there in any case.

The existence of a native animal group is, however, important. Generally, the prevalent type is the fur-bearing animal—naturally, to protect himself against the cold winters. The existence of these animals in abundance is important to a prosperous trapping industry. In brief, then, the regions are good largely for two things: lumbering and trapping.

The first large region in this group is **the North American taiga.** It extends all the way across North America from the coast of Labrador through central Alaska and includes the McKenzie taiga and highlands and the Hudson Bay taiga subregions. Mountains and other highlands are found within the over-all region, which might well be considered within the third or commercial stage of occupance, for here systematic lumbering is carried on to produce logs sold for outside processing. Concomitantly, systematic trapping of fur-bearing animals is done to obtain furs which are shipped outside for processing.

Although trapping might be considered partly a hunting industry, it also fits within the commercial stage of development. It is doubtful if this region can rise much above the commercial stage, even though large deposits of minerals are found, such as the iron reserves located in that portion south and east of Hudson Bay. All of the iron extracted from the area is shipped to the south outside the region for processing.

Another large region within this group is **the Asian taiga,** including the subregions of the Siberian Taiga and uplands, the Ob taiga, and the Russian taiga, which stretches in a similar belt of latitude all the way across the northern part of the Asian continent from Finland to the Kamchatka Peninsula and the Bering Straits, approaching Alaska to the east to form a continuous belt around the world. This huge region also is in the commercial stage of development and will probably not ascend above that. Forests are being cut down and animals are being trapped for processing outside the region. The Soviet government has vainly tried to encourage settlement in this region, fostering the growing of such hardy crops as kohlrabi, which can withstand this rigorous climate. The weather records of the region reflect some of the coldest recorded temperatures on earth, going frequently as low as 60 degrees below zero, with the all-time record having been set at 90 below at Verkhoyansk in Siberia. The Soviet settlement program has had only limited success, largely in the subregion known as the Russian taiga.

The region known as **the Scandinavian taiga** (Kjolen taiga and Baltic taiga), which includes northern Sweden and part of Norway and Finland, is quite different. Here the forest trees are systematically cropped, with one plot reaching maturity while others are being planted, so that continuous planting and cutting are going on and a constant supply of wood is provided. The region, however, is still within the third stage, for even the iron mined in the famous Kierunavaara district in Sweden is taken southward out of the area for processing in the Swedish manufacturing region.

The High Latitudes

These are the areas of the world above 65 degrees latitude, which is too cold for agriculture. They include the polar marine regions, which occupy the maritime edges of land in the polar easterlies wind belt between 65 and 85 degrees latitude (the Eurasian tundra, the Lapland tundra, the North American or Eskimo tundra, and the Antarctic tundra), the polar continental or ice cap regions, poleward of 85 degrees (Greenland and the Antarctica ice cap), and the inland areas in the polar easterlies realm.

The polar marine regions occupy those areas along the coast of the Arctic and Antarctic Oceans (Map 19) where the marine influence ameliorates somewhat the harshness of the polar climate and allows a brief period of warmth in the summer when the topsoil of the land is melted. This produces a tundra vegetation on which reindeer graze.

The Eurasian tundra region features nomadic pastoralism behind the reindeer. This is also true of the famous Lapland tundra of northern Finland and Norway. The regions, of course, are in the subsistence stage.

The North American tundra or Eskimo tundra region contains, of course, the Eskimos, most of whom are in the primeoriginal stage of hunting and fishing. Seal and walrus, as well as the polar bear, are hunted. The Antarctic tundra is not graced by any permanent human occupance.

The two major parts of **the polar continental or ice cap regions** are the Greenland and Antarctica ice cap regions, covered with thousands of feet of ice. The areas are naturally uninhabited (except for special teams of scientists), and are in no stage of occupance at all. With the great strides made by science today, however, and considering the accelerated amount of exploration taking place in these areas, one cannot say that these regions might not someday support an advanced and prosperous occupance.

SELECTED REFERENCES

Adams, Nicholson B. *The Heritage of Spain: Introduction to Spanish Civilization.* Rev. ed. New York: Holt, Rinehart and Winston, 1959.

Allen, Durward L. *Our Wildlife Legacy.* Rev. ed. New York: Funk & Wagnalls Co., 1962.

Ames, Oakes. *Economic Annuals and Human Cultures.* Cambridge, Mass.: Harvard University Press, 1939.

Angell, Norman. *Raw Materials, Population Pressure, and War.* New York: World Peace Foundation, 1936.

Atwood, Wallace W. *The Physiographic Provinces of North America.* Boston: Ginn & Co., 1940.

Bacon, L. B., and others. *Agricultural Geography of Europe and the Near East.* Washington, D.C.: Government Printing Office, 1948.

Berg, Lev S. *Natural Regions of the U.S.S.R.* New York: Macmillan Co., 1950.

Bowman, J. *The New World.* New York: World Bank Co., 1928.

Carlson, Fred A. *Geography of Latin America.* 3rd ed. New York: Prentice-Hall, 1951.

Coon, Carleton S. *The Races of Europe.* New York: Macmillan Co., 1935.

Cressey, George B. *Asia's Lands and Peoples.* 3rd ed. New York: McGraw-Hill Book Co., 1963.

Cumberland, Kenneth B. *Southwest Pacific, A Geography of Australia, New Zealand, and Their Pacific Island Neighborhoods.* New York: McGraw-Hill Book Co., 1956.

Dale, Tom, and Vernon G. Carter. *Topsoil and Civilization.* Norman: University of Oklahoma Press, 1955.

Fraenkel, Gerd, and Lindley J. Stiles. *Today's World in Focus: Israel.* Boston: Ginn & Co., 1963.

Freeman, Otis W. (ed.). *Geography of the Pacific.* New York: John Wiley & Sons, 1951.

Geographical Journal. London: Royal Geographical Society, quarterly.

Geographische Zeitschrift. Leipzig and Berlin: Teubner, monthly.

Gottmann, Jean. *A Geography of Europe.* 3rd ed. New York: Henry Holt, 1954.

Krueger, Ralph R., and others (eds.). *Regional and Resource Planning in Canada.* Toronto: Holt, Rinehart & Winston, 1963.

Krypton, Constantine. *The Northern Sea Route and the Economy of the Soviet North*. Research Program on the U.S.S.R., Studies no. 14. London: Methuen & Co., 1956.

Lovering, Thomas S. *Minerals in World Affairs*. New York: Prentice-Hall, 1943.

MacGowan, Kenneth. *Early Man in the New World*. New York: Macmillan Co., 1950.

Mayer, Harold M., and Clyde F. Kohn (eds.). *Readings in Urban Geography*. Chicago: University of Chicago Press, 1959.

Mills, Clarence A. *Climate Makes the Man*. New York: Harper & Brothers, 1942.

New International Year Book. New York: Funk & Wagnalls Co., yearly.

Pierce, Richard A. *Russian Central Asia, 1867–1917*. Berkeley: University of California, 1960.

Putnam, Palmer C. *Energy in the Future*. Princeton, N.J.: D. Van Nostrand Co., 1953.

Sauer, Carl O. *Agricultural Origins and Dispersals*. New York: American Geographical Society, 1952.

Symonds, Percival M. *The Dynamics of Human Adjustment*. New York: Appleton-Century Co., 1946.

Thoman, Richard S. *The Geography of Economic Activity*. New York: McGraw-Hill Book Co., 1964.

Thomas, William L., Jr., and others (eds.). *Man's Role in Changing the Face of the Earth*. Chicago: University of Chicago Press, 1956.

Toynbee, Arnold J. *A Study of History*, Vols. I–IV. London: Oxford University Press, 1956.

U.S. Bureau of the Census. *Statistical Abstract of the United States*. Washington, D.C.: Government Printing Office,

U.S. Department of the Interior. *Mineral Yearbook*. Washington, D.C.: Government Printing Office, yearly.

U.S. Foreign Commerce Department. *Our World Trade*. Washington, D.C.: Chamber of Commerce of the United States, quarterly.

Unstead, J. F. *A World Survey*. London: University of London Press, 1962.

Van Cleef, Eugene. *Trade Centers and Trade Routes*. New York: D. Appleton Co., 1937.

Van Valkenburg, Samuel, and Ellsworth Huntington. *Europe*. 2nd ed. with Colbert C. Held. New York: John Wiley & Sons, 1952.

Wechsler, David. *The Range of Human Capacities*. Baltimore: Williams & Wilkins Co., 1952.

Weigert, Hans W., and others (eds.). *New Compass of the World*. New York: Macmillan Co., 1953.

World Almanac. New York: New York World Telegram, yearly.

Ziegler, P. Thomas. *The Meat We Eat*. Danville, Ill.: Interstate Printers & Publishers, 1962.

MAPS

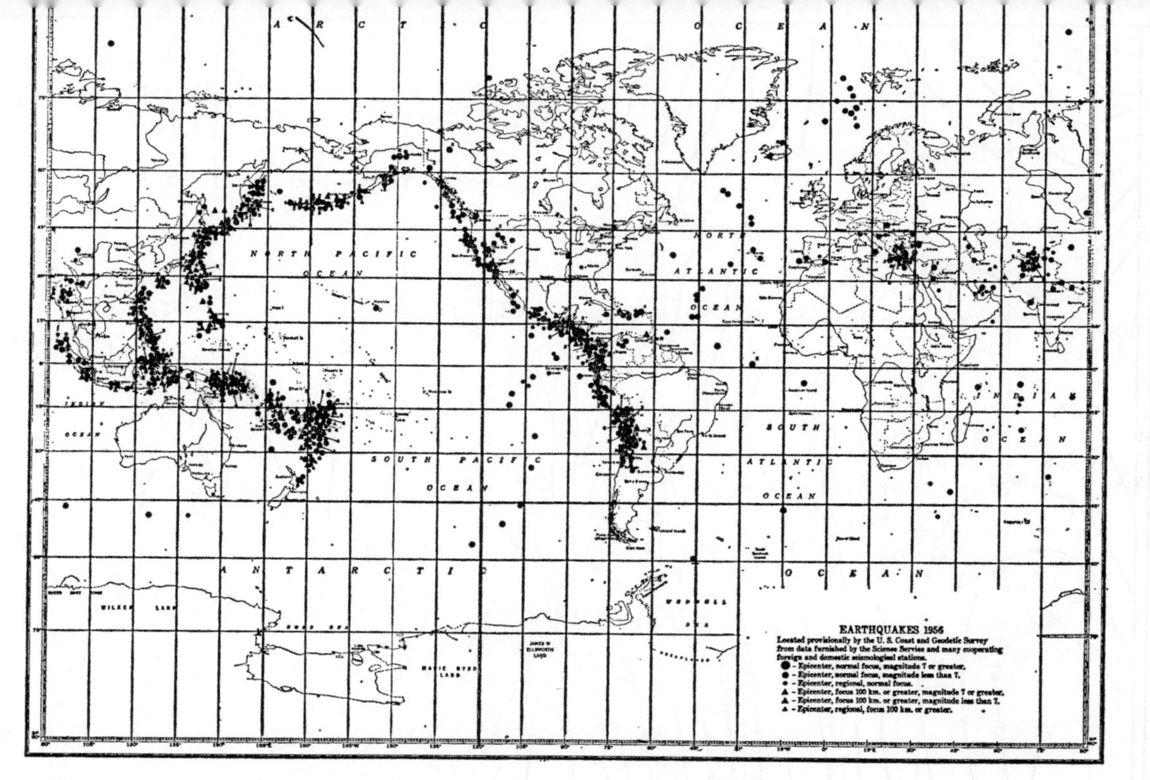

Map 1. Earthquake distribution in a typical year, 1956. *Courtesy U.S. Coast and Geodetic Survey.*

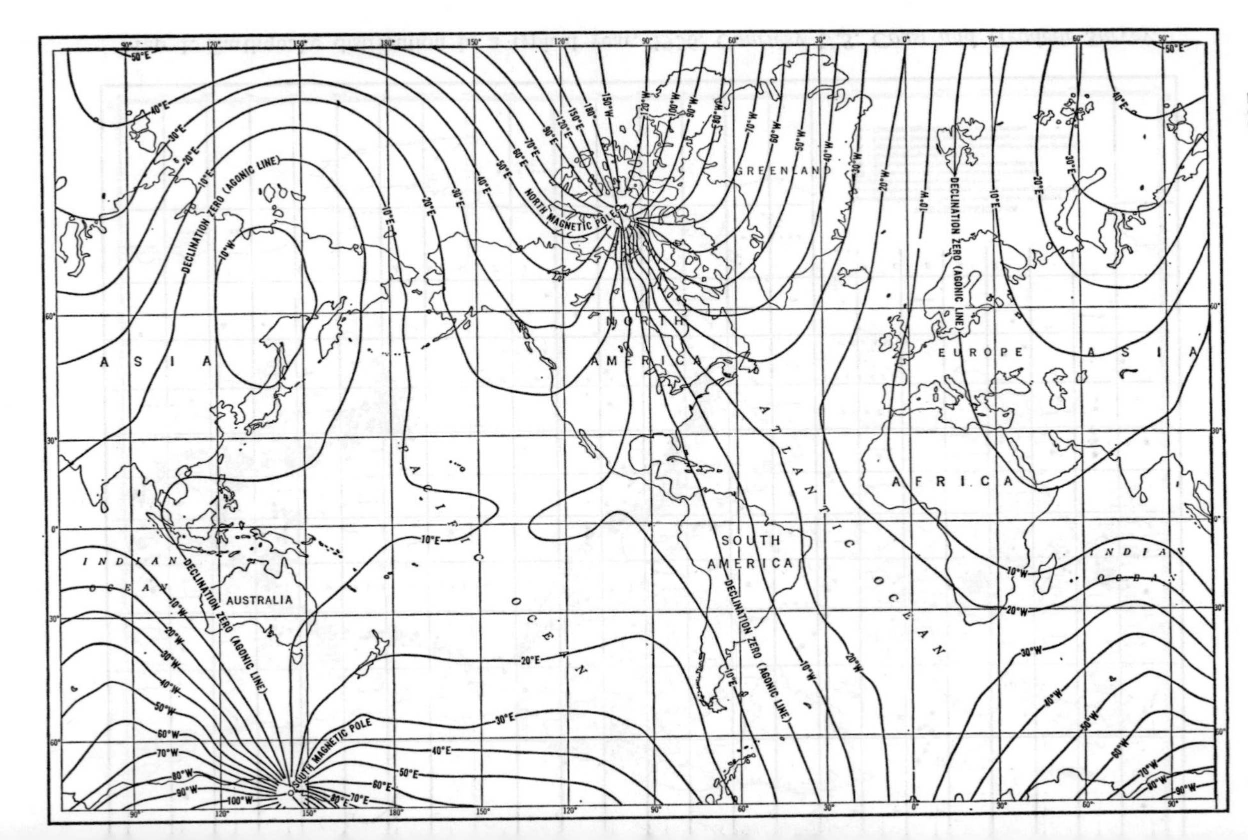

DECLINATION ZERO (AGONIC LINE)
NORTH MAGNETIC POLE
SOUTH MAGNETIC POLE
GREENLAND
NORTH AMERICA
SOUTH AMERICA
EUROPE
ASIA
AFRICA
AUSTRALIA
ATLANTIC OCEAN
PACIFIC OCEAN
INDIAN OCEAN

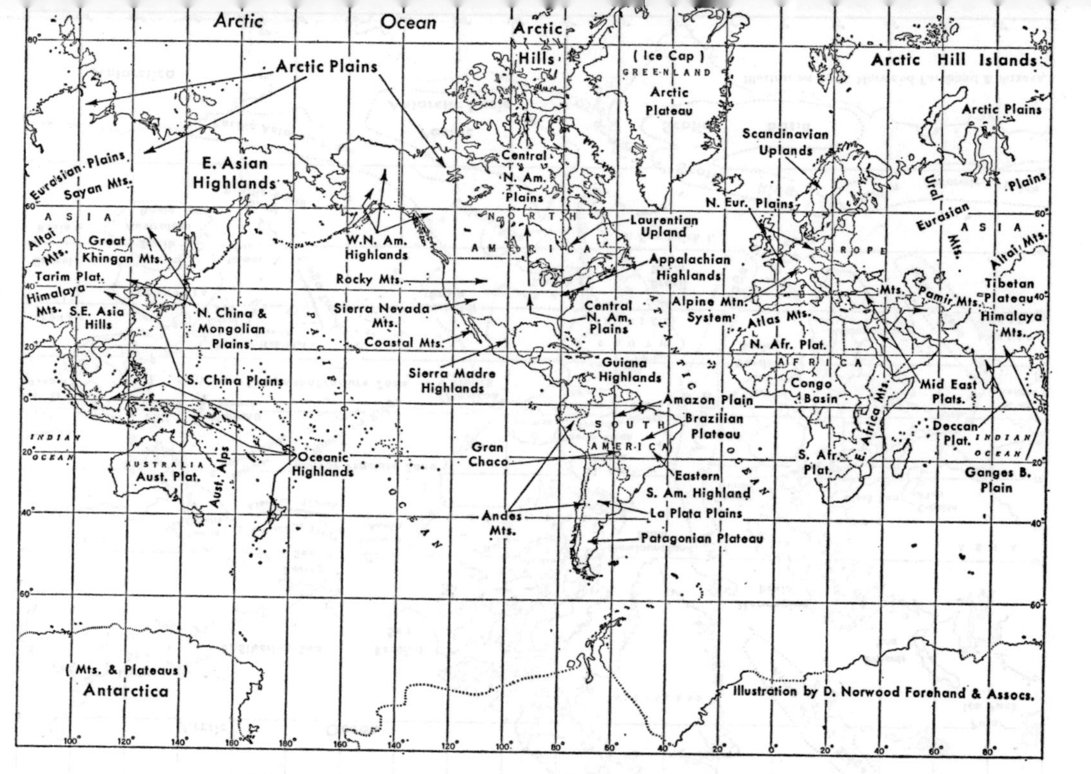

Map 3. Some major land forms of the earth's surface.

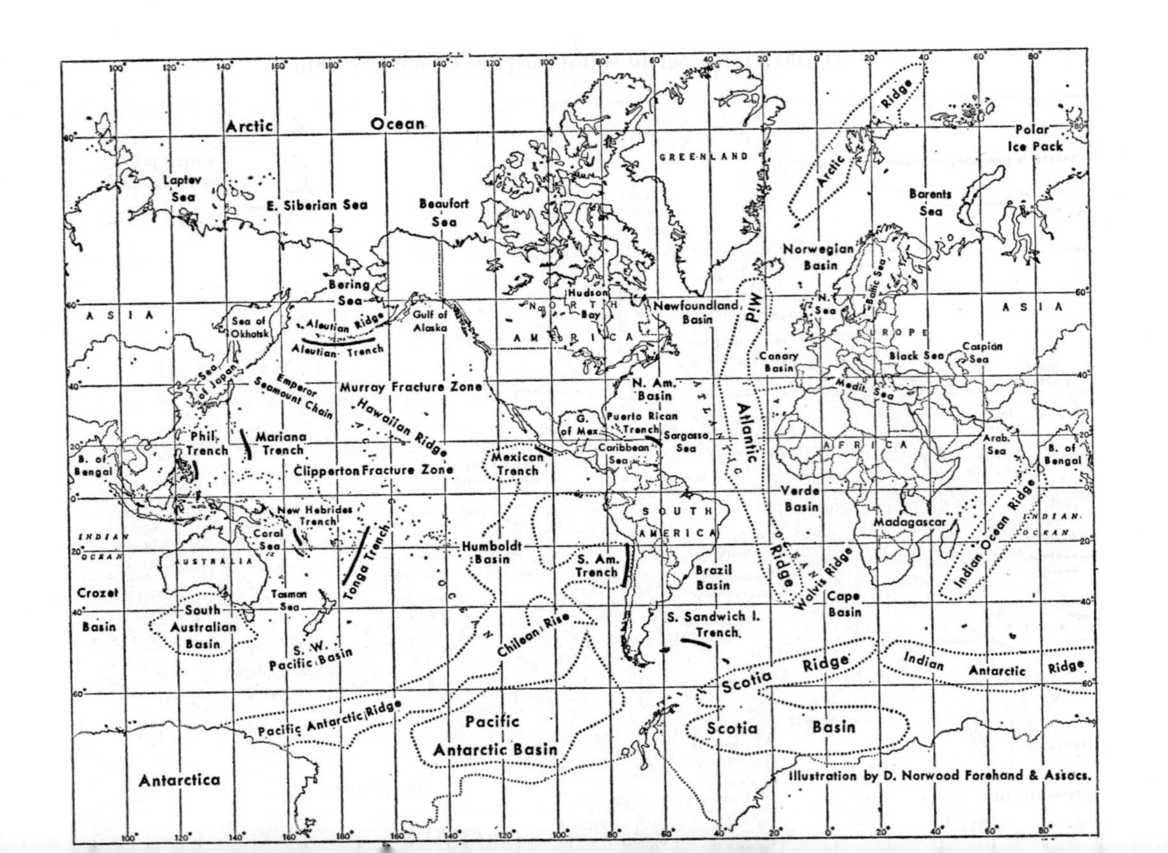
Arctic
Ocean
Polar
Ice Pack
GREENLAND
Laptev
Sea
E. Siberian Sea
Beaufort
Sea
Barents
Sea
Arctic
Ridge
Norwegian
Basin
Baltic Sea
N.
Sea
Bering
Sea
Aleutian Ridge
Aleutian Trench
Gulf of
Alaska
Sea of
Okhotsk
Sea of Japan
Hudson
Bay
NORTH
AMERICA
Newfoundland
Basin
Mid
Atlantic
Ridge
ASIA
EUROPE
Canary
Basin
Black Sea
Caspian
Sea
Medit. Sea
Emperor
Seamount Chain
Murray Fracture Zone
Hawaiian Ridge
N. Am.
Basin
ATLANTIC
OCEAN
G.
of Mex.
Puerto Rican
Trench
Sargasso
Sea
Caribbean
Sea
AFRICA
Arab.
Sea
B. of
Bengal
Phil.
Trench
Mariana
Trench
Clipperton Fracture Zone
Mexican
Trench
Verde
Basin
Indian Ocean Ridge
INDIAN
OCEAN
New Hebrides
Trench
Coral
Sea
Tonga Trench
PACIFIC
OCEAN
Humboldt
Basin
SOUTH
AMERICA
Madagascar
AUSTRALIA
S. Am.
Trench
Brazil
Basin
Walvis Ridge
Cape
Basin
Crozet
Basin
Tasman
Sea
South
Australian
Basin
Chilean Rise
S. Sandwich I.
Trench
S. W.
Pacific Basin
Scotia
Ridge
Indian
Antarctic
Ridge
Pacific Antarctic Ridge
Pacific
Antarctic Basin
Scotia
Basin
Antarctica
Illustration by D. Norwood Forehand & Assocs.

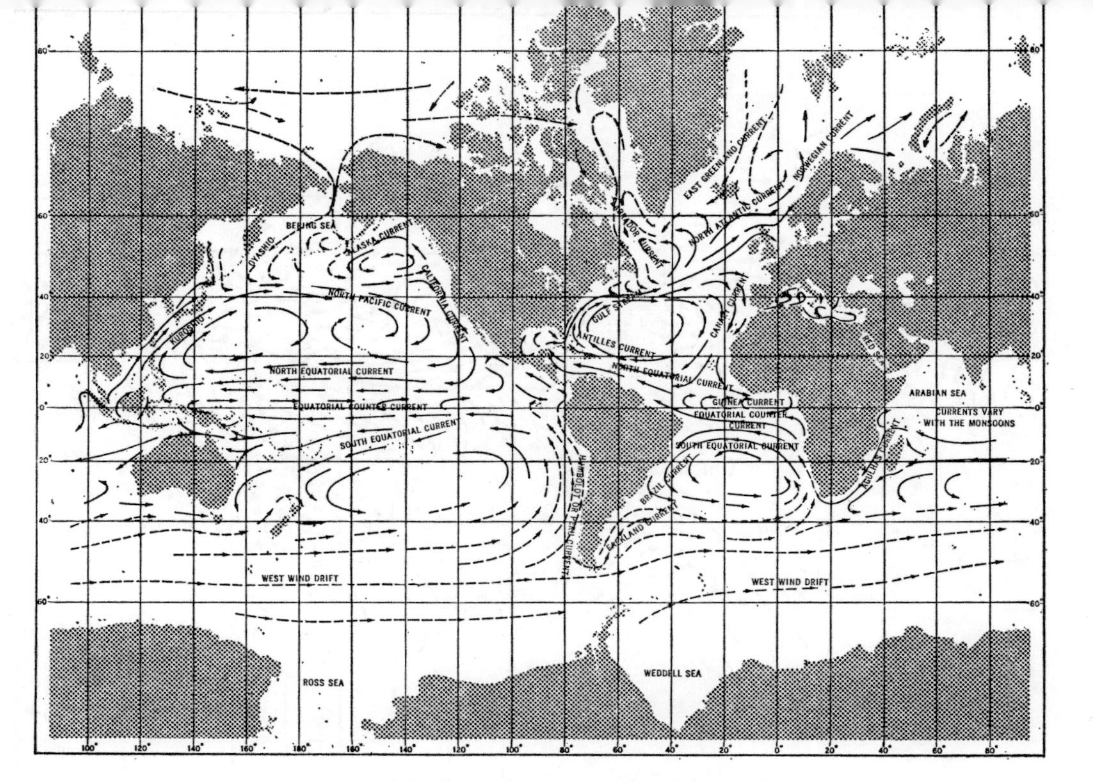

Map 5. Principal ocean currents of the world.

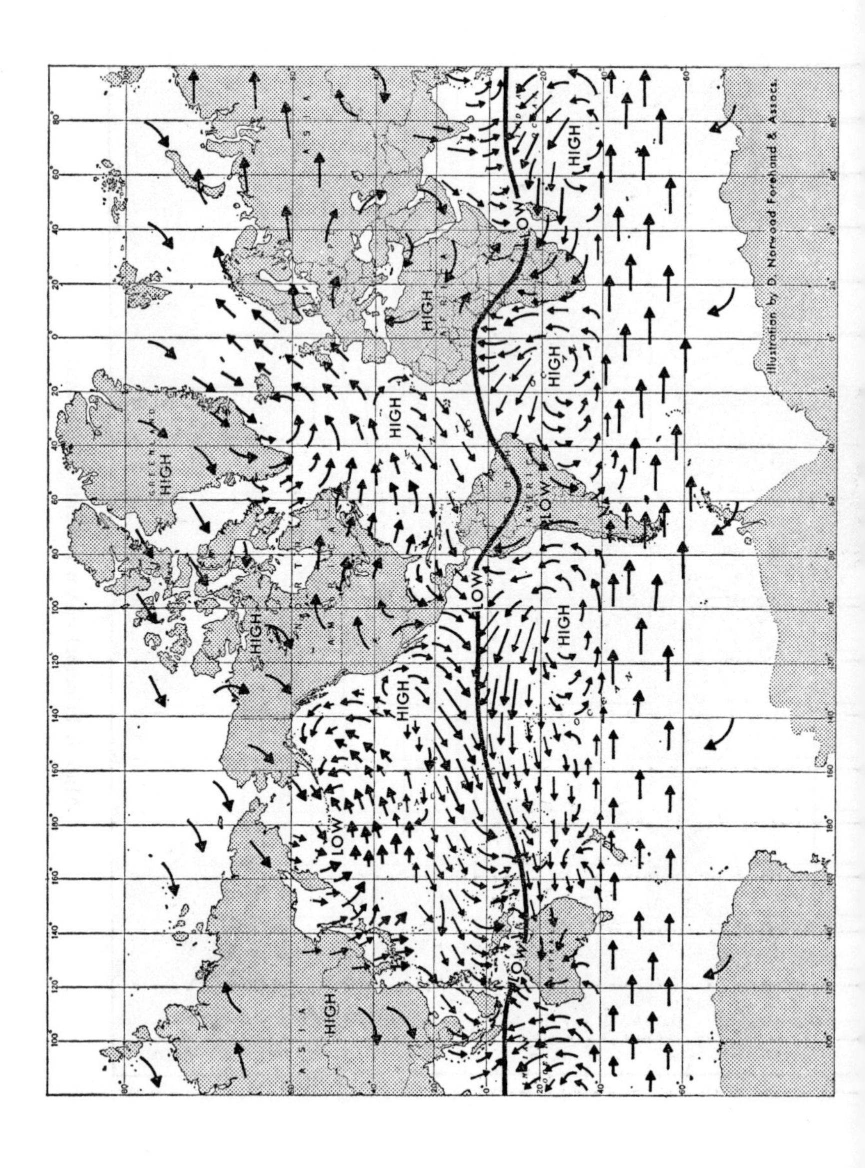
HIGH
LOW
HIGH
LOW
HIGH
HIGH
HIGH
LOW
HIGH
HIGH
HIGH
LOW
LOW
HIGH
HIGH
LOW
LOW
HIGH
Illustration by D. Norwood Forehand & Assocs.

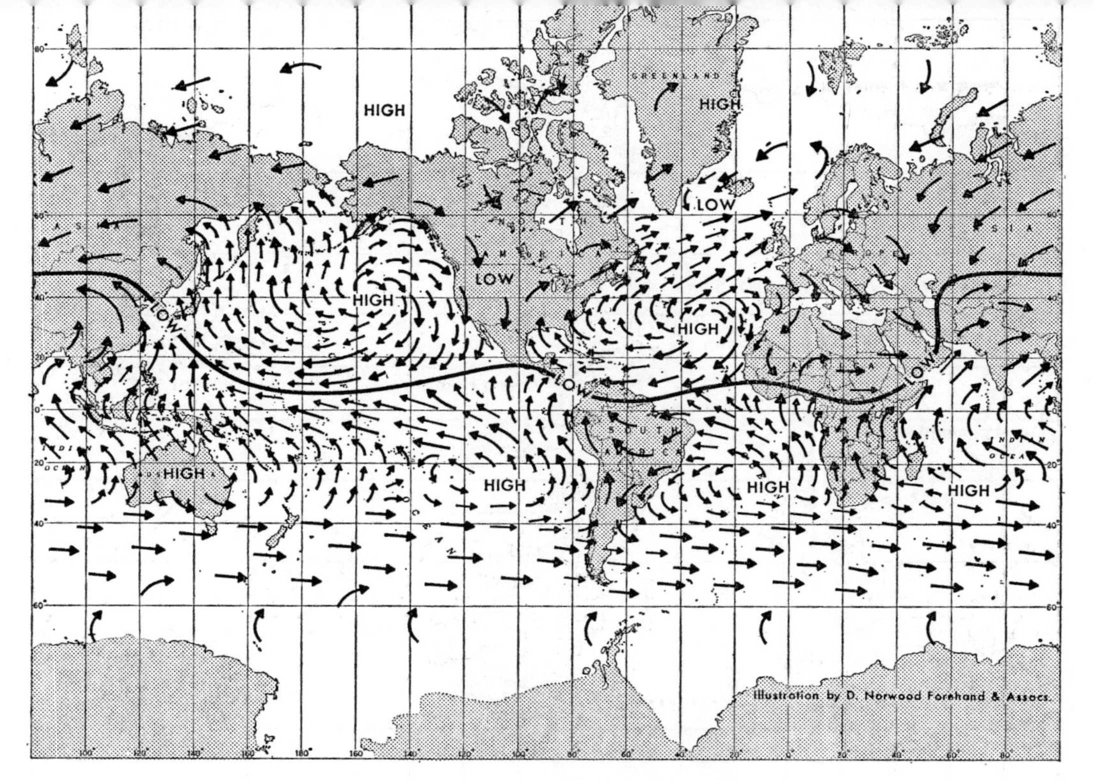

Map 7. Exaggerated seasonal winds—July.

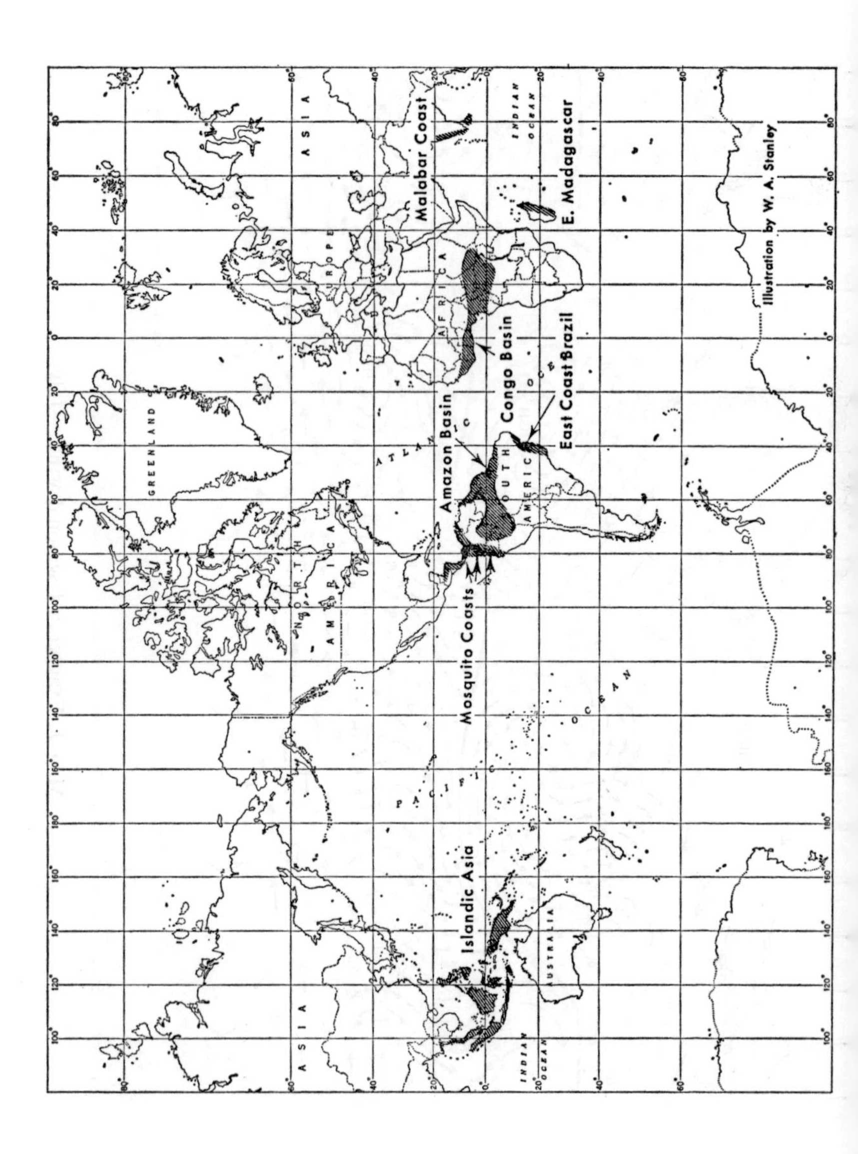
Malabar Coast
E. Madagascar
Congo Basin
East Coast Brazil
Amazon Basin
Mosquito Coasts
Islandic Asia
GREENLAND
AUSTRALIA
Illustration by W. A. Stanley

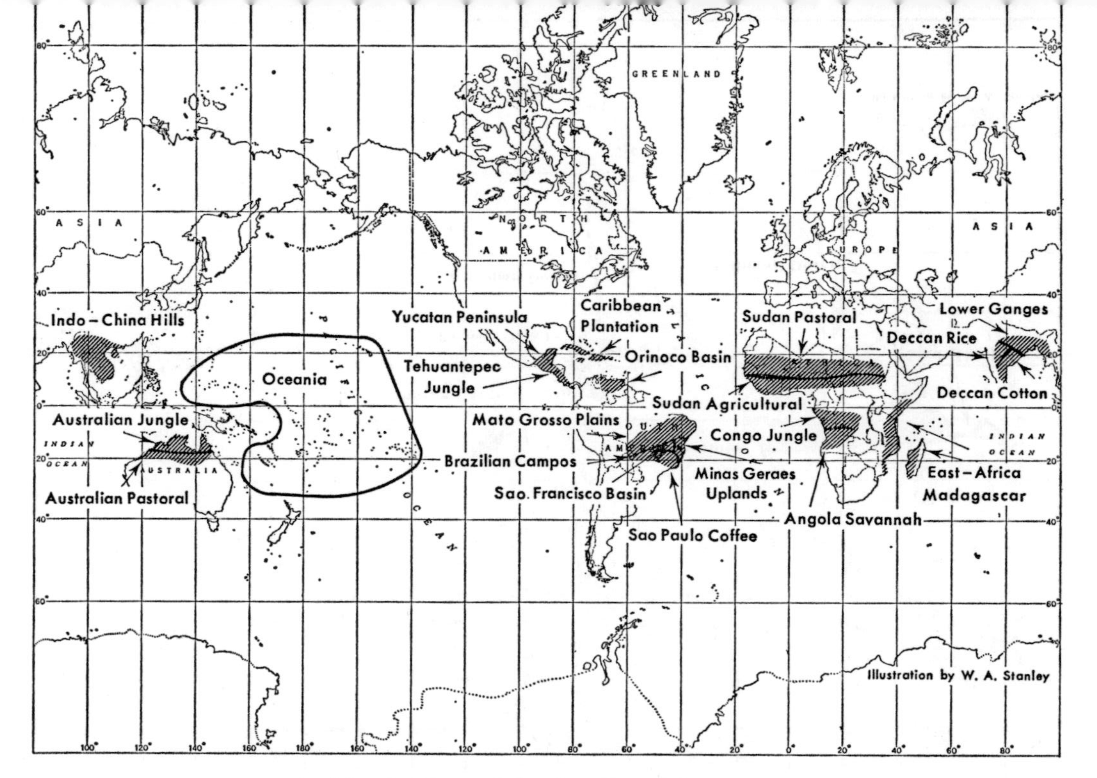

Map 9. Wet and dry low latitude regions.

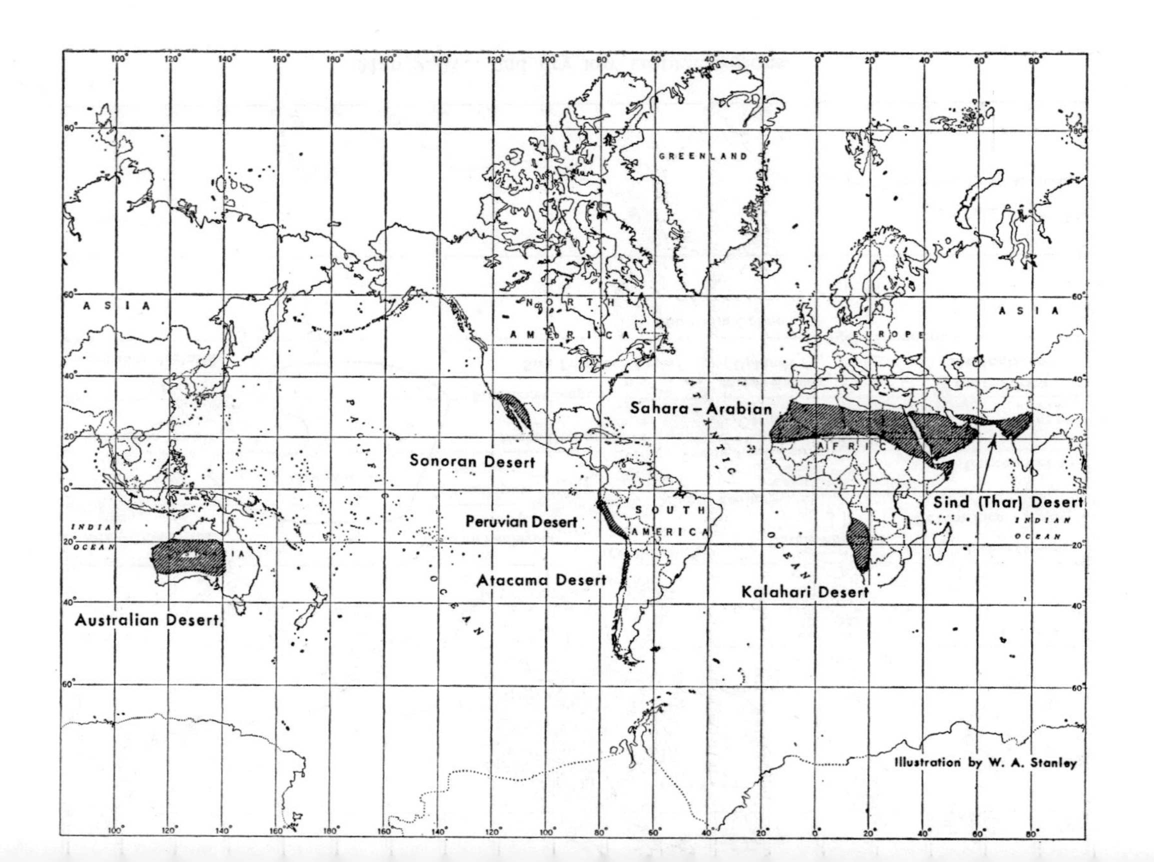
GREENLAND
ASIA
NORTH AMERICA
EUROPE
ASIA
Sahara – Arabian
AFRICA
Sonoran Desert
SOUTH AMERICA
Sind (Thar) Desert
INDIAN OCEAN
INDIAN OCEAN
Peruvian Desert
Atacama Desert
Kalahari Desert
Australian Desert
Illustration by W. A. Stanley

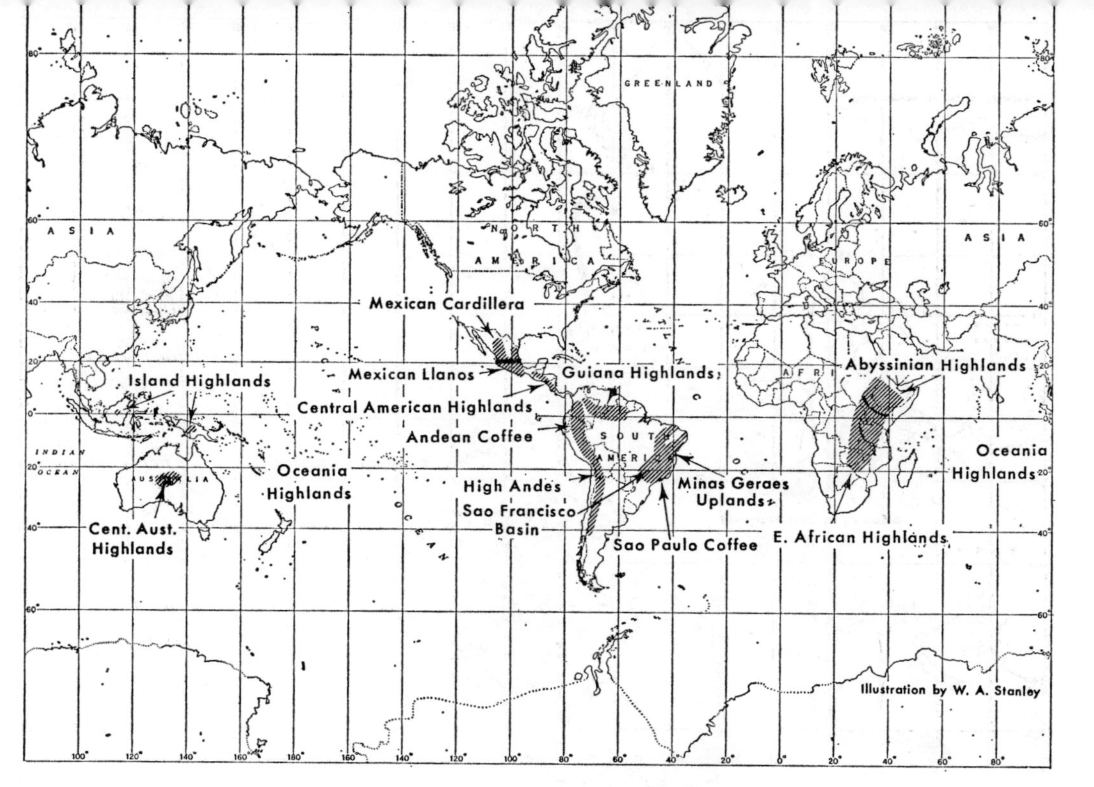

Map 11. Low latitude highlands.

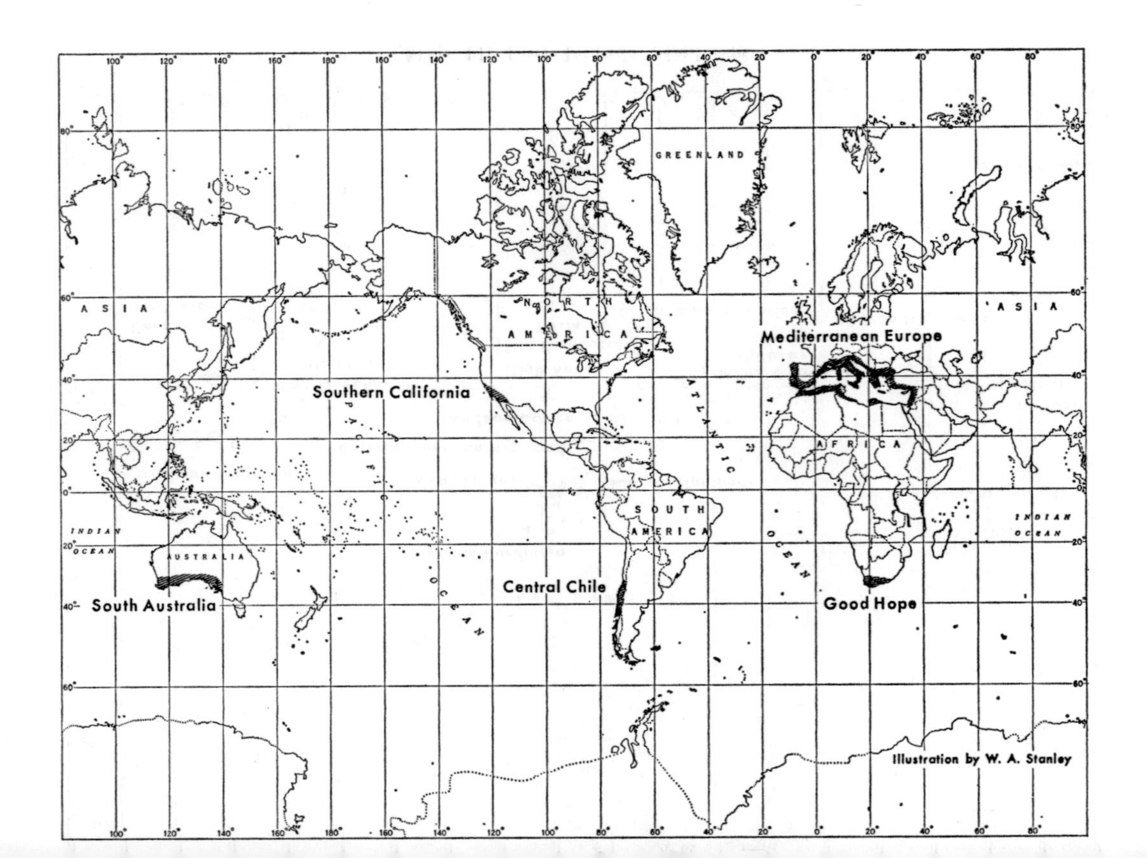
GREENLAND
ASIA
NORTH AMERICA
ASIA
Mediterranean Europe
Southern California
ATLANTIC
PACIFIC
AFRICA
SOUTH AMERICA
INDIAN OCEAN
INDIAN OCEAN
AUSTRALIA
OCEAN
OCEAN
Central Chile
South Australia
Good Hope
Illustration by W. A. Stanley

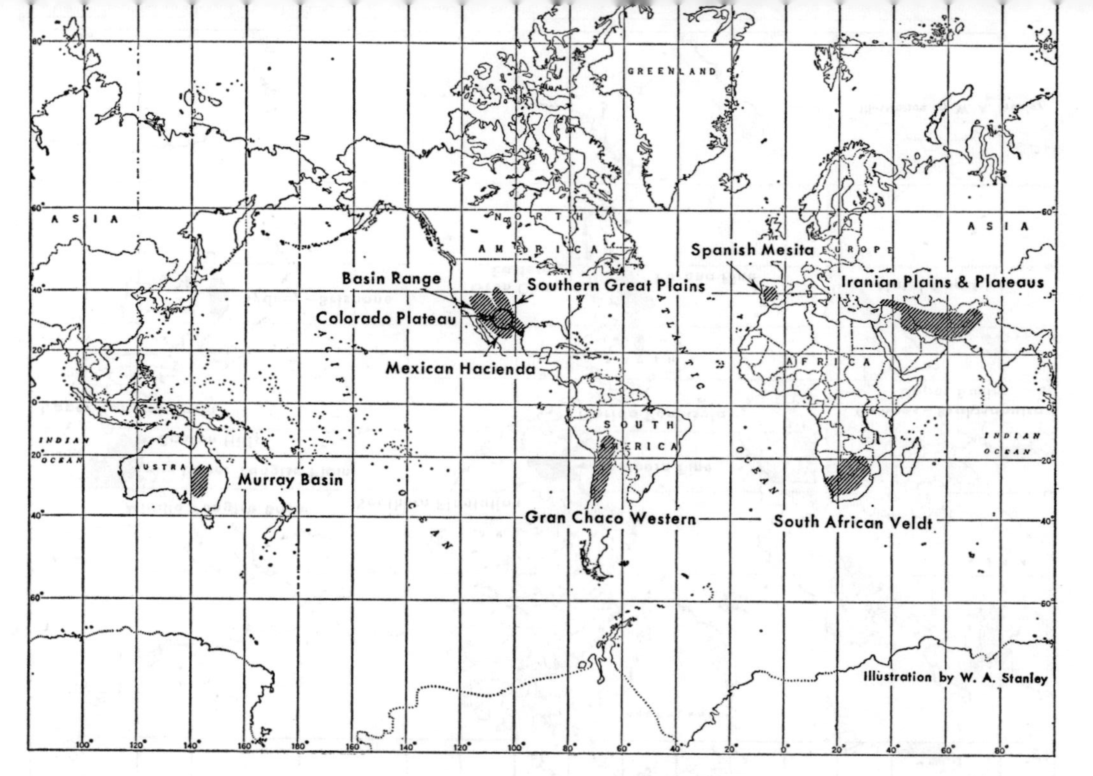

Map 13. Dry sub-tropical regions.

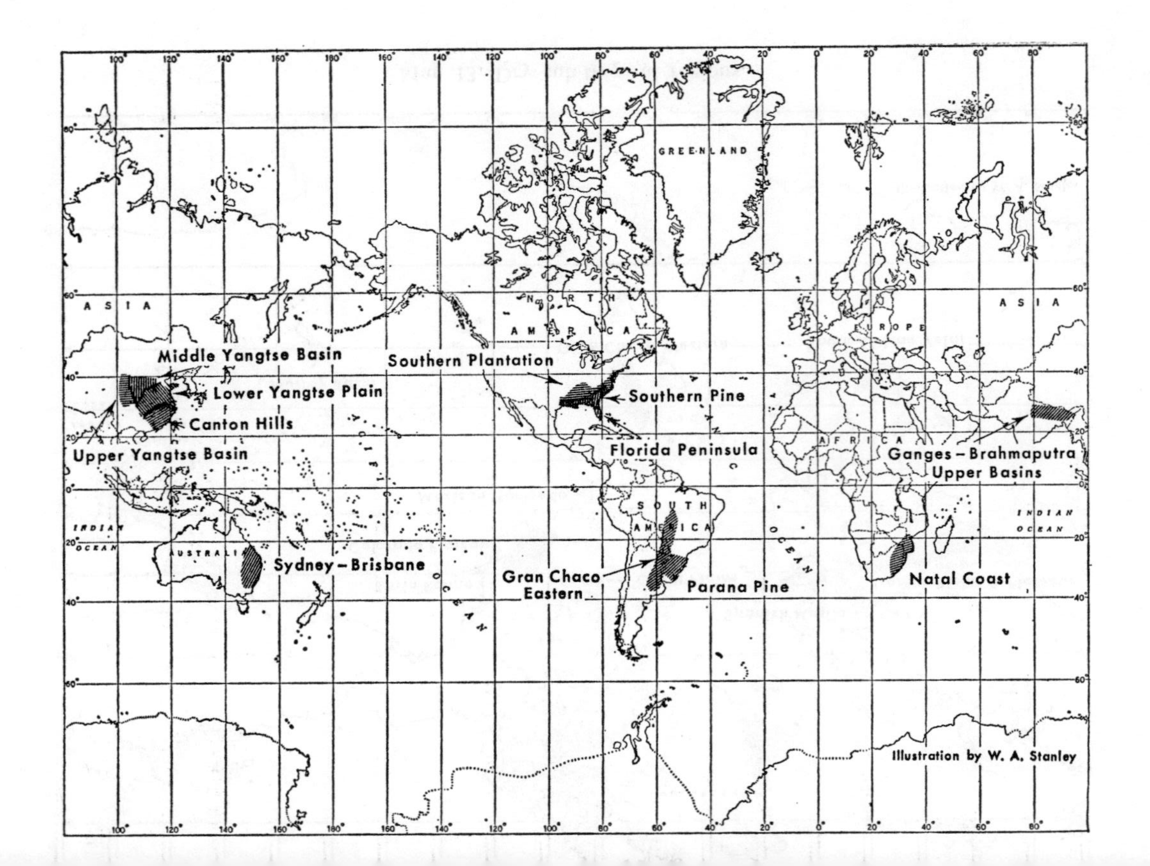
GREENLAND
ASIA
NORTH AMERICA
EUROPE
ASIA
Middle Yangtse Basin
Southern Plantation
Lower Yangtse Plain
Southern Pine
Canton Hills
AFRICA
Upper Yangtse Basin
Florida Peninsula
Ganges – Brahmaputra
Upper Basins
SOUTH AMERICA
INDIAN OCEAN
INDIAN OCEAN
AUSTRALIA
Sydney – Brisbane
Gran Chaco
Eastern
Parana Pine
Natal Coast
Illustration by W. A. Stanley

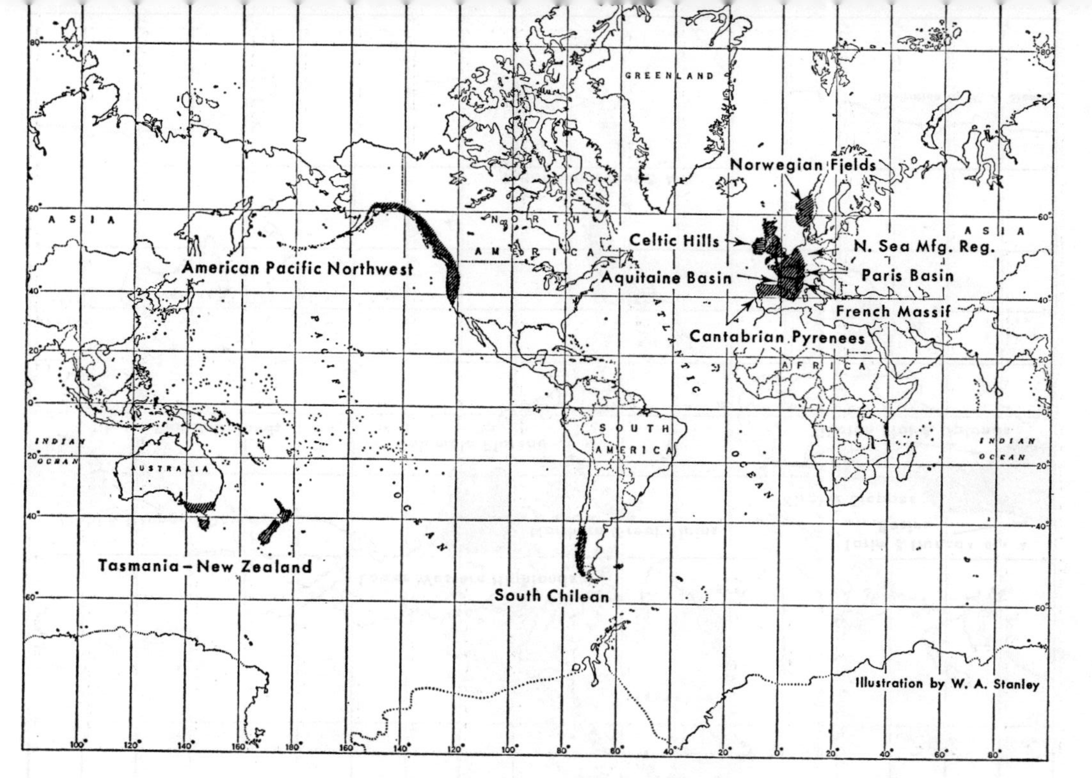

Map 15. Temperate marine regions.

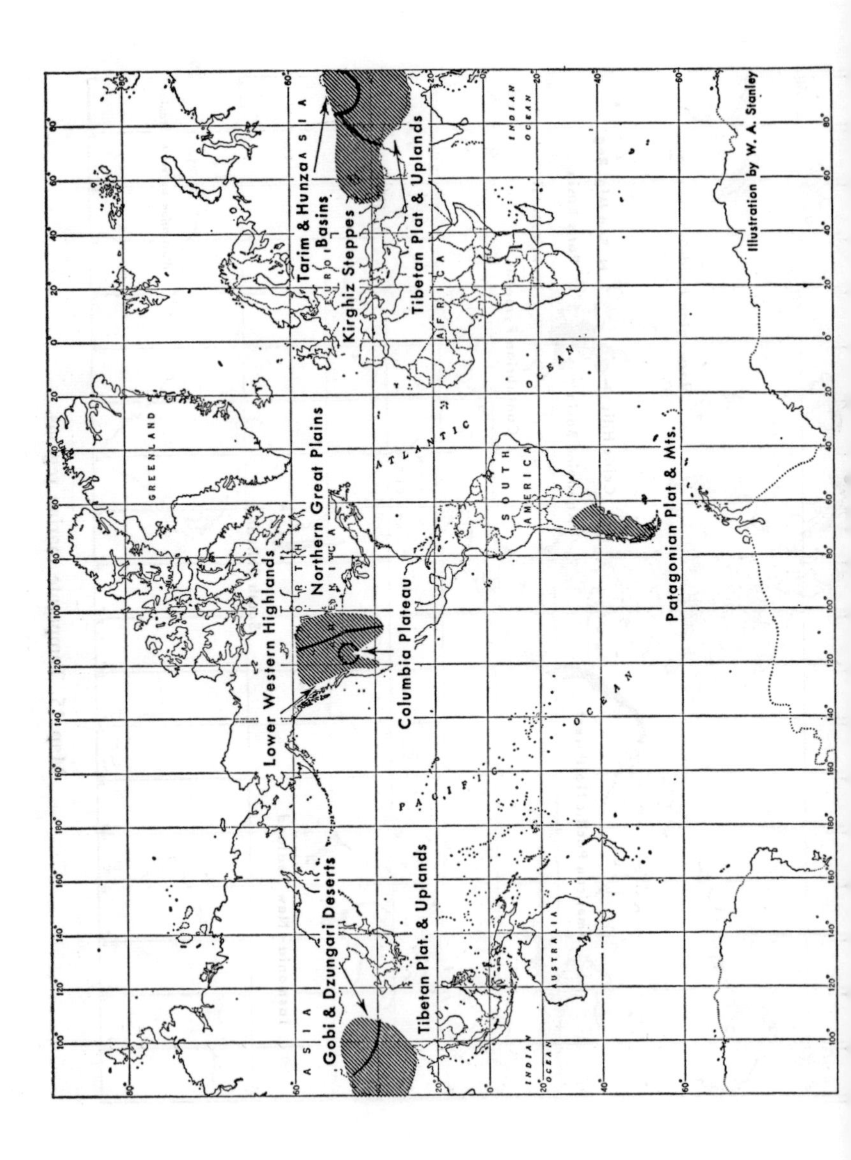
Tarim & Hunza Basins
Kirghiz Steppes
Tibetan Plat & Uplands
Northern Great Plains
Lower Western Highlands
Columbia Plateau
Patagonian Plat & Mts.
Gobi & Dzungari Deserts
Tibetan Plat. & Uplands
GREENLAND
ATLANTIC OCEAN
PACIFIC OCEAN
INDIAN OCEAN
SOUTH AMERICA
AFRICA
AUSTRALIA
ASIA
Illustration by W. A. Stanley

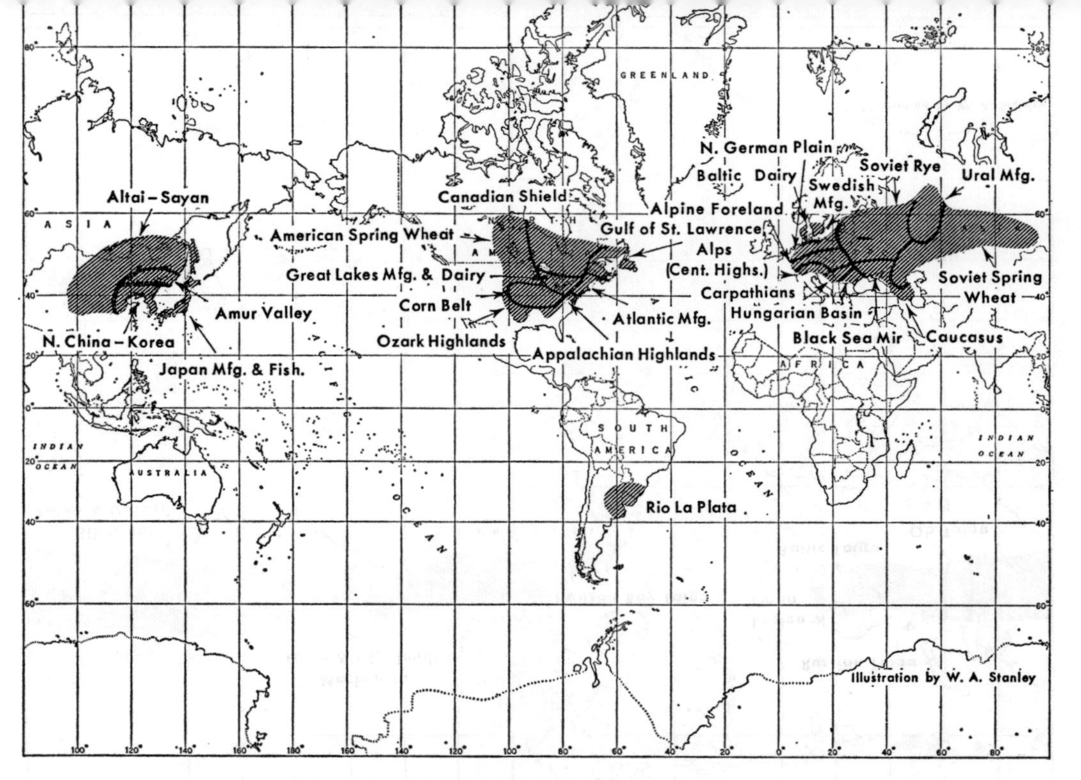

Map 17. Humid continental regions.

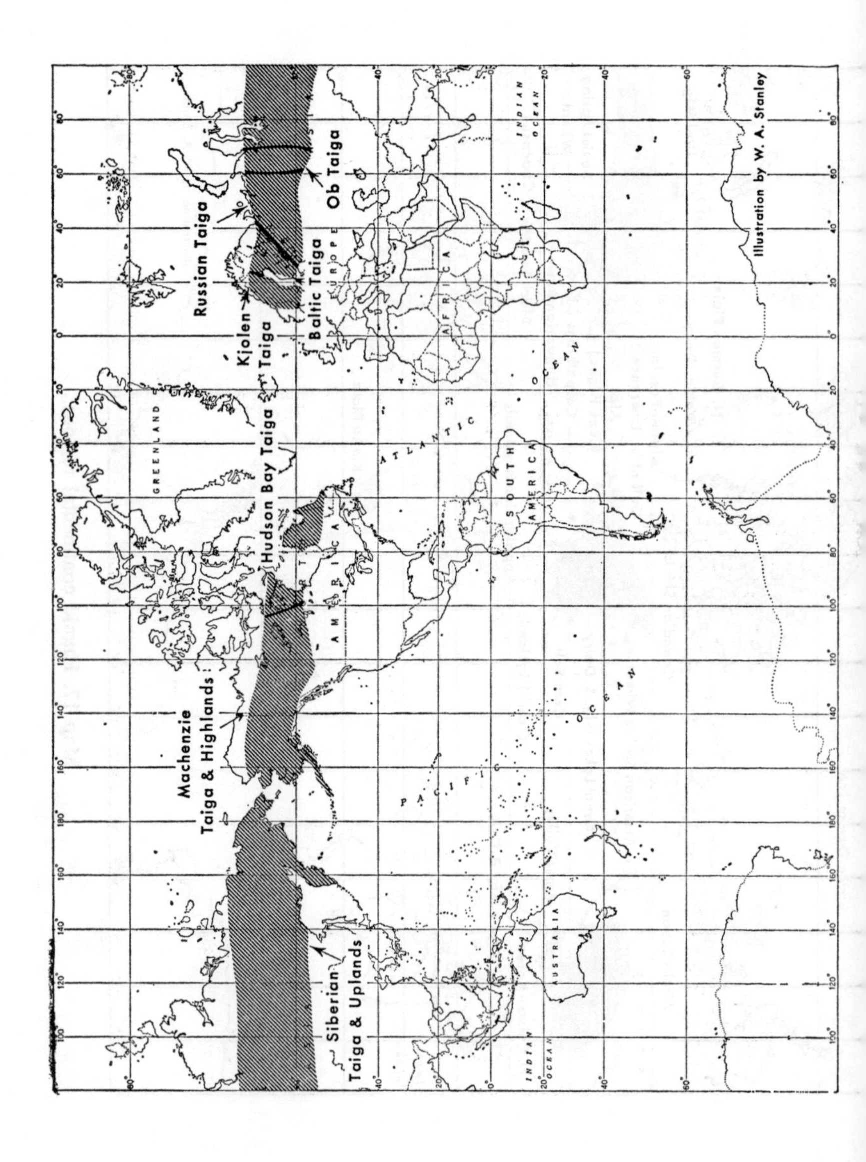

Russian Taiga
Kjolen
Baltic Taiga
Ob Taiga
Hudson Bay Taiga
Machenzie Taiga & Highlands
Siberian Taiga & Uplands
GREENLAND
EUROPE
AFRICA
ATLANTIC OCEAN
SOUTH AMERICA
PACIFIC OCEAN
INDIAN OCEAN
AUSTRALIA
Illustration by W. A. Stanley

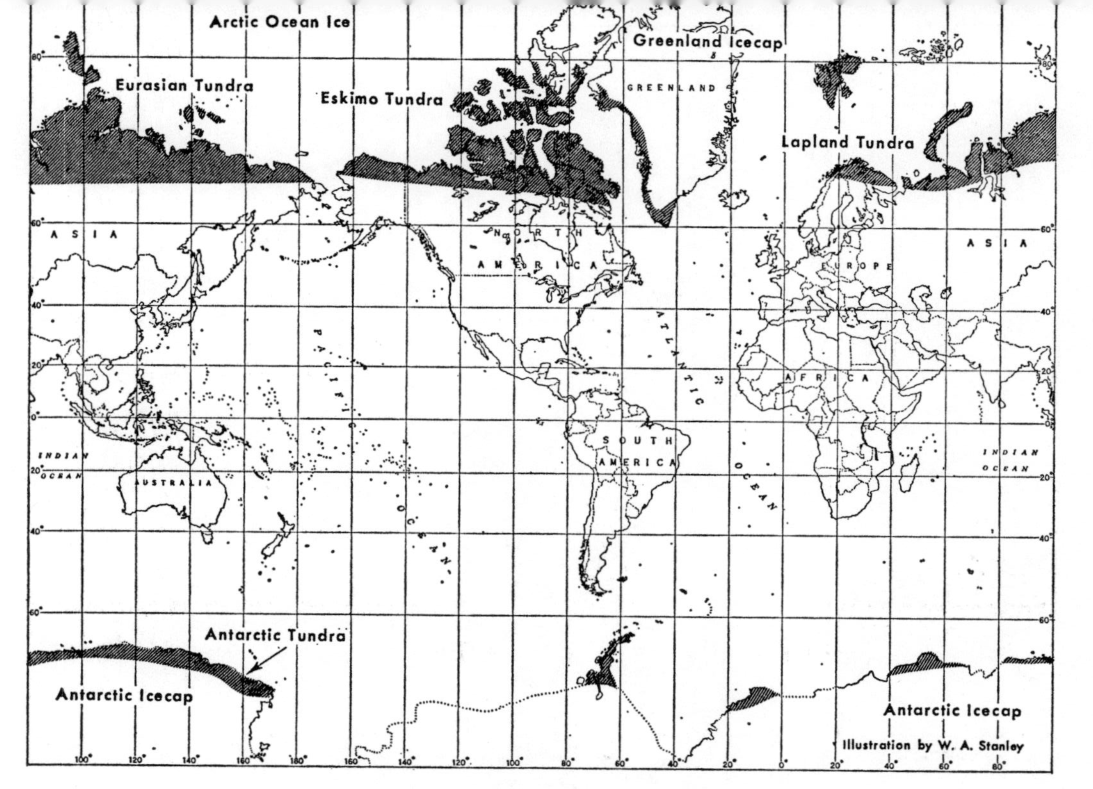

Map 19. Polar marine regions and polar ice cap.

Index

Page numbers in *italic* refer to illustrations.

A. Joseph Wraight

As a professional geographer of considerable stature, A. Joseph Wraight has traveled extensively and seen much of the world about which he writes and teaches.

His work as field geographer for the United States Coast and Geodetic Survey has taken him all over the North American continent into Alaska, Hawaii, and the Pacific. As an American representative to a number of international scientific conferences, he has visited Latin America, Asia, Western Europe, and Africa.

From 1951–52 the United States Government engaged Mr. Wraight as an expert witness on geographic matters in the Tidelands Oil Case Hearings before the Supreme Court.

Born in 1913 in St. Louis, Missouri, Mr. Wraight attended Washington University where he received his B.A. in 1939 and his M.S. in geology and geography in 1941. Clark University awarded him a doctorate in geography in 1951.

The author has taught in many universities, including those from which he received his degrees, St. Louis University and George Washington University.

Our Dynamic World follows seven other books in geography by A. Joseph Wraight. He has also written articles for the *Encyclopaedia Britannica, Harper Encyclopedia of Science,* and other scholarly publications.